The Advanced GNVQ Science Team

The Editors and Authors

Ken Gadd is Assistant Principal at Yeovil College. He is also Chair of the GNVQ Science National Working Group and a member of the NCVQ Science Advisory Committee. During a teaching career spanning over twenty years he has been extensively involved in resource development, having been co-ordinator of the Wessex A-level Modular Sciences scheme and President of the Education Division of the Royal Society of Chemistry.

John Holman is Headmaster of Watford Grammar School. He has directed the Salters Advanced Chemistry, Science and Technology in Society (SATIS) and Science across Europe projects. He is the author of a number of leading texts, including *Chemistry in Context*, and has acted as consultant on science and technology education to the Engineering Council as well as a number of industrial companies.

Michael Brimicombe is Senior Teacher at Cedars Upper School, Leighton Buzzard. He is a Chief Examiner for Physics and Electronics at A-level and GCSE, and has written a number of key texts, including *Physics in Focus*, *Introducing Electronic Systems* and *Electronic Systems*.

Roger Ellis has been a member of the Science Team at Yeovil College for over twenty years, during which time he has taught a wide variety of courses. He has contributed to the Wessex A-level Biology syllabus and wrote support material for the modules.

Neville Reed is Education Officer (Schools and Colleges) at the Royal Society of Chemistry. He was formerly Head of Chemistry at Eton College and Senior Lecturer in Organic Chemistry at Nene College. He has been a GCSE examiner since 1987.

Michael Reiss is Senior Lecturer in Biology at Homerton College, Cambridge. He taught in schools and colleges before moving into Higher Education, and has written or contributed to a number of leading texts, including *Biology: Principles and Processes* and *Advanced Practical Biology*. He is a Vice-President of the Institute of Biology and a Chief Examiner and Moderator.

The Advisers

John Avison
David Billings
Mary Jones
David Varnish
Doug Wilford

Safety Adviser

Peter Borrows

Acknowledgements

Photographs

The authors and publishers are grateful to the following for permission to reproduce copyright material. If any acknowledgement has been inadvertently omitted, this will be rectified at the earliest possible opportunity.

Cover: Science Photo Library
Figure I.1   Tropix/Veronica Birley
Figure 0.1   Science Photo Library
Figure 0.2   Alan Thomas
Figure 0.3   Alan Thomas
Figure 0.34   Alan Thomas
Figure 0.35   Alan Thomas
Figure 0.36   Alan Thomas
Figure 1.1   Science Photo Library
Figure 1.2   Science Photo Library
Figure 1.3   Tropix/Veronica Birley
Figure 1.4   Alan Thomas
Figure 1.6   Science Photo Library
Figure 1.7   Oxford Scientific Films
Figure 1.18   Science Photo Library
Figure 1.19 (both)   Alan Thomas
Figure 1.22 (left)   Alan Thomas
Figure 1.22 (right)   Geoscience Features
Figure 1.23 (all)   Alan Thomas
Figure 1.25   Jerry Mason
Figure 1.26   Alan Thomas
Figure 1.28   Alan Thomas
Figure 1.31   Alan Thomas
Unit 1 Case studies: page 74, Alan Thomas
Figure 2.1   Spectrum
Figure 2.2   Spectrum
Figure 2.3   Alan Thomas
Figure 2.6   Alan Thomas
Figure 2.7   Alan Thomas
Figure 2.8   Rover Group
Figure 2.9   Science Photo Library
Figure 2.10   Joseph Wedgwood and Sons
Figure 2.11   Britstock
Figure 2.17   Britstock
Figure 2.18   British Telecom
Figure 2.20   Environmental Picture Library
Figure 2.21   Science Photo Library
Figure 2.22   Alan Thomas
Figure 2.23   Science Photo Library/ NASA
Figure 2.37   Wellman Ltd
Figure 2.43   Halmatic Ltd.
Unit 2 Case studies: page 118, Trip (both); page 119, J. Allan Cash; page 120, Spectrum (both); page 122, Spectrum (bridge), Trip (Pompidou Centre), Science Photo Library (Lloyds Building)
Figure 3.1(left)   Lord Porter
Figure 3.1 (right)   Britstock
Figure 3.2   Bristol Myers Squibb
Figure 3.3   Heather Angel
Figure 3.5   Shades

Figure 3.8   Alan Thomas
Figure 3.9 (top)   Alan Thomas
Figure 3.9 (bottom)   BDH
Figure 3.12   Alan Thomas
Figure 3.13   Alan Thomas
Figure 3.14   J. Bibby Science Products
Figure 3.16   Alan Thomas
Figure 3.17   Geoscience Features
Figure 3.23   Paul Brierly
Figure 3.25   Johnson Progress
Figure 3.27   Alan Thomas
Unit 3 Case studies: page 161, Zeneca
Figure 4.1   Date Palm Developments
Figure 4.2   Alan Thomas
Figure 4.3   CP Pharmaceuticals
Figure 4.6   Science Photo Library
Figure 4.7(b)   Stuart Boreham
Figure 4.10(b)   Biophoto
Figure 4.12   Science Photo Library
Figure 4.15   Alan Thomas
Figure 4.16   Trip
Figure 4.17   Britstock
Figure 4.19   Oxford Scientific Films
Figure 4.20   Tropix
Figure 4.22   Britstock
Figure 4.23   Alan Thomas
Figure 4.24   Oxford Scientific Films
Figure 4.25   J. Allan Cash
Figure 4.29   Horticulture Research International
Figure 4.30   Holt Studios
Figure 4.31   Britstock
Figure 4.34   Science Photo Library
Figure 4.35   Tony Morrison
Figure 4.37   Plant Breeding Institute, Cambridge
Figure 4.38   Holt Studios
Figure 4.39   Plant Breeding Institute, Cambridge
Figure 4.41   Plant Breeding Institute, Cambridge
Figure 4.44   Alan Thomas
Figure 4.45   Science Photo Library
Figure 4.46   Science Photo Library
Figure 4.47   Spectrum
Figure 4.55   Philip Harris
Figure 4.64   Science Photo Library
Figure 4.65   Tropix
Figure 4.66   J. Allan Cash
Figure 4.68   Science Photo Library
Figure 4.70   Pharmaceutical Proteins
Figure 4.71   J. Allan Cash
Figure 4.72   University of Nottingham/ Professor D. Grierson
Figure 4.73   Science Photo Library
Figure 5.1   Ford Motors
Figure 5.2   Alan Thomas
Figure 5.3   Trip
Figure 5.10   Philip Harris
Figure 5.12   Quadrant
Figure 5.13   Quadrant
Figure 5.16   Ford Motors
Figure 5.17   Telegraph Colour Library
Figure 5.20   Ford Motors

Figure 5.22   Britstock
Figure 5.23   Image Bank
Figure 5.26   Stuart Boreham
Figure 5.28   Stuart Boreham
Figure 5.35   Trip
Figure 5.44   Britstock
Figure 5.47   Vosper Thornycroft
Figure 5.49   Alan Thomas
Figure 5.53(b)   Alan Thomas
Figure 5.54   Alan Thomas
Figure 5.56   Telegraph Colour Library
Figure 5.58   Philip Harris
Figure 6.1   Alan Thomas
Figure 6.2   Britstock/Zeneca
Figure 6.5   Science Photo Library
Figure 6.6   Alan Thomas
Figure 6.13(both)   Stuart Boreham
Figure 6.14   BDH
Figure 6.16   Paul Brierly
Figure 6.18   BDH
Figure 6.25   Alan Thomas
Figure 6.26   Paul Brierly
Figure 6.28   Zeneca
Figure 6.29   Spectrum
Figure 6.30   Shades
Figure 6.31   Hoyer plc
Figure 6.32   Alan Thomas
Figure 6.34 (both)   BP Oil UK
Figure 6.35   Telegraph Colour Library
Figure 6.36   Britstock
Unit 6 Case studies: page 282, Sporting Pictures (left), Tioxide plc (right); page 284, Stuart Boreham; page 285, Science Photo Library (above), Stuart Boreham (below)
Figure 7.1   Tropix/Veronica Birley
Figure 7.2   Science Photo Library
Figure 7.3   Telegraph Colour Library
Figure 7.4   Sporting Pictures
Figure 7.5   Science Photo Library
Figure 7.6   National Medical Slidebank
Figure 7.7(a)   St Mary's Hospital, Paddington
Figure 7.7(b)National Medical Slidebank
Figure 7.8   Chris Ridgers
Figure 7.9   J. Allan Cash
Figure 7.11   Alan Thomas
Figure 7.12   Britstock
Figure 7.14   Alan Thomas
Figure 7.15   John Clark
Figure 7.16   Science Photo Library
Figure 7.19   Omron Healthcare
Figure 7.20   Tropix/Veronica Birley
Figure 7.22   Science Photo Library
Figure 7.25   Science Photo Library
Figure 7.29   Biophotos
Figure 7.31   Oxford Scientific Films
Figure 7.32   Science Photo Library
Figure 7.41(both) Oxford Scientific Films
Figure 7.44   Oxford Scientific Films
Figure 7.45   Science Photo Library
Figure 7.49   Science Photo Library

Figure 7.50   Oxford Scientific Films
Figure 7.52   Science Photo Library
Figure 7.53   Science Photo Library
Unit 7 Case studies: page 325, Science Photo Library (both); page 326, University of Colorado
Figure 8.1   Science Photo Library
Figure 8.2(a)   Alan Thomas
Figure 8.2(b)   Science Photo Library
Figure 8.4   Image Bank
Figure 8.20   J. Allan Cash

Illustrations

Certain material in this book is based on already published sources as follows:

Figures 4.11, 4.33 and 4.36 Tortora, G.J., Funke, B.R. and Case, C.L. *Microbiology: An Introduction*, 3rd edition, Benjamin/Cummings, 1989
Figure 4.21 Tanner, J.M. *Foetus into Man: Physical Growth from Conception to Maturity*, Open Books, 1978
Figure 4.32 Newton, P. 'Hydroponics: growing plants without soil', *Biological Sciences Review* 4(3), 1992
Figure 4.61 Toole, G and Toole, S. *Understanding Biology for Advanced Level*, Hutchinson, 1987
Unit 4 Case study (Alcohol Production) Illustration 1 Tomkins, S.P., Reiss, M.J. and Morris, C. *Biology at Work*, Cambridge University Press, 1992
Figures 7.10 and 7.13 HMSO, *The Health of the Nation: A Strategy for Health in England Presented to Parliament by the Secretary of State for Health by Command of Her Majesty July 1992*, HMSO, 1992
Figures 7.17 Mackean, D.G. *Human Life*, John Murray, 1985
Figure 7.21 Hill, D.W. and Summers, R. *Medical Technology: A Nursing Perspective*, Chapman and Hall, 1994
Figure 7.23 Wallwork, J. and Stepney, R. *Heart Disease: What it is and How it's Treated*, Basil Blackwell, 1987
Figure 7.24 Andrews, C. and Smith, J. *Medical Nursing: A Concise Nursing Text*, Balliere Tindall, 1992
Unit 7 Case studies, Illustration 3 Taylor, D. *Human Physical Health*, Cambridge University Press, 1989

The Authors and Publishers are grateful to the following organisations for their co-operation in the production of this book:

New Scientist magazine, for extracts on pages 73, 125, 158, 159, 251, 327, 346 and 347, © *New Scientist* 1993–1994.
Alder Hey Children's Hospital, Liverpool

£20-99

A D V A N C E D

Science

Michael Brimicombe, Roger Ellis, Ken Gadd, Neville Reed & Michael Reiss

Editors: Ken Gadd & John Holman

Thomas Nelson and Sons Ltd
Nelson House   Mayfield Road
Walton-on-Thames   Surrey
KT12 5PL   UK

Nelson Blackie
Wester Cleddens Road
Bishopbriggs
Glasgow
G64 2NZ   UK

Thomas Nelson Australia
102 Dodds Street
South Melbourne
Victoria 3205   Australia

Nelson Canada
1120 Birchmount Road
Scarborough   Ontario
MIK 5G4   Canada

First published by Thomas Nelson and Sons Ltd 1995

I(T)P   Thomas Nelson is an International Thomson Publishing Company

I(T)P   is used under licence

ISBN 0-17-4482353
NPN 9 8 7 6 5 4 3 2 1

Printed in Spain by Mateu Cromo, S.A. Pinto (Madrid)

Contents

Contents

Contents

How to
use this
book

This book provides you with the essential tools needed for Advanced GNVQ Science. These will enable you to complete the units that make up the GNVQ. To get your GNVQ you will need to:
- show through your *coursework* that you have met the requirements of the qualification, and
- pass *tests* for the units.

In this book you will find information on the techniques, methods and related scientific ideas that are needed to tackle both coursework and tests.

The structure of the book

To work on any scientific problem you need the relevant knowledge, skills and understanding. This can be found in Units 0 to 8 of this book. You may need to look in more specialised texts or get information from other sources if you are undertaking an in-depth study of a particular problem. But then, this is one of the important skills a scientist must possess – the ability to find and use information.

Unit 0 covers the basic tools: methods and concepts which you will use extensively throughout the programme. They are general and do not relate specifically to any one unit.

Units 1-8 link directly to the mandatory science units. Each begins with an introduction which:
- describes the area of scientific work upon which the unit is based
- outlines some of the decisions you may have to make when tackling activities related to the unit.

The introduction is followed by information about relevant techniques and methods and important concepts and ideas. Advice on which techniques and methods to use in particular circumstances is given, as is guidance on their use.

Boxed *summaries* in the margin enable you to move through a section quickly and provide you with a *revision guide* for the *unit tests*. You can turn to the main text if, for example, there is a statement that you do not understand or that you want to read more about. The text also contains *figures* and *tables* which may be useful for revision as well as for coursework.

There are a number of *in-text questions* for you to try. These help you to check that you have understood the method or idea you have been reading about.

Finally, each unit contains some *case studies* which illustrate the application of techniques, methods and knowledge associated with the unit in real situations. The questions at the end of each case study give you the opportunity to collect evidence for your portfolio that some of the performance criteria and range of the elements in the unit have been met.

Finding information in the book

There are three ways in which you will find the information you need in this book:
- the contents list at the front
- the index at the back
- by 'pressing' the appropriate button in another section.

'*Buttons*' in the left-hand margin direct you to relevant sections. They are a cross-referencing system which allows you to find the information you need quickly. When you do look up something don't forget to mark your place in the book so that you can get back to it!

Buttons look like this:

▶ What do plant breeders do? page 184

heading to look for in the text   **page to turn to for further information**

Throughout the book, words in **bold** type direct you to boxes in the margin. Boxes provide summaries of the information you will need in order to pass unit tests. Other words, which need emphasis, are in *italic*.

Note to teachers on safety

When practical *instructions* have been given we have attempted to indicate hazardous substances and operations by using standard symbols and appropriate precautions. Nevertheless you should be aware of your obligations under the Health and Safety at Work etc. Act, Control of Substances Hazardous to Health (COSHH) Regulations and the Management of Health and Safety at Work Regulations. In this respect you should follow the requirements of your employers at all times.

In developing assignments, students should be encouraged to carry out their own risk assessments, i.e. they should identify hazards and suitable ways of reducing the risks from them. However, they must be checked by the teacher/lecturer.

The teachers/lecturers should be familiar and up to date with current advice from professional bodies.

Introduction

Advanced GNVQ Science: what do scientists do?

Advanced GNVQ Science is about what scientists do. Their activities fall into three broad categories:

They *obtain or make* things. For example they:
- obtain food, fuels and other useful materials from plants, animals and micro-organisms
- construct electronic control circuits
- make pharmaceuticals, dyes, food preservatives (and so on)

They *characterise* things. For example, they:
- determine the properties of materials used for construction, transport and other purposes
- analyse substances to establish composition or purity
- identify the characteristics of a healthy body

They *control* or *manage* change. For example, they:
- control moving objects, fluid movement, and the transfer of thermal energy
- control the rate of chemical and biological change
- contribute to the management of the healthcare of people
  GNVQ Science units are designed around these activities.

Underpinning a scientist's work is the ability to carry out scientific investigations by gathering, analysing, evaluating and communicating scientific data.

The structure of the qualification

GNVQ Science consists of *Science units* and *Core skills*.

Advanced GNVQ Science consists of:
8 mandatory units
4 optional units
3 core skill units.

Science units

Advanced GNVQ Science is divided into units, each based on a particular area of 'what scientists do'. The information needed for the eight mandatory units is provided in this book. Many of the methods, techniques and ideas will also be of value when you tackle your four optional units.

Each unit consists of three *elements*. These state what you must do to achieve the unit. In turn, each element consists of:
- *performance criteria*: a checklist of things you need to do to show that you can meet the requirements of the element

You will find that words in the performance criteria are explained in the range. For example,
- **Performance criterion: 'substance is prepared observing safe practice'**
- **Range: 'Substance: inorganic compounds (e.g. oxides, halides, salts of oxoacids, co-ordination compounds), organic compounds (e.g. alcohols, carboxylic acids, esters, amides, polymers)'.**

Core skill units:
- **Application of Number**
- **Communication**
- **Information Technology.**

You should have access to the full specifications for science and core skill units, as well as the grading criteria for merit and distinction.

- *range*: the particular situations in which the performance criteria are to be met.

Core skills

There are three core skill units that you must achieve: *Application of Number*, *Communication* and *Information Technology*. They should be achieved within the science activities that you undertake.

The requirements of these units are laid out in the same way as the Science units, with elements, performance criteria and range. There are five levels of core skills. For GNVQ Advanced, you must achieve at least level 3. However, you should strive to get higher levels. This extra achievement will be recognised on your certificate. It is worth working for.

Application of Number involves gathering and working on data, solving problems (for example, using graphs and equations), interpreting and presenting data (for example, using symbols and diagrams). The nature of science means that you will have lots of opportunities to meet the requirements of this core skill.

To meet the requirements for *Communication*, you will need to show that you can:
- write about science, using suitable illustrations such as diagrams and tables
- talk about science, with the help of visual aids such as posters or overhead projector transparencies.

Of course, some people know more about science than others; you need the ability to communicate with people with different experiences and knowledge.

The core skill of *Information Technology* is about word processing and using databases and spreadsheets. It is an invaluable aid to storing and communicating scientific data and ideas. You will have many opportunities to show that you can retrieve information from databases, word process scientific reports and use spreadsheets to handle data.

Assessment

There are two parts to the assessment.

Your *portfolio of evidence* is a collection of your *coursework*. It should contain evidence that you have carried out work to:
- meet the requirements of elements through the related performance criteria and range (and so achieve the units)
- meet the requirements of the core skill units
- show that you are worthy of a merit or distinction grade.

Unit tests are designed to allow you to show that you have covered all aspects of the mandatory units. If you do not pass a test you may take it again. Optional units do not have tests.

The activities designed by your school or college will have opportunities to meet these requirements built into them. However, an important aim of a GNVQ programme is that you begin to identify opportunities to gather evidence yourself. This may be, for example:
- extension work you have suggested in an activity
- experience gained on a work placement
- extra core skills you have used in an activity because of the way you chose to tackle it
- an activity that you designed and carried out.

It is important that you understand the GNVQ specifications and are able to recognise that you collected relevant evidence. This can be presented to your teacher or lecturer and you can 'claim' the appropriate part of the GNVQ. You are taking control of your own programme.

Meeting performance criteria

Your portfolio must show that you have met all the performance criteria for each element. You must show that the *breadth of the range* has been covered. This means showing that you understand the key features of each *range category* within a *range dimension*. Finally you must show for each element that you have looked in *depth* at those aspects of range which are the focus of the particular assignments you are tackling.

This probably sounds very complicated but an example will help. Consider the following performance criterion and related range:

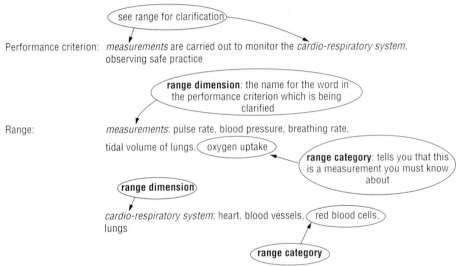

You would need to show that you understand how each of these measurements (pulse rate, blood pressure, breathing rate, tidal volume of lungs, oxygen uptake) are helpful in monitoring the cardio-respiratory system (heart, blood vessels, red blood cells, lungs). However, you would not be expected to carry out all of these measurements. For example, one assignment might focus on changes in breathing rate during exercise, relating this to the functioning of the lungs.

Evidence indicators

Each element has *evidence indicators*, showing the minimum amount of work you need to do. However, they are not prescriptive. Other types of evidence may be presented provided they are comparable in *coverage* (performance criteria and range) and *sufficiency* (number of activities).

For example, consider these evidence indicators:

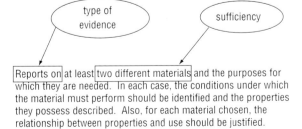

Alternative types of evidence might be posters for presentation at a scientific conference or an oral presentation (supported by appropriate visual aids). It is always helpful to look at the core skill specifications because the form of the evidence can often be tailored to meet core skill requirements as well.

Whatever the form, at least two materials must have been investigated. Between them, the investigations must show that performance criteria and range have been covered to the same extent as the evidence indicators given in the specifications.

Grading

Individual units are not graded. Instead you will be awarded a grade for the whole qualification. To gain a merit or distinction, at least a third of your evidence must meet the grading criteria for merit or the criteria for distinction. You will need to show that you can tackle activities using the knowledge, understanding and skills associated with Advanced GNVQ Science. The grading criteria also reflect the increasing responsibility that you are expected to take for the work you do. These are just the skills that employers and higher education are looking for.

There are four grading themes:

Planning
  1 drawing up plans of action
  2 monitoring courses of action
Information-seeking and information-handling
  3 identifying and using sources to obtain information
  4 establishing the validity of information
Evaluation
  5 evaluating outcomes and alternatives
  6 justifying particular approaches to tasks/activities
Quality of outcomes
  7 synthesis of knowledge
  8 command of scientific language

Grading criteria reward independent work – your ability to make many of the decisions about what to do and how to do it.

> **Grading themes:**
> - **Planning**
> - **Information-seeking and information-handling**
> - **Evaluation**
> - **Quality of outcomes**

Building up your GNVQ portfolio

A comprehensive GNVQ portfolio is vital to your success. This section offers you practical guidance on how to develop your portfolio.

Knowledge, skills and understanding

Your GNVQ programme will consist of various activities, such as lectures, discussions, experimental work, problem solving exercises, debates, presentations, discussions, information searches (library and electronic) and so on. You will be given increasing responsibility for your work.

The activities you undertake will have been designed to allow you to meet the requirements of elements and so achieve units. Your record of these activities will form the main part of your portfolio. You may be able to add relevant evidence from other sources such as work placements. To do this you will need a 'toolkit' of techniques and methods, together with the underpinning knowledge and understanding, to apply to the problem at hand. You will be able to use a technique most effectively if you understand the ideas upon which it is based.

> **A technique is a tool to investigate a problem in order to obtain required information, e.g. chromatography. A method is the adaption of a technique to a particular problem, e.g. the determination of the composition of a food colouring using thin layer chromatography.**

Activities: tasks and assignments

Here you will see how activities are designed so that you have opportunities to meet:

- requirements of the science units
- requirements of the core skill units
- grading criteria.

Understanding this will help you to devise extensions to activities or even your own investigations and projects. It is likely that you will build up to this by tackling activities of increasing complexity and taking increasing responsibility for your own work. Let's see what this might mean.

It is helpful to categorise activities as *tasks* or *assignments*. For the purposes of your Science GNVQ and this book, we will describe these as follows:

A *task* is a structured activity which allows you to collect evidence for science and core skill units. It is often a short piece of work which allows some or all of the performance criteria for one or more elements to be met. You are usually given precise instructions and there is little opportunity to meet grading criteria.

You may be given the opportunity to carry out extension work of your own design. In this way, the task may develop into an assignment.

An *assignment* is a more open-ended activity which allows you to collect evidence for science and core skill units. It also allows some or all of the grading criteria to be met. Assignments are not equally demanding. They may vary from *straightforward*, consisting of a number of discrete tasks, to *complex*, where the tasks involved are interrelated. Complexity will also increase depending on the extent of planning, information use and evaluation carried out, and the depth of knowledge shown.

This may be a little confusing, and some people may use the terms activity, task and assignment in different ways. Perhaps the important message is that some things you do will give you the chance to meet performance criteria and range requirements. However, you will not be able to show the skills associated with grading. On the other hand, some things will give you the opportunity to do both. For convenience, we are calling these tasks and assignments respectively.

An example will help to illustrate one approach to Advanced GNVQ Science.

Setting the scene

Your GNVQ programme might be designed around a number of themes based on topics such as health, food, transport and so on. One theme could be *Chemicals and Health*. It might involve an investigation of substances such as drugs, medicines, antiseptics and cleaning agents. Within this context, tasks and assignments would be designed to meet some of the requirements of Units 1, 3 and 7.

Tasks will usually consist of *worksheets* or *practicals*. Worksheets may involve calculating amounts of drugs from quantities given on labels, identifying functional groups in organic drugs, classifying inorganic drugs or choosing preparative routes to selected drugs. Practicals may involve the preparation of zinc oxide, the preparation of zinc sulphate, the preparation and analysis of aspirin, the preparation and analysis of paracetamol or the extraction of caffeine from coffee or tea.

Typical assignments might be to survey medicines that can be obtained

> **Tasks have precise instructions which you follow. No planning, information seeking and handling, or evaluating is needed. Assignments require you to take more control. Although they can be broken down into tasks, you will need to plan the approach and monitor how things are going, find and use information relevant to the problem, evaluate what you have done and show that you can bring together the relevant knowledge, skills and understanding.**

without prescription, to establish the identity of an unknown drug or to carry out an investigation of Folicin™.

In carrying out these activities, you could collect evidence for your portfolio. This could be supplemented by notes you make from this and other books or during lectures and discussions, worksheets, information-seeking exercises, problem-solving exercises, working on case studies from this book and so on.

Let us look at one task and one assignment within this theme. It will illustrate the difference between the two. The two are related in that the work carried out in the task helps to prepare you for the more open-ended assignment.

Task	**Preparation of zinc sulphate**
	Background Zinc sulphate is an inorganic compound which has both astringent and antiseptic properties. It is used in mouthwashes.
	Objective Your objective is to prepare a sample of zinc sulphate using the method given below.
CORROSIVE sulphuric acid	**Preliminary work** You are provided with 10 cm^3 2 mol dm^{-3} sulphuric acid and 5 g zinc granules. The equation for the reaction is:
	$$Zn(s) + H_2SO_4(aq) \rightarrow ZnSO_4(aq) + H_2(g)$$
	Zinc sulphate crystallises from solution as zinc sulphate-5-water, $ZnSO_4.5H_2O(s)$.
Element 3.2 PC1 (full range)	1. How many moles of sulphuric acid are there in 10 cm^3 2 mol dm^{-3} sulphuric acid? 2. How many moles of zinc must be added to react completely with the sulphuric acid? 3. What quantity of zinc must be added to react completely with the sulphuric acid? 4. How many moles of zinc sulphate would be formed? 5. What is the theoretical yield of zinc sulphate-5-water?
Eye protection must be worn. Element 3.2 PC2 (range: inorganic compounds)	**Method** Before beginning, make sure you are wearing eye protection. Using a 10 cm^3 measuring cylinder, place 10 cm^3 2 mol dm^{-3} sulphuric acid (**Caution: corrosive**) in a 100 cm^3 conical flask with a glass rod to prevent bumping. Use the same cylinder to add 10 cm^3 distilled water. Put the conical flask on a wire gauze supported by a tripod. Heat with a Bunsen burner so that the solution is just simmering. Now add zinc granules a little at a time until there is a slight excess (you will know roughly how much to add from your calculations above).

Element 3.3 PC2 (range: crystallisation, filtration)	Filter the hot solution through a folded filter paper and collect the filtrate in an evaporating dish. Place the dish on a hot water bath and evaporate gently until crystals begin to appear. Allow to cool. Separate the crystals by suction filtration and place in a desiccator to dry. Determine the actual yield of zinc sulphate-5-water crystals obtained by weighing the product.
Further work Element 3.3 PC4 (full range)	1. Calculate the percentage yield of zinc sulphate-5-water, using the formula: $$\text{percentage yield} = \frac{\text{actual yield / g}}{\text{theoretical yield / g}} \times 100\%$$
Element 3.2 PC3 (full range)	2. Conditions and operations used in the laboratory are not always easy to scale up. If the preparation were to be carried out on an industrial scale (100 kg of product) using a batch process, discuss the factors which must be considered, in particular equipment, transfer of materials, heating needs, use or disposal of co-products. **Assessment** Were all the performance criteria met?　YES/NO If NO, which ones were not met? _____

The instructions are precise. There is a clear link between the various parts of the task and the performance criteria (and associated range). You would be able to gather evidence for your portfolio. Since no planning, information finding and use, or evaluation is involved, you would not be able to show that you are worthy of a merit or distinction. However, you may decide to do some further work which would give you this opportunity. For example, you might undertake a survey of drugs which contain zinc compounds to find out what they are, what they are used for and proposing methods for making them in the laboratory.

Figure 1.1 Some women suffer from anaemia during pregnancy. They can be prescribed pills which supplement the iron intake of their normal diet.

Assignment

HARMFUL
copper(II) sulphate

Depending on the approach you take you have the opportunity to gather evidence for *Science units*
Element 1.2 PCs 1, 2, 3, 4
Element 1.3 PCs 1, 2, 3, 4
Element 3.1 PCs 1, 2, 3, 4
Element 3.2 PCs 1, 2
Element 3.3 PCs 1, 2, 4
Core skill units
Application of number
Element 3.2
Communication
Elements 3.1, 3.2
Grading
Planning
Information-seeking and information-handling
Evaluation
Quality of outcomes

Investigation of Folicin™

Background Folicin™ is used to treat anaemia during pregnancy. Manufactured by Link Pharmaceuticals, it comes in the form of white sugar-coated tablets. The Association of the British Pharmaceutical Industry (ABPI) Data Sheet Compendium give the composition of each tablet as

0.200 g dried iron(II) sulphate
0.0025 g copper(II) sulphate
0.0025 g manganese(II) sulphate
0.0025 g folic acid

Objectives You are provided with samples of iron(III) chloride, manganese(II) chloride and copper(II) oxide. You have access to the usual laboratory apparatus. Your objectives are to

1. describe the symptoms of anaemia and its causes

2. describe the role of (a) iron(II) ions and other metal ions, (b) folic acid in maintaining a healthy body.

3. plan the preparation of dried iron(II) sulphate, copper(II) sulphate and manganese(II) sulphate from the starting materials available, **including a risk assessment which must be checked by your teacher or lecturer**

4. prepare sufficient quantities of ingredients to make 100 Folicin™ tablets (*Caution: samples of these compounds made in the laboratory must not be consumed!*)

5. determine the yield of products obtained by your chosen methods of preparation.

6. establish by chemical analysis the percentage of iron in the prepared sample of dried iron(II) sulphate

Presentation of results

1. You should write a laboratory report of your investigation. You will be asked to discuss this with your teacher or lecturer.

2. The introduction to the report should explain why the compounds need to be prepared.

3. An appendix should contain your initial ideas and plans. It should show how these were modified during the course of the investigation, either from your own experiences in trying to carry out the work or through discussions with your teacher/lecturer or others.

4. In the report's conclusion you should evaluate the methods used and make recommendations for improvements should the work be repeated.

5. At the end of the report you should list those sources you used to find information. This should be cross-referenced in the report itself. Make sure it is clear why you chose some pieces of information but rejected others.

Assessment

Were all the performance criteria met?   YES/NO

If NO, which ones were not met? _____

Indicative grades:

Planning	(1)	M	D
	(2)	M	D
Information-seeking and	(3)	M	D
information-handling	(4)	M	D
Evaluation	(5)	M	D
	(6)	M	D
Quality of outcomes	(7)	M	D
	(8)	M	D

Supporting information

You will find an information pack in the Learning Resource Centre entitled 'Chemicals and Health'. You should read through this as it will provide you with valuable information, together with a list of other resources which may be useful.

This assignment provides you with the opportunity to meet a number of the requirements of your GNVQ, including meeting all of the grading criteria. With assignments of this kind, you may need help. Don't be afraid to ask. Just think carefully about your questions and make sure they are sensible.

Designing an assignment

As you develop your scientific knowledge and skills it is important to see where this is leading. Your goal is to be able to recognise a scientific problem that needs tackling, and then to design, carry out and evaluate possible solutions.

Let's look again at the Folicin™ assignment and see how it was set up.

Most ideas are triggered by something we see, hear or read about. The trigger for the Folicin™ assignment was:

Assignment trigger

Reading the labels on boxes and bottles in the local chemist's shows that many of the pills, tablets and lotions in them contain inorganic compounds.

What are these compounds?
What are the medicines used for that contain them?
How are they made and their purity checked?
What regulations govern the ingredients of medicines?
Could lead to possible assignments relating to Units 1, 3 and 7.

If a practical assignment is developed, it is essential that a risk assessment is made and checked by your teacher/lecturer.

You can probably think of more questions yourself. The list could become very long! So how do we set up an assignment? Firstly, we need to concentrate on one aspect. In this case the use of iron(II) salts for the treatment of anaemia was chosen. There are several products on sale which provide an iron supplement to the diet. One particularly interesting one is Folicin™. It contains four ingredients, three of which are inorganic salts and one of which is an organic compound.

The next stage is to consider the requirements of the GNVQ. The questions asked in the trigger point towards Unit 1 (Laboratory safety and analysis of samples), Unit 3 (Obtain new substances) and Unit 7 (Human physiology and healthcare management). The specifications of these units need to be looked at carefully and the assignment set up in such a way that it provides an opportunity for some of the units' requirements to be satisfied. Similarly, the core skill units need to be borne in mind.

The next stage is to identify some objectives which are likely to be attainable. For the Folicin™ assignment, the following were chosen:

1 describe the symptoms of anaemia and its causes
2 describe the role of (a) iron(II) ions and other metal ions, (b) folic acid in maintaining a healthy body

Both of these objectives relate to aspects of Element 7.3 (Unit 7), though in a minor way – as you will see if you look closely at the specifications. Other work would be needed to provide sufficient evidence for this element.

3 plan the preparation of dried iron(II) sulphate, copper(II) sulphate, manganese(II) sulphate from the starting materials available
4 prepare sufficient quantities of ingredients to make 100 Folicin™ tablets (*Caution: samples of these compounds made in the laboratory must not be consumed!*)

5 determine the yield of products obtained by your chosen methods of preparation

Objectives 3–5 match the demands of Unit 3 well. They allow many of the performance criteria to be met within the range 'inorganic compounds'. The starting materials were chosen so that more than one type of reaction would be involved in the preparations. The range for 'organic compounds' and related types of reactions (elimination, addition etc.) is not covered, nor is the use of melting points, boiling points or chromatography to assess purity. A further assignment based on organic compounds and appropriately designed would be suitable.

6 establish by chemical analysis the percentage of iron in the prepared sample of dried iron(II) sulphate

This meets the requirements of elements 1.2 and 1.3 from Unit 1, within the range 'quantitative chemical tests'.

Overall this assignment could be a major source of evidence for Unit 3, though other tasks or assignments would need to focus on organic compounds. This is why the list of activities included amongst the tasks the preparation and analysis of aspirin and of paracetamol, and another assignment – establishing the identity of an unknown drug. Some evidence can be gained for parts of Units 1 and 7, but more substantial assignments will be required. Here are two further assignments for you to consider.

In summary the process you should follow to arrive at an assignment is as follows:
- find a trigger
- decide which particular aspect to concentrate on
- look at the specifications of the units to which the work most closely relates
- keep at hand the core skill unit specifications and the grading criteria
- set objectives which are attainable
- write the assignment, perhaps using these headings:
    – Background
    – Objectives
    – Presentation of results
    – Assessment
- match the assignment to performance criteria, range and grading criteria that can be satisfied.

If you are given an assignment you may be directed towards some resources, such as information packs in your library. Of course you may not have this if you design your own assignment.

Assignment

Depending on the approach you take you may have the opportunity to gather evidence for
Science units
Element 4.1 PCs 1, 2, 3, 4, 5
Element 4.2 PC 5
Element 4.3 PCs 1, 2, 3, 4
Element 6.1 PCs 1, 5
Element 6.2 PCs 1, 2, 3
Element 6.3 PCs 1, 2, 3, 4
Core skill units
Application of number
Elements 3.1, 3.2
Communication
Elements 3.2, 3.3
Grading
Planning
Information-seeking and information-handling
Evaluation
Quality of outcomes

Making the most of yeast

Background
Yeast is a living organism, *Saccharomyces*, which plays a vital role in the production of alcoholic drinks. Yeast respires glucose anaerobically. The main end products are alcohol (strictly speaking, ethanol, CH_3CH_2OH) and carbon dioxide (CO_2).

Objectives
Your objectives are to:

1. Grow yeast in the laboratory and count how many cells there are in a culture.

2. Vary the conditions under which yeast is kept, so as to see which conditions suit it best.

3. Investigate how yeasts are used commercially.

Growing yeast cells in the laboratory and counting how many of them there are in a culture

Yeast cells reproduce asexually by budding. A few yeast cells are allowed to multiply in a nutrient medium for a about a week, and the concentration of yeast cells present is determined at regular intervals.

Requirements

Light microscope
Haemocytometer
Graduated cylinder (50 or 100 cm^3)
Conical flask (250 cm^3)
Cotton wool
Pipette
Linear (usual, arithmetical) graph paper
Nutrient medium for yeast (e.g. cider, 2% sucrose or malt broth)
Suspension of brewer's yeast

Procedure

1 Using a clean measuring cylinder, measure 50 cm^3 of nutrient medium (e.g. cider) and pour it into a 250 cm^3 conical flask.

2 Swirl a flask containing a suspension of brewer's yeast and, once they are well mixed, add one drop to the flask of nutrient medium.

3 Plug the neck of this flask with cotton wool and place it in a warm cupboard or incubator at 20–25 °C.

4 The yeast cells can be counted by means of a **haemocytometer**. You may need to get someone to show you how to use one. A haemocytometer is a sort of specialised microscope slide which can be set up to contain a small, known volume of liquid. You can use it to count the number of yeast cells in a sample. Take cell counts two or three times a day for between four and seven days as follows. (i) Swirl the flask before withdrawing a sample onto the haemocytometer slide – swirling helps ensure that the cells are evenly distributed before they are counted. (ii) There is no need to dilute the sample. On each occasion you should use at least two samples to carry out at least two independent cell counts. (iii) Choose an appropriately sized square on the haemocytometer grid. (iv) Decide whether or not you are going to count a yeast cell in the process of budding as one cell or two. (v) Count sufficient haemocytometer squares to get a reliable measure of the number of yeast cells – 100 yeast cells should be sufficient. (vi) Record your results systematically and use them to calculate the number of yeast cells per cubic centimetre.

Treatment of experimental data

● Plot your results on graph paper, with the number of cells per cubic centimetre on the vertical axis against time on the horizontal axis.

● Plot a second graph of the results with, as before, time on the horizontal axis, but with the logarithm of the number of cells per cubic centimetre on the vertical axis.

Interpretations and conclusions
● Compare your two graphs. Forgetting about any differences in scale, are there any differences between the two plots? If there are, suggest reasons for these differences. What is the purpose of plotting log (number of cells) against time?

● From your log graph determine the length of time it takes for the population size to double (the doubling time) when the population is growing fastest (during the exponential phase).

Under which conditions does yeast grow best?
It makes commercial sense to ensure that yeast is kept at close to its optimal growing conditions. Carry out a practical investigation to study what these conditions might be. For example, what is the optimal temperature? How important is the nutrient medium in which yeast is grown? What difference does the oxygen concentration or pH make?

   You will need to plan your investigation carefully. Don't try too much at once! It may help to carry out a trial run to see if what you intend to vary (e.g. type of nutrient medium) seems to make any difference at all. Decide on the best way of controlling and monitoring the physical conditions you are interested in. How sensitive does your equipment need to be? How often will you record the conditions? Is datalogging equipment appropriate?

How are yeasts used commercially?
Find out how yeasts are used commercially. You should be able to get information from a variety of sources. For example, try to arrange a visit to a local brewery. Use a library to research the uses of yeast. Interview an amateur wine- or beer-maker. What are the health implications of

drinking beer, wine or spirits? Don't forget that yeasts are also used to make bread. Visit a bakery or talk to someone who makes their own bread. See if you can find out anything about different types of yeast. Nowadays, some yeasts are genetically engineered. Find out about the regulations involved and the safety implications. Under present UK laws, bread that is made using genetically engineered yeast need not be labelled as such. Should it be?

Presentation of results

When you have finished your study write it up clearly so that someone unfamiliar with what you have done can understand it. Make sure that you show how your plans changed as a result of what you found out. A really good report will show evidence of appropriate background reading and demonstrate that you can evaluate your work. Think carefully about how you present your results and conclusions – by means of prose, graphs, photographs and tables, for example.

Assessment

Were all the performance criteria met?   YES/NO

If NO, which ones were not met? _____

Indicative grades:

Planning	(1)	M	D
	(2)	M	D
Information-seeking and	(3)	M	D
information-handling	(4)	M	D
Evaluation	(5)	M	D
	(6)	M	D
Quality of outcomes	(7)	M	D
	(8)	M	D

Supporting information

You will find valuable background information in a number of books in the library, particularly Taylor, J. *Micro-organisms and Biotechnology*, Nelson, 1990.

This specimen assignment resulted from the following trigger in Unit 4:

Assignment trigger

Yeast

Grapes ferment naturally. Home brew kits rely on sachets of yeast, and different yeasts are used for wine and for beer.

In what other processes are yeasts used?
What properties are important for each use?
What factors affect the use of yeasts?
How could you investigate these factors in the laboratory?

If a practical assignment is developed, it is essential that a risk assessment is made and checked by your teacher/lecturer.

Could lead to possible assignments relating to Units 4 and 6.

There is no single way to design and carry out an assignment. Here is a different approach to different subject matter.

Assignment

Depending on the approach you take you have the opportunity to gather evidence for

Science units
Elements 5.2 PCs 1, 2, 3, 4
Element 2.1 PCs 1, 2, 3, 4
Element 8.1 PCs 1, 2, 3, 4
Element 8.3 PCs 1, 2, 3, 4, 5

Core skill units
Application of number
Elements 3.1, 3.2, 3.3

Communication units
Elements 3.1, 3.2, 3.3

Information technology units
Element 3.1
Element 3.2
Element 3.3

Investigating gutters

Background

Rainwater on roofs drains away through gutters and down pipes. The gutters should be designed to allow even the heaviest rainfall to be dealt with safely. However, gutters are not regarded as objects of beauty, so they aren't built to be any larger than they need to be!

Objectives

You are provided with samples of guttering of various sizes made from plastic tube cut lengthways. You have access to the usual laboratory apparatus. Your objectives are to:

1. find out the maximum rainfall which can be expected in your locality,

2. do experiments to determine the rate at which guttering can remove water from a roof,

3. analyse your data to determine rules for calculating the guttering required for a particular roof,

4. consider the different materials from which gutters can be made,

5. determine the best material for gutters given the conditions under which they have to do their job.

<table>
<tr><td>

Grading
Planning
Information-seeking
and information-
handling
Evaluation
Quality of outcomes

</td></tr>
</table>

Presentation of results

1. You are to present the findings of your investigation to the rest of the group, together with one or two other invited members of staff. The presentation should last for 10 minutes and you should use suitable visual aids.

2 Your introduction to the presentation should explain why the information you gathered is needed to design good gutters.

3. A written record of your initial ideas and plans should be kept and available to look at. It should show how these ideas were modified in the course of the investigation. List secondary sources of information at the end of the report.

4. In the conclusion to your presentation evaluate the methods used and make recommendations should the work be repeated.

Assessment

Were all the performance criteria met?   YES/NO

If NO, which ones were not met? _____

Indicative grades:

Planning	(1)	M	D
	(2)	M	D
Information-seeking and information-handling	(3)	M	D
	(4)	M	D
Evaluation	(5)	M	D
	(6)	M	D
Quality of outcomes	(7)	M	D
	(8)	M	D

As you can see, this is a much more open-ended kind of assignment than the one on yeast. The trigger from which it was developed was:

Assignment trigger

Removing rainwater

Water that falls on roofs must speedily be directed into the drains. If the gutters don't work properly, rainwater can cause a lot of damage and discomfort.

How much water do gutters have to cope with?
What design of gutter does the best job?
What properties should a gutter have?
What are the best materials for a gutter?

If a practical assignment is developed, it is essential that a risk assessment is made and checked by your teacher/lecturer.

Could lead to possible assignments relating to Units 2 and 5.

So where can you get ideas for assignments? You may well come up with a trigger of your own. If not you may find the ones given throughout this book helpful.

Physical constants, conversion factors and other useful data

Quantity	Symbol	Value and units
Speed of light in a vacuum	c	$299\ 792\ 458\ \text{m s}^{-1}$
Permeability of a vacuum	μ_0	$4\pi \times 10^{-7}\ \text{H m}^{-1}$
Permittivity of a vacuum	ε_0	$1/\mu_0 c^2$
		$= 8.854 \times 10^{-12}\ \text{F m}^{-1}$
Gravitational constant	G	$6.672 \times 10^{-11}\ \text{N m}^{-2}\ \text{kg}^{-2}$
Planck constant	h	$6.626 \times 10^{-34}\ \text{J s}$
Rydberg constant	R_H	$1.097 \times 10^{7}\ \text{m}^{-1}$
Avogadro constant	N_A	$6.022 \times 10^{23}\ \text{mol}^{-1}$
Molar gas constant	R	$8.314\ \text{J mol}^{-1}\ \text{K}^{-1}$
Boltzmann constant	k	$1.381 \times 10^{-23}\ \text{J K}^{-1}$
Molar volume of ideal gas, RT/p ($T = 273.15\ \text{K}$, $p = 100\ \text{kPa}$)	V_m	$2.24 \times 10^{-2}\ \text{m}^3\ \text{mol}^{-1}$
Elementary charge	e	$1.602 \times 10^{-19}\ \text{C}$
Electron specific charge	$-e/m_e$	$-1.759 \times 10^{-11}\ \text{C kg}^{-1}$
Electron rest mass	m_e	$9.109 \times 10^{-31}\ \text{kg}$
Proton rest mass	m_p	$1.673 \times 10^{-27}\ \text{kg}$
Neutron rest mass	m_n	$1.675 \times 10^{-27}\ \text{kg}$
Acceleration of free fall (at latitude 51°N)	g	$9.81\ \text{m s}^{-2}$
Mass of Earth	m_E	$5.976 \times 10^{24}\ \text{kg}$
Radius of Earth at equator	r_E	$6.378 \times 10^{6}\ \text{m}$
Density of air ($T = 273.15\ \text{K}$, $p = 100\ \text{kPa}$)	ρ_{air}	$1.247\ \text{kg m}^{-3}$
Density of water ($T = 298\ \text{K}$)	ρ_{water}	$1000\ \text{kg m}^{-3}$
Density of mercury	ρ_{Hg}	$13550\ \text{kg m}^{-3}$
Specific heat capacity of water	c_{H_2O}	$4.19\ \text{kJ kg}^{-1}\ \text{K}^{-1}$
'Ice-point' temperature	T_{ice}	$273\ \text{K}$
Steam point temperature	T_{st}	$373\ \text{K}$
Faraday constant	F	$9.648\ 456 \times 10^{4}\ \text{C mol}^{-1}$

1 calorie (cal) = 4.184 J

1 electrostatic unit of charge = $3.335\ 640 \times 10^{-10}$ C

$L\,e\text{V}^b = 96.484\ \text{kJ mol}^{-1}$

1 atmosphere (atm) = 760 torr ($\approx$ 760 mmHg) = 101 325 N m^{-2} (Pa)

1 ångström (Å) = 10^{-10} m = 10^{-8} cm = 10^{-4} μm
= 10^{-1} nm = 10^{2} pm

1 litre (l) = 10^{-3} m^3 = 1 dm^3 = 10^3 cm^3

1 curie (Ci) = 3.7×10^{10} s^{-1}

Conversion of Celsius temperature to thermodynamic temperature:

$\theta_c/°\text{C} = T/\text{K} - 273.150$

$\ln x = 2.303 \log_{10} x$

0 | The basic toolkit

Every worker needs the correct tools for their job. This unit is a basic toolkit that any scientist might use. It describes basic techniques that you will need when carrying out scientific activities.

Figure 0.1 *This scientist is using a microscope to investigate a blood sample. The magnifying power of the microscope allows the observation of characteristics which the naked eye cannot see.*

Scientists are involved in three broad types of activity: obtaining, characterising and controlling. The things they investigate may be alive, dead or may never have lived. These may be large, tiny, static or moving. This toolkit gives information about basic techniques; more specialised ones are found in the relevant units later in the book.

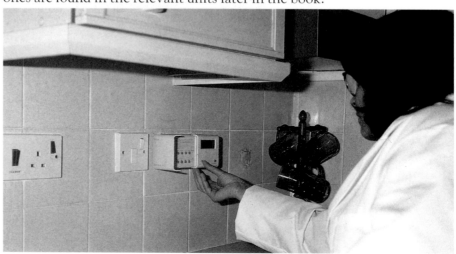

Figure 0.2 *This scientist is investigating the effectiveness of an electronic device for controlling a domestic central heating system.*

In carrying out your work in the laboratory you must ensure the safety of yourself and others. The importance of this is reflected in the first element of the Advanced GNVQ Science:

Element 1.1 Investigate health and safety practices in laboratories

You will need to:

- describe the hazards of working in laboratories
- identify the effects of safety regulations (e.g. regulations made under the Health and Safety at Work Act)
- review safety provision and practices in laboratories
- carry out a risk assessment and describe the safety procedure steps of an activity

▶ Assignment trigger: Hazards, page 4

▶ Assignment trigger: Waste, page 10

▶ Assignment trigger: Risk, page 11

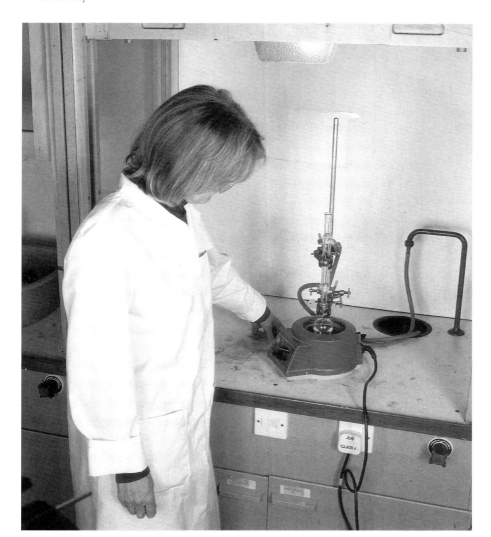

Figure 0.3 This scientist is taking all reasonable precautions while preparing a compound using chemicals which are known to be flammable and dangerous if inhaled.

This unit also covers two general aspects which you need to know about if you are to work successfully in science. You will need to be able to:

- classify and name the types of materials, substances and living things that scientists work with
- observe and make measurements of the properties and behaviour of these materials, substances and living things.

A hazard is anything that might cause harm
A risk is how likely it is that harm will be caused in a given situation

Safety regulations require
- **regular testing of electrical appliances**
- **control of substances hazardous to health**
- **prevention of exposure to hazardous substances**
- **definiton of danger areas**
- **defined procedures for emergencies**
- **use of personal protective equipment**

Safety in the laboratory

Fortunately most safe working practice is based on common sense, but this itself is not enough. You must acquire the specialist knowledge necessary to be able to identify **hazards**, reduce **risk** and be able to cope with dangerous situations if they arise.

To help employers and employees address risks at work seriously and effectively, a number of pieces of legislation have been passed by Parliament. The Health and Safety at Work Act (1974) (the HSW Act) empowered the Health and Safety Commission to produce detailed regulations. European Union directives on health and safety are implemented in the UK by means of regulations under the HSW Act. The Health and Safety Executive are responsible for appointing inspectors and enforcing the regulations. Some of the main safety regulations affecting you are shown in Table 0.1.

Table 0.1 Safety Legislation

Legislation	Examples of requirements
Management of Health and Safety at Work Regulations (1992)	*Employers must provide a safe working area and train and inform staff on safe working practice*
Control of Substances Hazardous to Health Regulations (1988) 'COSHH'	*Risk assessments arising from the use of hazardous substances must be made before they are used* Regulation 7: Preventing and Controlling Exposures *Measures must be taken to control or prevent exposure to hazardous substances*
Electricity at Work Regulations (1989) *for example: extension leads, kettles, power packs, self-illuminating microscopes*	*Regular maintenance and checking must be carried out by:* *–visual inspection by the user and a person appointed for the purpose* *–regular inspection and tests by a competent person* *Observe Health and Safety Executive guidelines on portable appliance testing*
Personal Protective Equipment (PPE regulations) at Work Regulations (1993)	Regulation 10: Proper Use of Protective Equipment *Employees must receive adequate training before using PPE and have a duty to use it as instructed* Regulation 11: Loss and Defects *Employees must take care of and report loss or defects in PPE*

Assignment trigger

Hazards

Many items in your laboratory have to carry safety warnings.

How do manufacturers tell consumers about the hazards of their products?
Why do they do it?
Is there an agreed system?

If a practical assignment is developed, it is essential that a risk assessment is made and checked by your teacher/lecturer

Could lead to possible assignments relating to Unit 1.

A safe working environment

Employers and educational establishments are legally obliged to provide you with a safe working environment, including laboratories. You must also be given training and information on safe working practice.

You are legally obliged to take reasonable care to protect your own and other's safety. This includes the correct use of safety equipment. You must:

- know what to do in an emergency such as a fire
- be able to carry out risk assessments for activities, especially those that you design for yourself
- make sure that your teacher or lecturer checks a risk assessment before practical work begins
- make yourself aware of the risks and safety measures **before** you start.

Table 0.2 Steps to carry out a risk assessment for an activity

Procedure	Notes and comments
1 Main stages/procedures of the activity are determined	These should be recorded in outline. How substances and equipment are to be used is determined, as are the quantities of any substances to be used
2 Hazards are identified	Common hazards and symbols are shown in Figure 0.4 and Table 0.3. Useful references for the identification of hazards are listed on page 6
3 Risks are assessed	Methods by which you and others may be exposed to risk are determined, including possible accidents. How likely is harm to occur?
4 Methods to reduce risks to acceptable levels are determined	Change to a safer alternative procedure or possibly smaller scale working. Use of protective equipment may be necessary. Take suitable control measures such as the use of a fume cupboard. Procedures must be in place for possible accidents, e.g. to deal with spills and to give access to first aid. Disposal of wastes must be taken into account. If risk cannot be reduced to acceptable levels, the activity must not be carried out.
5 Safety measures are recorded	Everyone involved must receive adequate information on the risks. Site procedures must be taken into account, for example laboratory rules and action in case of emergency such as fire.

toxic

oxidising

corrosive

explosive

risk of electric shock

harmful or irritant

radioactive

flammable

biological hazard (biohazard)

laser radiation

Figure 0.4 *Common hazard symbols*

Table 0.3 Some examples of hazards

Hazard	Effect	Examples/Notes
Pathogen	disease causing organism	typhoid bacillus
Carcinogen	causes cancer	benzene, aflotoxin
Mutagen	changes genetic code (DNA)	X-rays
Teratogen	damages developing fetus	thalidomide
Explosive		hydrogen/air
Oxidising	oxidising agent (helps things to burn)	sodium peroxide; risk of fire or explosion if reacts with combustible material
Flammable	can ignite	*flash point* means temperature at which the vapour above liquid ignites when flame applied *auto-ignition point* means temperature at which vapour ignites spontaneously e.g. hexane −28 °C (flash point) and 250 °C (auto-ignition point)
Toxic	poisonous	hydrogen cyanide, mercury compounds; may enter through skin, ingestion, inhalation
Harmful	not in another category: less obvious longer term effects	greater than $0.01 \, mol \, dm^{-3}$ lead salts can accumulate in the body
Corrosive	attacks and dissolves materials	greater than $0.5 \, mol \, dm^{-3}$ nitric acid, 35% ammonia solution
Irritant	causes skin inflammation or rashes/ dangerous to eyes	nitric acid less than $0.5 \, mol \, dm^{-3}$ greater than $0.1 \, mol \, dm^{-3}$
Radiation	higher levels are mutagenic and carcinogenic	radiation from uranium salts, ultraviolet light
Electrical	shock or fire	portable mains appliances particularly risky

Useful sources of risk assessments include:
- CLEAPSS *Hazcards* (new edition free to members, 1995)
- CLEAPSS *Laboratory Handbook* (safety sections updated, 1995)
- *Merck Index*
- BDH and other manufacturers'/suppliers' catalogues and data sheets
- *Hazardous chemicals: a manual for schools and colleges* (SSERC, 1979)
- *Topics in safety* (ASE, 1988)
- *Microbiology: an HMI guide for schools and Further Education*, (HMSO, 1990)
- *Safeguards in the school laboratory* (ASE, 1990)

Q 1 What are the procedures in case of fire in each of the rooms that you use? Where are the nearest fire alarms and telephones?

Safe working in the laboratory and with chemicals

Fortunately accidents in the laboratory are rare. You are more likely to suffer an injury at home. However, there are certain precautions and procedures that you can adopt to reduce risk. Most of these amount to common sense, but it is important to appreciate that you need to be alert to identify hazards and need to make safe working practice a habit. You should make yourself aware of the meanings of the hazard warning symbols on things that you use and the precautions that are necessary. You should be able to find the correct sources to be able to conduct your own risk assessments (though you should never do anything without first checking with your supervisor). It is wise to treat all chemicals as potentially dangerous. You should also know the procedures that should be followed in the case of accidents.

Remember that the law requires you to take reasonable care to protect yourself and others. The COSHH Regulations require you to find out what safety precautions are necessary before you start any practical work. Your first duty when using unfamiliar chemicals or apparatus is to find out about the safety aspects. Sometimes your supervisor will have indicated the hazards to you. If so you must take note of their advice. If not, you must establish the hazards and associated risks for yourself and then check these with your supervisor before you start. Table 0.4 (Safe working practice in laboratories) lists important safety points that you should remember and always carry out. Note that this list is for general guidance only and is *not* comprehensive. *You* must be alert to the hazards and risks for each specific situation in which you find yourself.

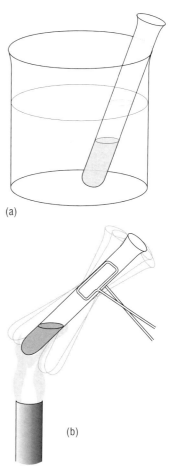

(a)

(b)

Figure 0.5 *(a) Flammable liquids with low boiling points should be heated in a boiling tube, no more than one-fifth full, placed in a beaker of hot water. (b) Non-flammable material should be heated gently in a Pyrex boiling tube, over a blue Bunsen flame. The tube should again be no more than one-fifth full, tilted so that the tube-holder is to one side of the flame and the mouth of the tube is pointing away from anybody nearby. The tube should be shaken gently.*

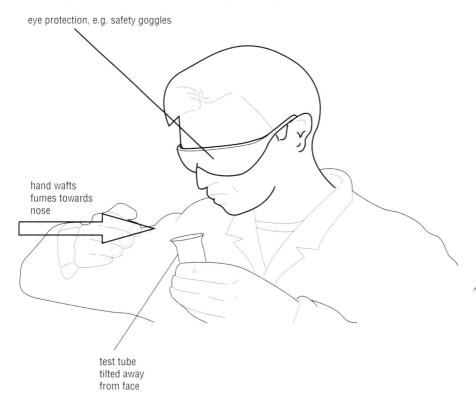

eye protection, e.g. safety goggles

hand wafts fumes towards nose

test tube tilted away from face

Note: Fill lungs with air *before* smelling and waft gently with extreme caution. *Inform your teacher/lecturer if you are asthmatic.*

Figure 0.6 *Correct procedure for smelling gases.*

Table 0.4 Safe working practice in laboratories

Area for special consideration	Common problems	Action
Heating	Fire, scalds and burns e.g. flammable solvent or long hair ignites, boiling liquid spurts out of test tube.	**Use correct procedures for:** • *heating flammable liquids (no naked flames)* • *heating with a Bunsen burner* *These are illustrated in Figure 0.5*
Glassware	Glass is fragile and will break or shatter if dropped or heated inappropriately. Broken glass is razor sharp and can cause from minor cuts to severe lacerations.	**Care** *is essential:* • *place apparatus on firm surface* • *avoid clutter and crowding* • *do not attempt to push glass tubing or thermometers into bungs or remove them without special training* • *never hold bottles by the neck* • *never attempt to force tight stoppers or to push stoppers in too tight* • *use correct type and size of Pyrex vessels when heating* • *wear eye protection if there is any risk of glass breaking* • *do not use cracked, chipped or scratched glassware* • *dispose of broken glass with care; a special bin should be provided* • *tie back long hair*
Personal Protection	Skin contact with, absorption, ingestion or inhalation of harmful, irritant, corrosive or mutagenic chemicals or harmful organisms causing e.g. burns, allergic reactions, asphyxiation, infectious diseases	**Prevent or restrict contact:** **Always** 1. Use appropriate protective clothing: • *wear a buttoned up lab coat* • *wear shoes that will protect your feet (not open-toed sandals)* • *use eye or face protection (e.g. goggles or mask) when any operation hazardous to eyes is being conducted by anyone in the lab* • *wear gloves if there is a risk of contact with dangerous chemicals* 2. Follow the correct procedures: • *use the minimum quantities of materials necessary* • *make sure all containers are labelled appropriately* • *use safety fillers when pipetting liquids* • *smell gases with extreme caution using the correct procedure illustrated in Figure 0.6* • *use a fume cupboard when working with toxic, irritant or corrosive chemicals* • *use a safety screen if there is any risk of apparatus shattering or exploding* • *check in advance the procedure for dealing with any spillage* • *report all accidents, spills or breakages to your supervisor, no matter how small they may be* • *clean/clear up apparatus and surfaces after use* • *dispose of materials safely at the end of a practical session* • *wash hands after practical work*

Table 0.4 Continued

Area for special consideration	Common problems	Action
		Never • *put your thumb over the end of a test tube to shake it: stopper with a bung* • *taste or smell anything unless instructed to do so* • *eat, drink, smoke or apply cosmetics in the laboratory*
Heavy objects	Incorrect lifting can cause permanent back damage; dropped objects may injure feet	**Use correct lifting procedure**, *keeping back straight or ask for assistance. Make sure heavy items are placed on strong, stable surfaces.*
Emergencies	Accidents, injuries or fire require prompt action to take remedial action or raise the alarm	**Never work alone.** *For each area that you work in, know the locations of nearest:* • *fire alarm and fire evacuation assembly point* • *isolation switches/valves for electricity and gas* • *telephone* • *eyewashing tap or bottle* • *trained first aider* • *first aid kit* • *fire extinguisher (but priorities are raise alarm, evacuate area)* • *learn basic first aid procedures and ideally obtain a first aid qualification.*

 2 A typical set of laboratory rules could be:
- Wear appropriate protective clothing
- Know what to do in the case of fire
- Do not carry out any hand to mouth operations in the laboratory
- Report accidents
- Take care with glassware
- Know hazard warning signs
- Be organised
- Be tidy

a) How would you explain the need for each of these rules to a newcomer to the laboratory?
b) Rewrite those that you think could be expressed better or need further explanation.
c) What rules would you add?
d) Try to place these or other sets of rules in order of importance. Discuss this with others.

> **Laboratory provision and practice require regular safety reviews.**

Safe working with micro-organisms

This is covered in detail by the HMSO publication *Microbiology: an HMI guide for schools and Further Education* (HMSO, 1990). Some of the main issues are outlined here.

- *Aseptic* (sterile) techniques should always be employed when cells are cultured in the laboratory. This prevents the accidental contamination of laboratory cultures or laboratory workers.

- *All* cultures of micro-organisms at school or college level should be treated as though they contain *pathogens* (disease-causing organisms). This is because they may accidentally enter a culture from outside, or a micro-organism may change, for example by gene mutation.
- Culture techniques lead to very large numbers of microbes being grown, increasing the *risk* associated with them. They can enter the body by inhalation, ingestion or through cuts in the skin.

Q 3 A single bacterium that enters a culture from the air can divide once every 20 minutes in the ideal conditions of temperature and food provided. How many bacteria could such a single cell have increased to after a three-day incubation?

Figure 0.7 Reducing risks when culturing microbes

Microbes are in the air

Remove lids from culture bottles and plates for the minimum time necessary.

Holding the lid over the dish helps prevent entry of microbes.

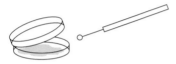

Tape lids on Petri dishes, but do not seal.

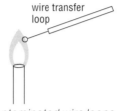
wire transfer loop

Resterilise contaminated wire loops by gradually introducing them into the Bunsen flame. Heat to red heat up to handle.

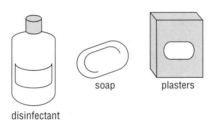
soap   plasters
disinfectant

Strict hygiene: wash hands thoroughly; clean work surfaces (preferably using disinfectant) before and after work to reduce risk of contaminating cultures. Take care with sharp instruments and cover cuts with waterproof plasters to prevent entry of micro-organisms.

Pathogens may be present in cultures.

incubator

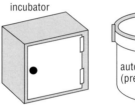

autoclave (pressure cooker)

Incubate at 25 °C using nutrient agar, not at 37 °C using e.g. blood agar. Autoclave (pressure cook) cultures unopened.

Assignment trigger

Waste

Houses, factories, hospitals all produce harmful waste which must be disposed of.

How do they dispose of it?
Are there regulations which have to be adhered to?

If a practical assignment is developed, it is essential that a risk assessment is made and checked by your teacher/lecturer.

Could lead to possible assignments relating to Unit 1.

Safe working with electricity

Electricity is an important hazard in the laboratory. There are two main risks: *shock* and *fire*. Safe practice includes:
Safe handling:
- avoid water
  - do not handle equipment or switches with wet or damp hands or when standing on a wet floor
  - no water on bench or likely risk of spillage over apparatus

- no trailing leads
- avoid extension leads
- less than 20V for open terminals (60V can be fatal)
- care with flammable liquids or gases (e.g. charging lead/acid batteries generates a hydrogen/oxygen mixture)
- HT (high tension) equipment should be clearly labelled and treated with caution
- know how to switch off the supply (labs have isolating switches)

Safe maintenance:
- visual check for
  - broken plugs
  - frayed or cracked leads
  - inner insulation visible (e.g. cable pulling out of plug)
  - loose or damaged casings
- competent person checks equipment and records this regularly (including fuses and earths)

Other safety considerations

Each situation generates its own hazards and risks which the scientist must take into account.

 4 Each area will have its own site procedures to ensure safety:
a) What are the rules for each laboratory that you work in?
b) Are they adequate?
c) How can you isolate the gas and electricity supplies?
d) What provision is there for the disposal of wastes?
e) How often are electrical equipment and fume cupboards tested?

Keep alert! Safety problems can arise unexpectedly. A mysterious series of explosions in school refrigerators was eventually traced to rats kept for dissection. The rats were killed using ether. Sufficient remained in their lungs to diffuse into the air in the refrigerators. This formed an explosive mixture, detonated by the sparks of the thermostat micro-switches!

Assignment trigger

Risk

Everything in life is risky. This includes work in the laboratory. By law, all procedures must be preceded by a risk assessment.

What is a risk assessment?
Who lays down the regulations?
What is the difference between a risk and a hazard?

If a practical assignment is developed, it is essential that a risk assessment is made and checked by your teacher/lecturer.

Could lead to possible assignments relating to Unit 1.

Naming substances and living things

It is vitally important to have unambiguous and systematic ways of naming and classifying things, whether living or non-living.

The world around us may be living (animals, plants, microbes) or non-living, which can be further sub-divided into:
- once living (fossils, coal, oil)
- never living (rocks and minerals).

Living and non-living

Perhaps surprisingly, living and non-living things have much in common. Living things (called *organisms*) are made up of chemical compounds, just as non-living material is. However, living systems organise and concentrate chemical compounds that are not common in non-living materials. This requires energy.

The part of the Earth in which we find organisms is known as the *biosphere*. When we look more closely, we find it is made up of numerous ecosystems. An ecosystem consists of a community of organisms and their non-living environment.

Table 0.5 Elements of the earth

The approximate composition of the Earth and the Earth's crust (expressed as percentage by mass)					
	Earth	**Earth's crust**		**Earth**	**Earth's crust**
iron	34.6	5.1	sodium	0.57	2.8
oxygen	29.5	46.4	chromium	0.26	<0.1
silicon	15.2	28.0	manganese	0.22	<0.1
magnesium	12.7	2.0	cobalt	0.13	<0.1
nickel	2.4	<0.1	phosphorus	0.10	0.11
sulphur	1.9	0.10	potassium	0.07	2.5
calcium	1.1	3.5	titanium	0.05	0.58
aluminium	1.1	8.1			

Note: The Earth's crust is the relatively thin outer layer of our planet. However, it is an invaluable reservoir of resources, both organic and inorganic.

Table 0.6 Elements of the human body

The composition of the human body (expressed as percentage by mass)			
oxygen	65.0	sulphur	0.25
carbon	18.0	sodium	0.15
hydrogen	10.0	chlorine	0.15
nitrogen	3.0	magnesium	0.05
calcium	1.5	iron	0.0004
phosphorus	1.0	zinc	0.0004
potassium	0.35		

Organisms: living things

What distinguishes a living organism such as yourself from non-living material such as a crystal of salt? Since you are essentially a collection of chemical compounds, you have much in common!

A living system is able to carry out these processes:

- reproduction
- respiration
- excretion
- growth
- nutrition
- movement
- sensation

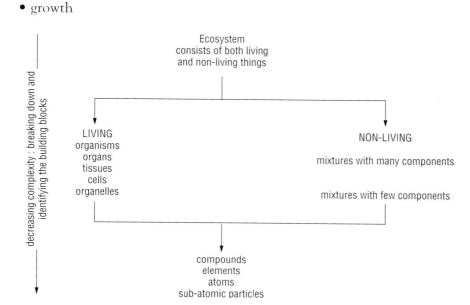

Figure 0.8 *A classification of living and non-living things*

Elements, compounds and mixtures

All matter can be classified into one of the three basic groups: elements, compounds and mixtures.

Elements

Elements are the building blocks from which all material is made, whether it is living or non-living. Over 100 are known. About 90 occur naturally (either alone or in chemical combination with other elements) and nearly twenty more have been made. Each element is given a name and a symbol and has its own characteristic properties.

An element cannot be broken down into a simpler chemical substance. All of the atoms which make up a particular element contain the same number of protons in their nuclei and therefore the same number of electrons. Atoms of the same element but with different numbers of neutrons are called isotopes.

Elements are often described as metals or non-metals. The division is not sharp, however, and some elements possess properties which make it difficult to classify them. Silicon is an example.

Elements may be gases, liquids or solids under normal conditions.

- noble gases consist of uncombined atoms;
- other gaseous elements are molecular (e.g. oxygen and chlorine)
- solid elements have simple molecular structures (e.g. sulphur, phosphorus), giant covalent structures (e.g. carbon, silicon) or giant metallic structures (e.g. copper, sodium).

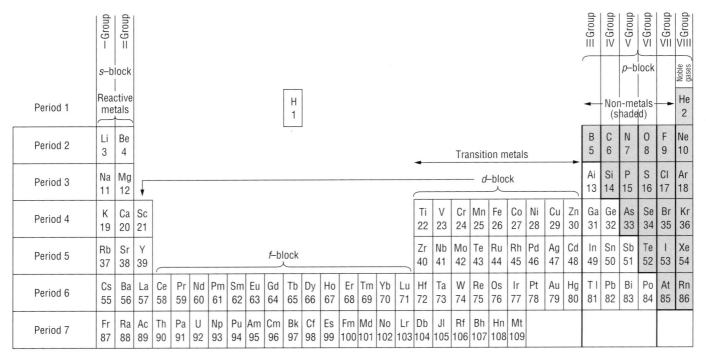

Figure 0.9 *The elements are arranged in order of increasing atomic number in the form of a table, the Periodic Table. The properties of the elements change from left to right across a row (called a Period). For example, the elements tend to change from metals to non-metals. A Period ends and a new one is started so that elements with similar properties are found in the same column. The columns are called Groups.*

> Over 100 elements are known. They combine chemically to form compounds, of which more than 10 million are known. Compounds can be broken down into simpler substances, elements cannot.

Compounds

Elements combine to form chemical **compounds**. A compound consisting of just two elements is called a binary compound. Others consist of three or more elements. Generally:

- metals do not form compounds with other metals (though they are often 'mixed' to produce useful materials called alloys)
- metals combine with non-metals to form ionic compounds
- non-metals combine with one another to form covalent compounds.

A characteristic of a compound is that its elements are always present in a constant ratio. For example:

1. any sample of magnesium oxide contains 60% by mass magnesium and 40% by mass oxygen;
2. any sample of calcium carbonate contains 40% calcium, 12% carbon and 48% oxygen (all by mass).

Compounds have different properties to the elements from which they are formed. For example, sodium chloride (common salt) is a hard white crystalline solid, soluble in water and essential to a healthy diet. Yet sodium is a soft, shiny metal which reacts violently with water and chlorine is a yellow-green gas which is extremely poisonous.

Compounds can be broken down into the elements from which they are made (though not always easily). For example, sodium chloride is formed when sodium is burnt in chlorine; molten sodium chloride is broken down into its constituent elements again by electrolysis.

Compounds which are gases or liquids at room temperature and pressure have simple molecular structures. The atoms in a molecule are held together by covalent bonds. Solid compounds are either molecular (covalent bonding within molecules) or have giant structures. The atoms in compounds with giant structures are held together by covalent or ionic bonds.

We may classify compounds as *organic* or *inorganic*. Those which contain the element carbon are generally said to be organic, others are inorganic. Oxides of carbon, carbonates, hydrogencarbonates and cyanides are considered inorganic even though they contain carbon.

Compounds which can be extracted from plants and animals are called *natural products*. They are usually organic (e.g. amino acids, proteins, carbohydrates). Some biologically important compounds are organometallic (for example, some enzymes).

Mixtures

Any number of elements or compounds may be physically combined to give mixtures. Although all living things are mixtures of compounds, we usually use the term to refer to non-living systems. Mixtures may have large numbers of components or few. A component may be present in relatively small or large quantities.

The components of a mixture may be separated by physical methods such as filtration, distillation or chromatography. Air is a mixture made up of nitrogen, oxygen, argon, water vapour and carbon dioxide and other gases. It can be separated into its components by fractional distillation. This is used industrially, for example to obtain pure nitrogen and pure oxygen.

Nomenclature: naming compounds

Naming compounds must be unambiguous. Misunderstanding must be avoided and effective communication promoted. To help, the Commissions of the International Union of Pure and Applied Chemistry (IUPAC) has made recommendations for naming chemical compounds. They cover inorganic and organic compounds.

> **Systematic naming is called nomenclature.**

Oxidation numbers

Oxidation numbers are helpful in chemical nomenclature. An oxidation number is a numerical value assigned to atoms of an element when that element is:

- in the free state, e.g. Cl_2
- present in ionic or covalent compounds, e.g. NaCl or $SiCl_4$
- present in simple or complex ions, e.g. Cl^- or ClO_4^-

The rules for assigning oxidation numbers to atoms of an element are:

1 The oxidation number of atoms in an uncombined element is zero.

2 In combination with other elements, the oxidation number of atoms of some elements remains the same, whether they are found in ionic or covalent compounds, simple or complex ions:

> **The oxidation ($Ox(B)$) number of an atom, (B), may be thought of as the charge it would carry if all the other atoms in the species were removed as their common ions.**

Table 0.7 Oxidation numbers and exceptions

Element	Oxidation number	Exceptions
fluorine	-1	none
oxygen	-2	F_2O, $Ox(O) = +2$; peroxides, $Ox(O) = -1$
hydrogen	+1	ionic hydrides, $Ox(H) = -1$
Group I	+1	
Group II	+2	
chlorine	-1	compounds formed with fluorine and oxygen

3 The sum of the oxidation numbers of atoms in a compound is zero.

4 The sum of the oxidation numbers in an ion equals the charge on the ion.

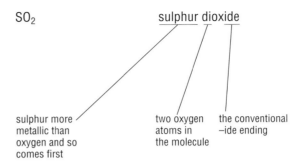

Figure 0.10 *The naming patterns for binary compounds with simple molecular structures*

Prefixes used in naming organic and inorganic compounds	
Number of atoms	**Prefix**
1	mono
2	di
3	tri
4	tetra
5	penta
6	hexa
7	hepta
8	octa
9	nona
10	deca

Binary inorganic compounds

By convention the most metallic element comes first in both the name and formula of the compound. Binary compounds end in -ide. There are a few exceptions. Non-metal hydrides such as water, ammonia and methane are common ones.

In binary compounds with simple molecular structures, the most metallic element comes first in the name. The numbers of atoms of each element present (given by the molecular formula) are shown in the name by prefixes (see Figure 0.10).

In binary compounds with giant structures or non-simple molecular structures, again the most metallic element comes first in the name. Roman numerals in brackets are called oxidation numbers (see Figure 0.11).

The oxidation number is omitted for elements which always display the same value. For example, sodium is always +1 and so NaBr is simply sodium bromide rather than sodium(I) bromide. Other examples are: KCl, potassium chloride; $MgCl_2$, magnesium chloride; CaO, calcium oxide; Al_2O_3, aluminium oxide; $ZnCl_2$, zinc chloride.

Note that the sum of the oxidation numbers for each atom of the compounds in Table 0.8 is zero.

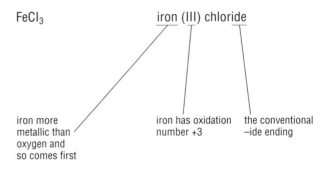

Figure 0.11 *The naming patterns of binary compounds with giant structures*

Table 0.8 Names of binary compounds: examples of the use of oxidation numbers

Name and formula	Oxidation numbers
Simple molecular oxides	
carbon monoxide, CO	$Ox(C) = +2$; $Ox(O) = -2$
carbon dioxide, CO_2	$Ox(C) = +4$; $Ox(O) = -2$
nitrogen dioxide, NO_2	$Ox(N) = +4$; $Ox(O) = -2$
dinitrogen tetraoxide, N_2O_4	$Ox(N) = +4$; $Ox(O) = -2$
sulphur trioxide, SO_3	$Ox(S) = +6$; $Ox(O) = -2$
Other oxides	
phosphorus(V) oxide, P_2O_5	$Ox(P) = +5$; $Ox(O) = -2$
phosphorus(III) oxide, P_2O_3	$Ox(P) = +3$; $Ox(O) = -2$
iron(II) oxide, FeO	$Ox(Fe) = +2$; $Ox(O) = -2$
iron(III) oxide, Fe_2O_3	$Ox(Fe) = +3$; $Ox(O) = -2$
copper(II) oxide, CuO	$Ox(Cu) = +2$; $Ox(O) = -2$
copper(I) oxide, Cu_2O	$Ox(Cu) = +1$; $Ox(O) = -2$
Simple molecular halides	
bromine pentafluoride, BrF_5	$Ox(Br) = +5$; $Ox(F) = -1$
phosphorus trichloride, PCl_3	$Ox(P) = +3$; $Ox(Cl) = -1$
disulphur dichloride, S_2Cl_2	$Ox(S) = +1$; $Ox(Cl) = -1$
tin tetrachloride, $SnCl_4$	$Ox(Sn) = +4$; $Ox(Cl) = -1$
titanium tetrachloride, $TiCl_4$	$Ox(Ti) = +4$; $Ox(Cl) = -1$
Other halides	
iron(II) fluoride, FeF_2	$Ox(Fe) = +2$; $Ox(F) = -1$
tin(II) chloride, $SnCl_2$	$Ox(Sn) = +2$; $Ox(F) = -1$
copper(II) chloride, $CuCl_2$	$Ox(Cu) = +2$; $Ox(F) = -1$
copper(I) iodide, CuI	$Ox(Cu) = +1$; $Ox(I) = -1$

An acid may be defined as a compound which dissociates (or ionises) in water to give hydrated hydrogen ions, $H^+(aq)$. The hydrogen atoms in an acid which dissociate like this are called 'ionisable hydrogen atoms'. Only ionisable hydrogen atoms can be replaced when a salt is formed.

Not all oxoanions have parent oxoacids which can be isolated as pure compounds. For example, carbonic acid 'H_2CO_3' does not exist but hydrogen carbonates and carbonates do.

Oxoacids and their salts

Oxoacids contain oxygen. Table 0.9 is a list of the names of some important oxoacids and oxoanions. Some important examples are sulphuric acid (H_2SO_4), nitric acid (HNO_3) and phosphoric(V) acid (H_3PO_4).

Salts form in acid-base reactions. Ionisable hydrogen atoms in an acid are replaced by metal or ammonium ions. When they are all replaced, a normal salt is formed, for example, calcium sulphate ($CaSO_4$). The two hydrogen atoms in H_2SO_4 have been replaced by one calcium atom.

When only some of the ionisable hydrogens are replaced, an acid salt is formed. For example, H_3PO_4 forms a normal salt Na_3PO_4 and two acid salts, Na_2HPO_4 and NaH_2PO_4. Of course, acids with only one ionisable hydrogen can only form normal salts.

Table 0.9 Oxoacids and oxoanions. In each $Ox(H) = +1$ and $Ox(O) = -2$

Formula and common name	Oxidation number	Sum of oxidation numbers
H_2SO_4, sulphuric acid	$Ox(S) = +6$	0
HSO_4^-, hydrogensulphate ion	$Ox(S) = +6$	-1
SO_4^{2-}, sulphate ion	$Ox(S) = +6$	-2
H_2SO_3, sulphurous acid	$Ox(S) = +4$	0
HSO_3^-, hydrogen sulphite ion	$Ox(S) = +4$	-1
SO_3^{2-}, sulphite ion	$Ox(S) = +4$	-2
HNO_3, nitric acid	$Ox(N) = +5$	0
NO_3^-, nitrate ion	$Ox(N) = +5$	-1
HNO_2, nitrous acid	$Ox(N) = +3$	0
NO_2^-, nitrite ion	$Ox(N) = +3$	-1
HCO_3^-, hydrogencarbonate ion	$Ox(C) = +4$	-1
CO_3^{2-}, carbonate ion	$Ox(C) = +4$	-2
H_3PO_4, phosphoric(V) acid	$Ox(P) = +5$	0
$H_2PO_4^-$, dihydrogenphosphate(V) ion	$Ox(P) = +5$	-1
HPO_4^{2-}, hydrogenphosphate(V) ion	$Ox(P) = +5$	-2
PO_4^{3-}, phosphate(V) ion	$Ox(P) = +5$	-3
MnO_4^-, manganate(VII) ion	$Ox(Mn) = +7$	-1
$Cr_2O_7^{2-}$, dichromate(VI) ion	$Ox(Cr) = +6$	-2
CrO_4^{2-}, chromate(VI) ion	$Ox(Cr) = +6$	-2

Hydrates

Many compounds crystallise from aqueous solution as hydrates. These are compounds which have a fixed amount of water present. In the formula, a full stop is used to separate the formula of the anhydrous compound from the amount of water present in the hydrate. Naming always follows the pattern in the example below.

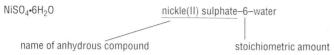

Figure 0.12 *Naming pattern of typical hydrate*

Other examples include $CuSO_4.5H_2O$, copper(II) sulphate-5-water, and $Na_2CO_3.10H_2O$, sodium carbonate-10-water.

Naming hydrocarbons

The nomenclature for **organic compounds** is based on the systematic naming of hydrocarbons.

Hydrocarbons are organic compounds which contain the elements hydrogen and carbon only. There are four categories: alkanes, alkenes, alkynes and arenes (also called aromatic hydrocarbons). Alkanes are said to be saturated because each carbon atom has four other atoms bonded to it (the maximum allowed by its valency of 4). The others are unsaturated because at least one carbon atom in the molecule has three or less other atoms bonded to it.

Alkanes are the simplest of the hydrocarbons. Each carbon atom in an alkane is bonded to four other atoms (either hydrogen atoms or carbon atoms). They may have unbranched, branched or ring structures (see Figure 0.13).

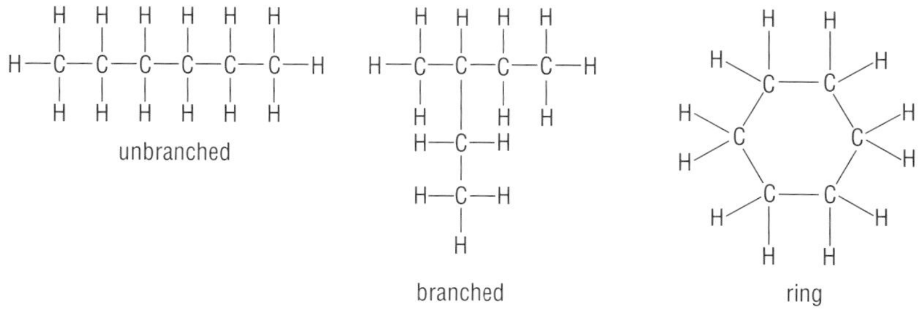

Figure 0.13 *Six carbon atoms may be joined in different ways. The arrangement of the carbon atoms (ignoring other atoms) is often called the carbon skeleton.*

The names of all aliphatic organic compounds derive from the names of the unbranched alkanes (Figure 0.14).

CH_4	methane
$CH_3 CH_3$	ethane
$CH_3 CH_2 CH_3$	propane
$CH_3 CH_2 CH_2 CH_3$	butane
$CH_3 CH_2 CH_2 CH_2 CH_3$	pentane
$CH_3 CH_2 CH_2 CH_2 CH_2 CH_3$	hexane

Figure 0.14 *The first six unbranched alkanes. The names of all alkanes end in -ane and the prefix tells us how many carbon atoms are present. Nomenclature of aliphatic compounds is based on the names of the unbranched alkanes.*

Organic compounds fall into two broad categories:
1 aliphatic – containing only discrete carbon-carbon bonds (whether they are single, double or triple);
2 aromatic – containing delocalised carbon-carbon bonds, most commonly in six-membered rings called benzene rings.
Both types derive their names from the parent hydrocarbons.

Alkanes are saturated, aliphatic hydrocarbons
- saturated – since four is the maximum number of bonds a carbon atom can form;
- aliphatic compounds – since they contain only localised covalent bonds;
- hydrocarbons – since they consist only of carbon and hydrogen

Homologous series: compounds which differ only in their chain length, increasing by a – CH_2 unit as the series is ascended. For example, $CH_3OHCH_3CH_2OH$, $CH_3CH_2CH_2OH$, $CH_3CH_2CH_2CH_2OH$, $CH_3CH_2CH_2CH_2CH_2OH$ are members of the homologous series of unbranched primary alcohols.

We often refer to fragments of the alkane which appear in more complicated organic molecules. These fragments are called alkyl groups. They may be thought of as alkanes from which a hydrogen atom has been removed. Table 0.10 shows the formulae of the alkyl groups derived from the simple, unbranched alkanes.

Table 0.10 Alkyl groups derived from unbranched alkanes

Parent alkane	Alkyl group	Name
CH_4	$-CH_3$	methyl
C_2H_6	$-C_2H_5$	ethyl
C_3H_8	$-C_3H_7$	propyl
C_4H_{10}	$-C_4H_9$	butyl
C_5H_{12}	$-C_5H_{11}$	pentyl
C_6H_{14}	$-C_6H_{13}$	hexyl

The name for a **branched alkane** must tell us:
- the name of the alkane from which the longest unbranched carbon skeleton derives
- the names of substituent alkyl group
- the number of substituents
- the positions of substituents.

An example will show how this works. The alkane below is called 2,3-dimethylpentane.

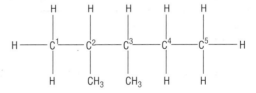

Figure 0.15 *2,3-dimethylpentane*

The name is made up as follows:

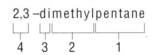

Figure 0.16 *Arriving at the name 2,3-dimethylpentane*

1 The longest unbranched chain has five carbon atoms.
2 The substituents are methyl groups.
3 There are two such groups.
4 They are located on the second and third carbon atoms in the chain (they could be considered to be on the third and fourth carbon atoms if we count from the opposite direction, but the rule is that the numbers used are as low as possible).

Alkenes contain a $>C=C<$ bond. The name of an alkene is based on the alkane of the same chain length. The ending -ene indicates the double bond.

> **The principles behind naming branched alkanes apply to naming all organic compounds.**

Arenes are ring compounds. It is the delocalised electrons, shared by carbon atoms in the ring, which distinguish aromatic compounds from aliphatic compounds.

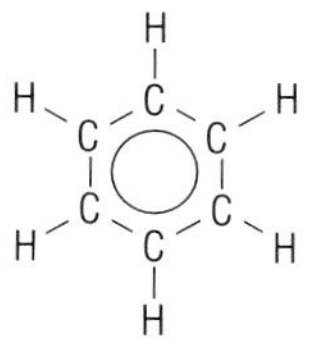

benzene

usually written as

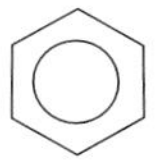

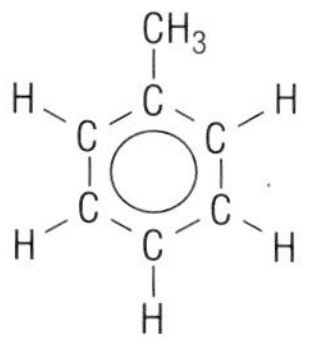

methylbenzene

usually written as

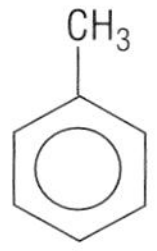

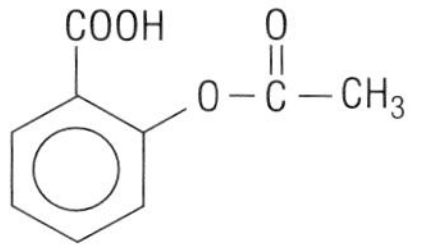

aspirin
– a painkiller

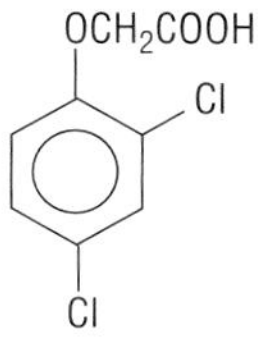

2,4–D
– a weedkiller

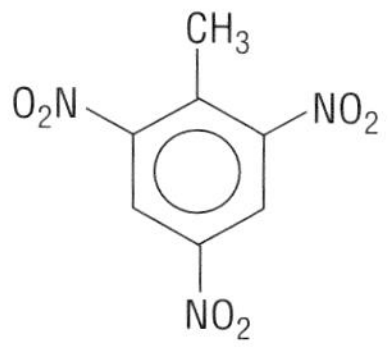

TNT
– an explosive

Esters are named by treating them as if they were derived from an alkyl group and a group based on a carboxylic acid. The name of the alkyl group is placed first, followed by the name for the alkanoate.

Figure 0.17 *The most common aromatic ring is the benzene ring, with six carbon atoms. The benzene ring is found in many thousands of organic compounds.*

Functional groups are shown in a name by using suffixes or prefixes.

Table 0.11 Naming organic compounds containing functional groups

(a) Naming the compounds in the following classes is similar to alkenes and alkynes. The 'e' is removed from the name of the alkane and replaced by the appropriate suffix ending.

Class of organic compound	Functional group	Suffix	Class of organic compound	Functional group	Suffix
alcohol	$-OH$	-ol	ester	$-C\underset{OR}{\overset{O}{<}}$	-alkyl...oate
aldehyde	$-C\underset{H}{\overset{O}{<}}$	-al	acid chloride	$-C\underset{Cl}{\overset{O}{<}}$	-oyl chloride
ketone	$>C=O$	-one	amide	$-C\underset{NH_2}{\overset{O}{<}}$	-amide
carboxylic acid	$-C\underset{OH}{\overset{O}{<}}$	-oic acid	nitrile	$-C\equiv N$	-onitrile

Table 0.11 Continued

(b) Naming compounds in the following classes is similar to alkyl substituents.
   The prefix is followed by the name of the alkane.

Class of organic compound	Functional group	Prefix
halogenoalkane	–X	halo (fluoro, chloro, bromo, iodo)
amine	–NH_2	amino
nitroalkane	–NO_2	nitro

Table 0.12 Examples of compounds based on propane

Compound	Structural formula	Functional group	Compound	Structural formula	Functional group
Hydrocarbons			propanoic acid	CH_3CH_2COOH	carboxylic acid
propane	$CH_3CH_2CH_3$	–	propanoyl chloride	CH_3CH_2COCl	acid chloride
propene	$CH_3CH=CH_2$	alkene	methyl propanoate	$CH_3CH_2COOCH_3$	ester
propyne	$CH_3C\equiv CH$	alkyne	propanamide	$CH_3CH_2CONH_2$	acid amide
Functional groups			propanenitrile	CH_3CH_2CN	nitrile
1-chloropropane	$CH_3CH_2CH_2Cl$	chloro	1-nitropropane	$CH_3CH_2CH_2NO_2$	nitro
propan-1-ol	$CH_3CH_2CH_2OH$	alcohol	1-aminopropane	$CH_3CH_2CH_2NH_2$	amine
propanal	CH_3CH_2CHO	aldehyde			
propanone	CH_3COCH_3	ketone			

Nomenclature: naming living things

Just as it is essential that elements and compounds are named unambiguously, so it is vital that living things can be identified or distinguished accurately.

Categories or levels	Groups to which you belong:	You share these groups with:
kingdom	Animalia	Platyhelminthes (flatworms) Annelida (ringed worms) Mollusca Arthropoda etc.
phylum	Chordata	Pisces (fish) Amphibia Reptilia Aves (birds) etc.
class	Mammalia	Monotremata (egg-laying mammals e.g. duck-billed platypus) Marsupialia (pouched mammals e.g. kangaroo) Carnivora (e.g. cats and dogs) Cetacea (whales and dolphins) etc.
order	Primata	Cebidae (New world monkeys) Cercopithecidae (Old world monkeys)
family	Hominidae	*Australopithecus* (extinct)
genus	Homo	*Homo erectus* (extinct human ancestor)
species	*Homo sapiens* (Linnaeus)	

Binomial system of nomenclature: generic name / specific name / (author's name: name of the person who first gave that name to the species, not usually used)

Figure 0.18 Human taxonomy

Figure 0.18 shows the seven main groups (or taxa) that you belong to. Examples of organisms that you are thought to share common ancestry with at each level are shown.

It is usual today to recognise six *kingdoms*, if viruses are included. See Table 0.13.

Table 0.13 The six kingdoms of living organisms

Virales:	Viruses. Simple parasites composed of nucleic acid and protein only, e.g. measles, HIV.
Prokaryotae:	Bacteria and blue green algae. Simple organisms with small prokaryotic cells lacking nuclei and membranous organelles such as mitochondria and Golgi bodies, e.g. typhoid bacterium, *Salmonella*.
Protoctista:	Algae, protozoa, slime moulds. Mainly unicellular. A mixed bag not having the characteristics of the other groups, e.g. *Amoeba*, *Euglena*, *Fucus* (wrack seaweed).
Plantae:	Plants. Cells have walls. Usually photosynthetic.
Fungi:	Usually composed of tubular strands called *hyphae*. Heterotrophic.
Animalia:	Animals. Multicellular. Heterotrophic.

The last three kingdoms are all *eukaryotic*: the cells possess nuclei and have membrane-bound organelles.

5 What does heterotrophic mean?

Members of a *species* are capable of interbreeding to produce fertile offspring. They are physically more alike to each other than to the members of any other species. They are named using the *binomial system* ('two names'). The first name is that of the *genus* to which the organism belongs. It is given a capital letter. The second or *species name* has a small letter.

Keys: recognising living things

Keys are methods for sorting organisms into groups using convenient, easily recognisable external features wherever possible. This is a type of artificial classification, but if we use the system to *sort* organisms out, we can use it to assign them to their conventional taxa, to species level if necessary.

A *dichotomous key* provides two choices at each step. A feature is chosen to split the possible organisms into two roughly equal groups. This is repeated until a choice leaves only one possible organism.

(a) Flowchart

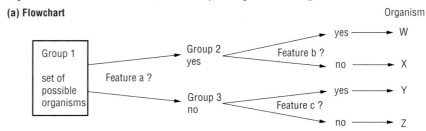

For more possible organisms, more stages are necessary.

(b) The flow chart is written as a key in this form:

1	a	Feature a is present	go to 2
	b	Feature a is not present	go to 3
2	a	Feature b is present	organism W
	b	Feature b is not present	organism X
3	a	Feature c is present	organism Y
	b	Feature c is not present	organism Z

Figure 0.19 How a key works

6 As far as possible, keys use easily distinguishable external features. Write your own key for four organisms, e.g. butterfly, locust, woodlouse and shrimp.

Making observations and measurements

Scientific method starts with *observation*. To be able to formulate and test theories and laws, scientists need to establish the 'way things are'. They need to determine characteristic properties and the nature and causes of change.

In seeking to characterise things, scientists must be able to describe their features accurately.

Any items of information are called *data* (singular: datum). Data concerning characteristics which change are called *variables*. Things capable of change, but held constant, are called *parameters*. By controlling parameters scientists can determine the effects of change by experiment. The effect of changing temperature on the volume of a gas can be investigated if pressure is kept constant. If only one variable is allowed to alter at a time, its effect on other variables can be found.

Qualitative data allow categorisation, so that you can place things into groups with common attributes. *Living or non-living, colour* and *shape* are examples.

Quantitative data require a system of units to quantify (give numerical value to) all the different kinds of measurable variables.

Qualitative data describe properties without measurement. They are non-numerical.
Quantitative data are described by number. The measurement of size, quantity or amount is necessary.

Measurement: units

Communication of numerical data and calculations using different measured physical quantities require a single universally accepted system of units. The Système International d' Unités (SI) is the internationally accepted form of the metre-kilogram-second system. It is the convention accepted by scientists.

Table 0.14 SI units

Measured quantity	Name of SI unit	Symbol
Length	metre	m
Mass	kilogram	kg
Amount of substance	mole	mol
Time	second	s
Electric current	ampere	A
Temperature	kelvin	K
Luminous intensity	candela	cd

There are seven base units for which dimensions, names and symbols are specified (see Table 0.14). All other measurements can be *derived* by combining these units. The most useful ones are also given special names and symbols.

Table 0.15 Some common derived SI units

	Name of unit	Symbol	Definition in basic SI units
Velocity	–	–	ms^{-1}
Acceleration	–	–	ms^{-2}
Force	newton	N	$kg\, m\, s^{-2}$
Energy	joule	J	$kg\, m^2\, s^{-2}$
Power	watt	W	$kg\, m^2\, s^{-3}$

Table 0.15 Continued

	Name of unit	Symbol	Definition in basic SI units
Momentum	–	–	$kg\ m\ s^{-1}$
Area	–	–	m^2
Volume	–	–	m^3
Density	–	–	$kg\ m^{-3}$
Pressure	pascal	Pa	$kg\ m^{-1}\ s^{-2}$
Concentration	–	–	$mol\ dm^{-3}$
Electric charge	coulomb	C	$A\ s$
Electric potential difference	volt	V	$m^2\ kg\ A^{-1}\ s^{-3}$
Electric resistance	ohm	Ω	$m^2\ kg\ A^{-2}\ s^{-3}$
Electric conductance	siemens	S	$s^3\ A^2\ kg^{-1}\ m^{-2}$
Electric capacitance	farad	F	$s^4\ A^2\ kg^{-1}\ m^{-2}$
Frequency	hertz	Hz	s^{-1}
Radioactivity	becquerel	Bq	s^{-1}
Enzyme activity	katal	kat	$mol\ substrate\ s^{-1}$

Multiples of units
Prefixes are used to indicate multiplication factors of units.

Table 0.16 Prefixes for units

Multiples of units

10^{18}	exa	E		10^{-1}	deci	d
10^{15}	peta	P		10^{-2}	centi	c
10^{12}	tera	T		10^{-3}	milli	m
10^{9}	giga	G		10^{-6}	micro	μ
10^{6}	mega	M		10^{-9}	nano	n
10^{3}	kilo	k		10^{-12}	pico	p
10^{2}	hecto	h		10^{-15}	femto	f
10	deca	da		10^{-18}	atto	a

As you can see from Table 0.16, this makes it easy to represent large multiples or small fractions. Deca-, deci- and centi- have been included because you are likely to come across them. They are not strictly SI units.

Q 7 It is very important to use capital or small letters correctly. For example, why must you distinguish between G and g? What other examples can you find?

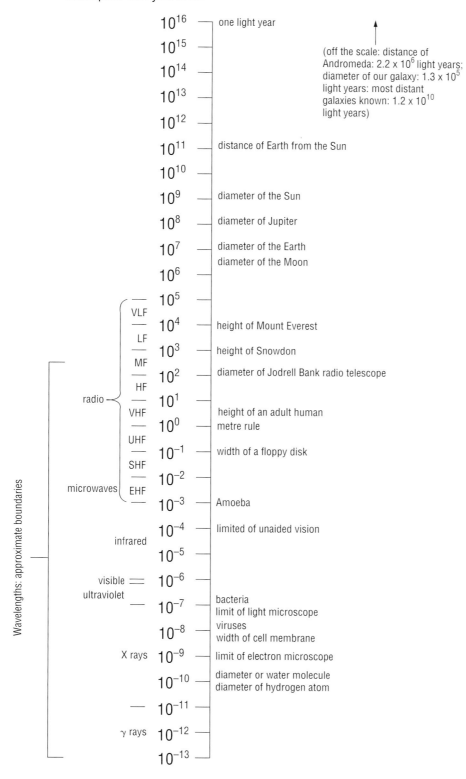

Figure 0.20 *Relative sizes compared/metres*

Amount of substance

When chemical reactions occur, whether in laboratory reactors or living things, particles (atoms, molecules and ions) collide and react. We want to be able to measure out numbers of these particles. However, we cannot count them out in the laboratory. What we can do is measure masses and volumes. We need, therefore, to be able to convert these quantities to amounts of substances.

We cannot measure the masses of atoms but we can determine their relative masses. An atom of the carbon-12 isotope, $^{12}_{6}C$, is the standard with a relative mass of 12.00. The masses of all other atoms are measured relative to it.

Magnesium atoms are roughly twice the mass of carbon-12 atoms ($A_r[Mg]=24.3$). Therefore 2 g magnesium contains about the same number of atoms as 1 g carbon-12. Titanium atoms are four times the mass of carbon-12 atoms ($A_r[Ti]=47.9$). Therefore 4 g titanium contains about the same number of atoms as 2 g magnesium and 1 g carbon.

> Relative isotopic mass =
>
> $\dfrac{\text{mass of one atom of the isotope}}{^1/_{12}\text{th mass of one atom of } ^{12}_{6}C}$
>
> The relative atomic mass, A_r, of an element is the average of the relative isotopic masses of its isotopes, taking account of their naturally-occuring relative abundances.

> If we weigh out quantities of elements in the same proportions as their relative atomic masses, they will contain the same number of atoms as one another.

Table 0.17

The masses in each column contain the same number of atoms as one another				
$A_r[C] = 12.0$	12.0 g	1.20 g	0.240 g	60.0 g
$A_r[N] = 14.0$	14.0 g	1.40 g	0.280 g	70.0 g
$A_r[Na] = 23.0$	23.0 g	2.30 g	0.460 g	115.0 g
$A_r[S] = 32.1$	32.1 g	3.21 g	0.642 g	160.5 g
$A_r[Ca] = 40.1$	40.1 g	4.01 g	0.802 g	200.5 g

Table 0.18 The elements: symbols, atomic numbers and relative atomic masses (brackets show most stable isotope)

Element	Symbol	Atomic number	Relative atomic mass	Element	Symbol	Atomic number	Relative atomic mass
Actinium	Ac	89	(227)	Californium	Cf	98	(251)
Aluminium	Al	13	27.0	Carbon (graphite)	C	6	12.0
Americium	Am	95	(243)	Cerium	Ce	58	140.1
Antimony	Sb	51	121.75	Chlorine	Cl	17	35.5
Argon	Ar	18	39.9	Chromium	Cr	24	52.0
Arsenic (α, grey)	As	33	74.9	Cobalt	Co	27	58.9
Astatine	At	85	(210)	Copper	Cu	29	63.5
Barium	Ba	56	137.3	Curium	Cm	96	(247)
Berkelium	Bk	97	(247)	Dysprosium	Dy	66	162.5
Beryllium	Be	4	9.0	Einsteinium	Es	99	(254)
Bismuth	Bi	83	209.0	Erbium	Er	68	167.3
Boron	B	5	10.8	Europium	Eu	63	152.0
Bromine	Br	35	79.9	Fermium	Fm	100	(253)
Cadmium	Cd	48	112.4	Fluorine	F	9	19.0
Caesium	Cs	55	132.9	Francium	Fr	87	(223)
Calcium	Ca	20	40.1	Gadolinium	Gd	64	157.3

Table 0.18 Continued

Element	Symbol	Atomic number	Relative atomic mass	Element	Symbol	Atomic number	Relative atomic mass
Gallium	Ga	31	69.7	Potassium	K	19	39.1
Germanium	Ge	32	72.6	Praseodymium	Pr	59	140.9
Gold	Au	79	197.0	Promethium	Pm	61	(147)
Hafnium	Hf	72	178.5	Protactinium	Pa	91	(231)
Helium	He	2	4.0	Radium	Ra	88	(226)
Holmium	Ho	67	164.9	Radon	Rn	86	(222)
Hydrogen	H	1	1.0	Rhenium	Re	75	186.2
Indium	In	49	114.8	Rhodium	Rh	45	102.9
Iodine	I	53	126.9	Rubidium	Rb	37	85.5
Iridium	Ir	77	192.2	Ruthenium	Ru	44	101.1
Iron	Fe	26	55.8	Samarium	Sm	62	150.4
Krypton	Kr	36	83.8	Scandium	Sc	21	45.0
Lanthanum	La	57	138.9	Selenium	Se	34	79.0
Lawrencium	Lr	103	(257)	Silicon	Si	14	28.1
Lead	Pb	82	207.2	Silver	Ag	47	107.9
Lithium	Li	3	6.9	Sodium	Na	11	23.0
Lutetium	Lu	71	175.0	Strontium	Sr	38	87.6
Magnesium	Mg	12	24.3	Sulphur	S	16	32.1
Manganese	Mn	25	54.9	Tantalum	Ta	73	180.9
Mendelevium	Md	101	(256)	Technetium	Tc	43	(99)
Mercury	Hg	80	200.6	Tellurium	Te	52	127.6
Molybdenum	Mo	42	95.9	Terbium	Tb	65	158.9
Neon	Ne	10	20.2	Thallium	Tl	81	204.4
Neodymium	Nd	60	144.2	Thorium	Th	90	232.0
Neptunium	Np	93	(237)	Thulium	Tm	69	168.9
Nickel	Ni	28	58.7	Tin	Sn	50	118.7
Niobium	Nb	41	92.9	Titanium	Ti	22	47.9
Nitrogen	N	7	14.0	Tungsten	W	74	183.9
Nobelium	No	102	(254)	Uranium	U	92	238.0
Osmium	Os	76	190.2	Vanadium	V	23	50.9
Oxygen	O	8	16.0	Xenon	Xe	54	131.3
Palladium	Pd	46	106.4	Ytterbium	Yb	70	173.0
Phosphorus	P	15	31.0	Yttrium	Y	39	88.9
Platinum	Pt	78	195.1	Zinc	Zn	30	65.4
Plutonium	Pu	94	(242)	Zirconium	Zr	40	91.2
Polonium	Po	84	(210)				

A mole is the amount of a substance which contains the same number of chemical entities as there are atoms in exactly 12.000 g of carbon -12. This number is 6.02×10^{23}

A chemical entity may be an atom, molecule or ion.

The mole: the scientist's counting unit

Scientists need a convenient counting unit for chemical substances. The counting unit for amounts of substances is the **mole** (mol). 1 mole of any substance contains the same number of particles. Its counting value is 6.02×10^{23}.

A quantity of substance (mass or volume) can be converted into the amount of substance if we know the relative atomic masses of the atoms present. It is essential to say what the entity is. For example, '2 mol oxygen' is too imprecise. We must say whether we mean '2 mol oxygen atoms', '2 mol oxygen molecules' or even '2 mol oxygen cylinders'.

Calculating the mass of one mole of chemical entities

The mass of one mole of chemical entities is called the molar mass, M. Its unit is g mol^{-1} ('mass per mole'). It has the same numerical value as the sum of the relative atomic masses of the atoms present.

The relative atomic mass of calcium is 40.1 (A_r[Ca] = 40.1), and so its molar mass is 40.1 g mol^{-1}. Some elements exist as molecules. These are the chemical entities present. The chemical entity must be stated when giving molar masses. For example, 1 mol sulphur atoms has molar mass 32.1 g mol^{-1} but 1 mol sulphur molecules (S_8) has molar mass $(8 \times 32.1) = 256.8$ g mol^{-1}. We write this as:

$$M[S] = 32.1 \text{g mol}^{-1} \; ; \; M[S_8] = 256.8 \text{g mol}^{-1}$$

To determine the molar mass of a compound we need to know:
- either its molecular formula (if it is a molecular compound), since the chemical entity is a molecule
- or its empirical formula (if it has a giant structure), since the chemical entity is an empirical formula unit.

To calculate the molar mass of a compound, the relative atomic masses of its atoms are added up, each multiplied by their stoichiometry. Here are two examples:

Glucose, $C_6H_{12}O_6$, has a molecular structure. Using its molecular formula, we can calculate its molar mass:

$$A_r[C] = 12.0; A_r[H] = 1.0; A_r[O] = 16.0$$

1 mol $C_6H_{12}O_6$ molecules contains
6 mol C atoms, 12 mol H atoms, 6 mol O atoms

$$M[C_6H_{12}O_6] = 6(12.0) + 12(1.0) + 6(16.0) = 180.0 \text{ g mol}^{-1}$$

Calcium carbonate, $CaCO_3$, has a giant structure. Using its empirical formula, we can calculate its molar mass:

$$A_r[Ca] = 40.1; A_r[C] = 12.0; A_r[O] = 16.0$$

1 mol $CaCO_3$ empirical formula units contains
1 mol Ca atoms, 1 mol C atoms, 3 mol O atoms

$$M[CaCO_3] = 40.1 + 12.0 + 3(16.0) = 100.1 \text{ g mol}^{-1}$$

The amount of substance is calculated from its mass, m, simply by dividing by the molar mass, M.
$$n = m/M$$
The mass of a given amount of substance may be calculated by rearranging the equation to give
$$m = nM$$

Calculating quantities and amounts of substance

To calculate amount of substance, the mass of the sample is divided by its molar mass ($n = m/M$). Here are some examples:

Table 0.19 Calculations of amount of substance

Substance	Molar mass/g mol^{-1}	Mass of sample/g	Amount/mol
Copper, Cu	63.5	6.35	0.1
Potassium, K	39.1	391	10
Iodine, I_2	253.8	2.538	0.01
Calcium oxide, CaO	56.1	56.1	1
Sodium chloride, NaCl	58.5	5.85	0.1
Magnesium carbonate, $MgCO_3$	84.3	42.15	0.5
Hexane, C_6H_{14}	86.0	172.0	2
Ethanol, C_2H_5OH	46.0	0.230	0.005

To calculate the mass of a sample, the amount of substance is multiplied by its molar mass ($m = nM$). Here are some examples:

Table 0.20 Mass samples from molar mass

Substance	Molar mass/g mol^{-1}	Amount of sample/mol	Mass/g
Sodium, Na	23.0	0.1	2.30
Chlorine, Cl_2	71.0	5	355
Magnesium chloride, $MgCl_2$	95.3	1	95.3
Calcium bromide, $CaBr_2$	199.9	0.1	19.99
Potassium hydroxide, KOH	56.1	0.5	28.05
Pent-1-ene, C_5H_{10}	70.0	2	140.0
Butan-1-ol, C_4H_9OH	74.0	0.005	0.37

Concentrations of solutions are usually given in mol dm^{-3}. Provided we know the volume of solution we can calculate the amount of solute present.

Amount of solute, n = concentration (mol dm^{-3}) × volume (dm^3).

For example, in 20 cm^3 (i.e. 0.02 dm^3) 0.5 mol dm^{-3} NaCl(aq), the amount of NaCl present = 0.5 × 0.02 = 0.01 mol.

Notice that the volume (20 cm^3) has been converted to dm^3 (0.02 dm^3).

> Gases are usually measured by volume rather than mass. The amount of substance can be calculated using the equation
> $$n = V/V_m$$
> where V = volume of gas/dm^{-3}
> V_m = molar volume / dm^3 mol^{-1}
> At room temperature and pressure, $V_m = 24$ dm^3 mol^{-1}.

Measurement: accuracy, precision and errors

No measurement is ever perfect. Its accuracy and precision are always limited by the quality of the instrument and the way in which it is used.

Accuracy is shown by measurements that are close to the real values.
Precision is shown by measurements that are close to each other.
Bias or systematic error may give precision but not accuracy.
Random error gives neither precision nor accuracy.

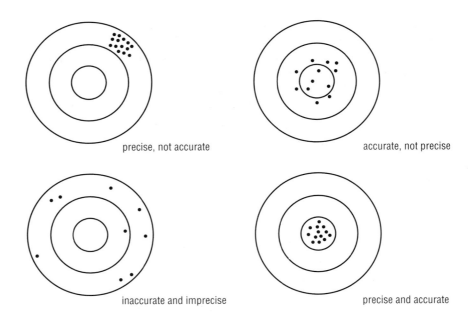

precise, not accurate

accurate, not precise

inaccurate and imprecise

precise and accurate

Figure 0.21 *Target model of precision and accuracy*

Errors

Human error can be a major factor in distorting data. Perception is crucial. What you see depends on what you have previously experienced.

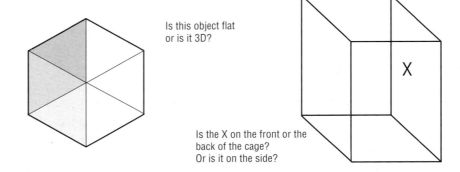

Is this object flat or is it 3D?

Is the X on the front or the back of the cage? Or is it on the side?

Figure 0.22 *Two people observing the same event may report quite differently. Microscopy presents many difficulties to the inexperienced observer. This is compounded by* **artefacts** *caused by the preparation of materials to be viewed by a microscope.*

Comparing measurements to detect errors

Careless or poor technique, for example misreading a scale, can also cause errors. *Comparison* of results with others (repeating your own measurements and comparing your results with other peoples') is an effective way to detect *human error* and you should always do this if you can. Plotting *graphs* is another good method for detecting suspect data.

These methods will not detect *systematic errors*, for example if a balance is calibrated incorrectly. Maintenance of instruments should include regular comparison by measuring the same quantity using another instrument or by using a standard such as an accurate known mass. This will check the *accuracy*.

Precision of instruments and measurement error

The *likely error* in a measurement is always fixed by the smallest scale division on the instrument being used. For example, a ruler will have divisions at intervals of 1 mm. This means that a ruler can be used to measure the distance between two points with a *precision* (at best) of 0.5 mm.

The *error* of any measurement of length with the ruler is ± 0.5 mm. This means that an article whose length is 12.8 cm according to the ruler, may in fact be anything between 12.85 cm and 12.75 cm long. So the length of this article is best quoted as 12.80 ± 0.05 cm.

The same rule applies when using a balance. If you place your pen on a balance and it tells you that it has a mass of 12.4 g, the *precision* of this measurement is ± 0.05 g. The *accuracy* depends on how well the balance was calibrated when it was made and how well it has been maintained since. The quickest way to check the accuracy of a measurement is to repeat it with different instruments.

Percentage error

It is often useful to know the *percentage error* of a measurement.

$$\text{Percentage error} = \left(\frac{\text{error}}{\text{value}}\right) \times 100$$

Supposing that you measure the length of your pencil and obtain a value of 14.8 cm. To calculate the percentage error:
- find the size of the smallest unit being used to make the measurement: 1 mm
- find the likely error of the instrument by halving this: ±0.05 mm
- convert value and error to the same units: 14.8 cm = 148 mm
- divide the error by the value and multiply by 100:

$$\left(\frac{0.05}{148}\right) \times 100 = 0.03\%$$

The error in each single measurement must be taken into account when measurements are combined to find the **compound error**.

Estimating compound error

Suppose that you want to find the density of a sample of metal wire. You will need to measure the length and diameter to be able to calculate the volume. Then you will need to measure the mass to calculate the density.

How can you estimate the likely error in cases like this, where errors in individual measurements combine to give a compound error?

For a sample 25.0 cm long, 0.94 mm in diameter and of mass 0.9 g, the volume is calculated:

$$V = ?\, m^3$$
$$V = \pi r^2 l$$
$$\text{length} = 25 \times 10^{-2}\, m$$
$$\text{radius} = 0.47 \times 10^{-3}\, m$$
$$V = 3.14 \times (0.47 \times 10^{-3})^2 \times 25 \times 10^{-2}$$
Therefore $V = 1.73 \times 10^{-7}\, m^3$

Then the density is calculated:

$$D = ?\, kg\, m^{-3}$$
$$D = m/V$$
$$m = 0.9 \times 10^{-3}\, kg$$
$$V = 1.73 \times 10^{-7}\, m^3$$
$$D = \frac{0.9 \times 10^{-3}}{1.73 \times 10^{-7}}$$
Therefore $D = 5.20 \times 10^3\, kg\, m^{-3}$

Compound error occurs whenever measurements are combined in calculations. It can be estimated by finding the percentage errors for each measurement and adding them together each time that they are used in a calculation.

Next, the percentage error for each measurement is found. This is shown in Table 0.21.

Table 0.21 Finding percentage error

Quantity	Value	Precision	% error
Length	25.0 cm	± 0.05 cm	0.2
Radius	0.474 mm	± 0.005 mm	0.5
Mass	0.9g	± 0.05g	5.6

The percentage error for the density is found by adding together the percentage errors for each measurement used in calculating the final answer. Notice that the error for the radius is doubled in the calculation. This is because you have to square the radius in order to find the volume of the wire.

$$\text{Total \% error} = 0.2 + (2 \times 0.5) + 5.6 = 6.8$$

Finally, you work out the *compound error* from the value of the density and its percentage error:

$$\text{Compound error} = \frac{6.8}{100} \times 5.20 \times 10^3 = 0.35 \times 10^3$$

So the actual value of the wire's density can be given as $5.2 \pm 0.35 \times 10^3 \, \text{kg m}^{-3}$.

The estimates for likely error are based on the assumption that instruments are being used correctly to their levels of precision. Errors that are made by scientists in making measurements cannot be included in these estimates. This means that you need to be careful, especially when errors are compounded. Remember that you can compare your results with someone else's to check for human error.

Combining measurements

A single measurement will tell you very little, but if you measure the same quantity in several different ways you can find out more about how accurate your final value is likely to be.

Suppose that you are trying to find a value for the conductivity of a metal. The sample is a long narrow wire. You need a value for the wire's cross sectional area A, so you use a micrometer screw gauge to measure its diameter.

Instead of making a single measurement at a position chosen at random, you make a series of measurements evenly spread along the length of the sample. Table 0.22 shows your data.

Table 0.22

Position/cm	5	15	25	35	45
Diameter/μm	250	270	280	240	260

The arithmetic average or *mean* of these values is found by adding them and dividing by the number of values. Here, mean = 1300 ÷ 5 = 260 μm.

The usefulness of the value for the mean depends on the kind of variation found in our sample of results. To consider the pattern of variation, we need to know the *range, mode* and *median* as well as the mean (See Table 0.23).

Table 0.23

Range	the difference between the maximum and the minimum value in a set of results
Mean	the arithmetic average = total of individual values divided by number of values used
Mode	the most frequently occurring value
Median	the central value, found by placing all the values in order of magnitude (the average of the central values, if there is an even number of values)

The mean value of 260 μm in Table 0.22 does not tell us about the precision of our data. (See Figure 0.21).

The range tells us how widely the values are spread out. Here we have 280 – 240 = a range of 40 μm.

A narrow range indicates precision, a wide range indicates lack of precision.

The micrometer used to make the measurements here has a precision of ± 5 μm, a range of 10 μm. Assuming that the instrument has been used correctly (negligible human error), the larger range of 40 μm in the measurements indicates *random* variation in the actual thickness of the wire. This is more significant than the error caused by deficiences in the instrument itself. Estimating likely error by considering the precision of the micrometer would give an underestimate.

Most measurements show variation. Some samples show a very wide range, so that the mean is only an indicator of a *typical* result. Measuring adult human heights or weights would be examples. Wherever variation occurs, a Gaussian or normal distribution with a bell shaped curve is usually found. This is shown in Figure 0.23. When measurements vary in this way, likely error can be estimated by finding the **standard deviation (σ)**.

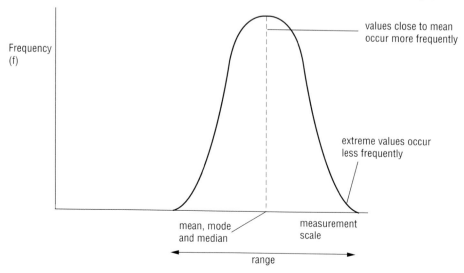

Figure 0.23 Gaussian or normal distribution

Likely error caused by random error in a set of measurements can be found by calculating the standard deviation. This can be done by using the $\sigma_n - 1$ button on a statistical calculator. If a large number of measurements is made (over 25), the σ_n button can be used.

The standard deviation of a set of figures is calculated from:

$$\sigma_{n-1} = \sqrt{\frac{\Sigma d^2}{n-1}}$$

Where: Σ = 'sum of'

d = deviation of measured values from the mean

n = number of measurements made

This is easier than it looks, especially if you use a statistical calculator or computer spreadsheet to do the calculation for you! The steps are:

1 calculate the mean of the set of measurements
2 calculate the deviation of each result from the mean (mean − measurement = d)
3 square each deviation (d^2)
4 add the squared deviations (Σd^2)
5 divide by one less than the number of measurements made ($\Sigma d^2/n - 1$)
6 find the standard deviation from the square root of this last value (σ_{n-1})

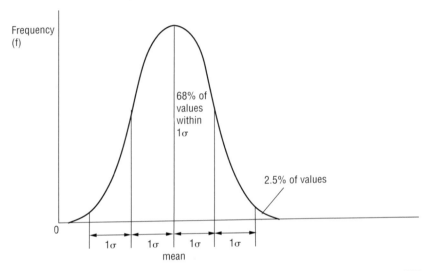

Figure 0.24 The relationship of the standard deviation to the normal distribution. The standard deviation is used as an estimate of the likely error because most of the measurements will occur within this value from the mean.

Q 8 Standard deviation can be calculated to estimate likely error. What is the likely error for the diameter of the wire for which measurements are given in Table 0.22?

You should obtain a value of 16 μm, so you can state that the diameter of the wire is 260 ± 16 μm. Check your working against Table 0.24 below.

Table 0.24 Likely error calculation for the diameter of a wire

Position/cm	5		15		25		35		45
Diameter/μm	250		270		280		240		260
Mean of diameter	250	+	270	+	280	+	240	+	260
					5				
Deviation from mean	-10		+10		+20		-20		0
Deviation²	100		100		400		400		0
$\Sigma d^2/n - 1$	100	+	100	+	400	+	400	+	0
					5 − 1				

$$\sigma_{n-1} = \sqrt{250} = 16 \text{ μm}$$

Sample size: how many measurements do you need to take?

The value of standard deviation tends to fall as the number of measurements increases. This is because the the value for the mean is becoming a more accurate estimate.

You need to consider how accurate your measurements need to be and what error limits are acceptable for the purpose that you have in mind. This determines your choice of measuring instrument and the number of measurements that you need to make. Sometimes crude measurements are acceptable. A qualitative test adding a reagent to give a colour change can be done by counting drops using a single sample. A pharmacist testing a drug may be measuring tiny amounts of an active ingredient to a high level of precision and accuracy. Repeated samples would be needed to check levels of random error and very precise measuring instruments would be needed.

Efficient working means being confident in obtaining reliable results using the minimum number of measurements necessary.

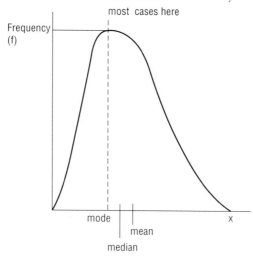

Figure 0.25 *Skewed distributions*

More about mode and median

The mean may not always be the best estimate of 'average' value. Sometimes sets of measurements are *skewed*. This is shown in Figure 0.24. Mode is useful as it indicates which values are likely to occur most freqently. This is vital information for manufacturers of protective clothing. The median indicates the point at which half the values lie above and half below. It gives a better 'average' for heavily skewed distributions, in which a few very high or very low values can alter the mean dramatically.

Using graphs

Straight line graphs are widely used by scientists as a means of combining the results of many measurements.

Best straight line

An equation linking measured quantities can be written for a *straight line graph*:

$$y = mx$$

The features of a straight line graph with this equation are as follows (see Figure 0.26).

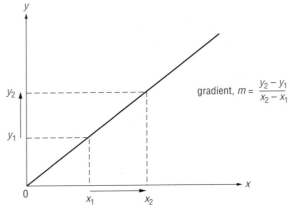

gradient, $m = \dfrac{y_2 - y_1}{x_2 - x_1}$

Figure 0.26 A straight line graph with equation y = mx

1 line passes through the origin $(0, 0)$

2 m is the **gradient** of the line; it is usually the value of the property that you are trying to find

3 x and y are paired combinations of measurements

An example will illustrate the use of such a graph: when determining the resistance of a metallic conductor (kept at a constant temperature), Ohm's law tells us that resistance R of a conductor is a constant. It is equal to the ratio of the potential difference V to the current I. This can be written

$$R = \frac{V}{I}$$

which can be converted to

$$V = RI$$

which is of the form

$$y = mx$$

The potential difference across a sample of a metal conductor can be increased through a series of steps and this can be measured using a voltmeter. The equivalent changes in current can be found using an ammeter. The pairs of measurements can then be plotted on a graph to give a straight line which should pass through the origin (see Figure 0.27). If voltage is plotted on the vertical axis and current is plotted on the horizontal axis, the resistance will be the gradient of the line through the points.

Error bars have been added to the points. They indicate the extent of the likely error of each measurement. A best straight line has been drawn to give the best estimate of the resistance of the conductor.

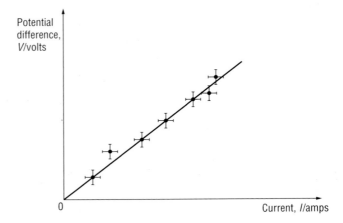

Figure 0.27 A straight line graph to find the resistance of a conductor.

The best straight line can also be found by using a *least squares fit*. This and other values such as the gradient and standard deviation can most easily be found using computer programs.

Spotting bad data

Graphs can combine results to make bad data stand out. Such results can be re-measured or ignored when drawing the line of best fit.

 9 Anomalous data are those that do not fit into the pattern shown by the rest. Which point on the graph in Figure 0.27 is an example of anomalous data?

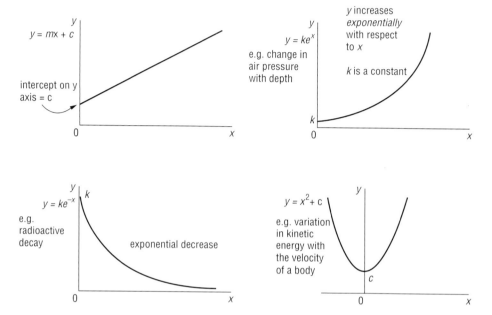

Figure 0.28 Some common graphs which you may come across

The tools for the job

There are a number of standard procedures which are used in the science laboratory. These are outlined in this section.

Measuring length and area accurately

Using a ruler gives only limited precision. Vernier callipers, micrometers and microscopes with measuring devices can be used to obtain the greater precision required for smaller objects. See Figures 0.29, 0.30 and 0.31.

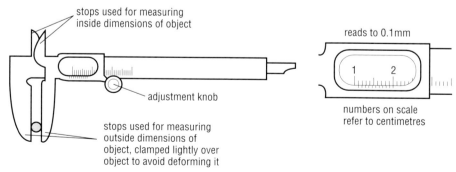

The numbers on the fixed scale are centimetres, sub-divided into millimetres. The moving scale has 10 divisions in the space of 9mm of the fixed scale. Use it to measure to the nearest tenth of a millimetre by finding the line on the moving scale most closely in line with a line on the fixed scale.

Figure 0.29 How to use Vernier callipers. Precision can be improved by using a Vernier scale.

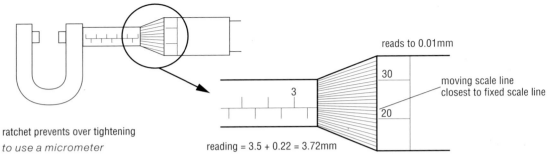

reads to 0.01mm

moving scale line closest to fixed scale line

reading = 3.5 + 0.22 = 3.72mm

Figure 0.30 How to use a micrometer screw gauge.

A micrometer screw gauge measures to the nearest 0.01mm. Clamp the object to be measured. The numbers on the scale are millimetres. Read the number to the left of the moving scale (3.5 in Figure 0.30 above). Use the numbers on the moving scale to find the measurement to 0.1mm (3.5 + 0.2 above). Then count the number of small divisions from the 0.1mm value to the line along the centre of the fixed scale and add this as the 0.01mm value. 3.5 + 0.20 + 0.02 = 3.72mm.

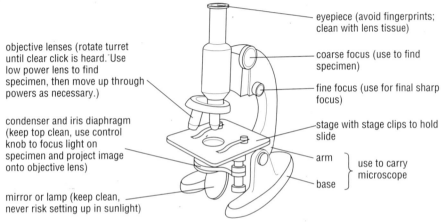

eyepiece (avoid fingerprints; clean with lens tissue)

objective lenses (rotate turret until clear click is heard. Use low power lens to find specimen, then move up through powers as necessary.)

coarse focus (use to find specimen)

fine focus (use for final sharp focus)

condenser and iris diaphragm (keep top clean, use control knob to focus light on specimen and project image onto objective lens)

stage with stage clips to hold slide

arm ⎤ use to carry microscope

mirror or lamp (keep clean, never risk setting up in sunlight)

base ⎦

Figure 0.31 The parts of a microscope

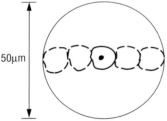

50μm

If roughly 5 of the specimens could be fitted into the field of view, they must be 1/5 of the diameter. In this case 50/5 = 10μm.

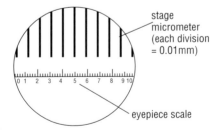

stage micrometer (each division = 0.01mm)

eyepiece scale

Figure 0.32 Using a microscope for measuring. A stage micrometer can be used to find the diameter of the field of view of a microscope and to calibrate an eyepiece graticule for the accurate measurement of very small objects down to the size of bacteria.

Here are some tips:
- set up the microscope firmly on a bench in a position out of direct sunlight where you can be comfortable
- select low power
- clip slide to stage, positioning it so that the specimen is in the light from the condenser
- focus with coarse then fine focus knobs
- if specimen cannot be found focus on edge of coverslip and search for specimen. If still not visible try next power
- close iris diaphragm, then open to point where further opening does not increase brightness
- focus the condenser by placing a pencil or mounted needle tip on the light source and focusing until the specimen and point are in focus together
- if necessary use the iris diaphragm to adjust the light intensity (not too bright)
- use the fine focus for higher powers. Be careful: high-power objectives can break slides and the lenses can be damaged
- if there is difficulty focusing using high power, watch the objective and move it close to the slide. Attempt to focus by moving the slide away from the lens
- readjust the illumination using the iris diaphragm
- if lenses appear dirty, check by rotating the eyepiece. If the dirt remains stationary, check the objective and condenser lenses. Use lens tissues only. Ordinary tissues scratch lenses.
- when finished, remove the slide, return to low power and check the microscope is clean and dry. Report any faults.

Measuring with the microscope

Use a slide with a graticule or stage micrometer to measure the diameter of the field of view for each objective. This is a microscope ruler that you focus on. Keep a record of these values for the microscopes that you use. Approximate measurements can then be obtained for any specimen that you view, by comparing it to the width of the field of view. In Figure 0.32 (left) 5 of the specimens fit into a field of view of diameter 50μm. So the average width is about 10μm.

More accurate measurements

An eyepiece graticule (micrometer scale) can be seen when viewing a specimen, but the dimensions vary for each objective. It must be calibrated by superimposing the scales of the eyepiece and stage micrometers. Move the slide until the scales are aligned. The stage micrometer is used to measure the sizes of the eyepiece divisions. For example, if a distance of the lines on the stage micrometer of 0.1mm is selected, the number of eyepiece divisions (n) to fill this should be found, when size of each eyepiece division = $\frac{0.1}{n}$ mm. The eyepiece scale can then be used to measure objects viewed at that power.

   Note: An instrument known as a **travelling microscope** can be used to measure very small distances, such as the diameter of the bore of a capillary tube. It is moved across the specimen using a screw with a Vernier scale.

Table 0.25

Device	Range	Precision
Tape measure	30 m	0.5 mm
Ruler	1 m	0.5 mm
Vernier callipers	100 mm	0.05 mm
Micrometer screw gauge	10 mm	5 μm
Microscope graticule	10 mm	0.5 μm

   Perimeters, surface areas and volumes can be calculated from dimensions for many simple regular shapes. See Table 0.26

Table 0.26

Shape		Perimeter	Area
Square	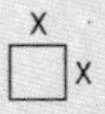	$4x$	x^2
Rectangle	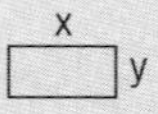	$2(x + y)$	xy
Right-angled triangle	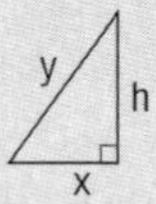	$x + y + h$	$\frac{1}{2}hx$
Any triangle	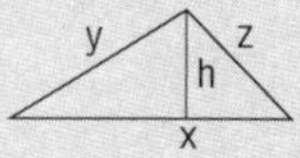	$x + y + z$	$\frac{1}{2}hx$

Table 0.26 continued

Shape		Surface area	Volume
Cube		$6x^2$	x^3
Cuboid		$2xy + 2xz + 2yz$	xyz
Sphere		$4\pi r^2$	$\dfrac{4\pi r^3}{3}$
Cylinder		$2\pi rh + 2\pi r^2$	$\pi r^2 h$

For irregular shapes it is possible to trace the outline of the object onto graph paper and count all the squares covered by a half or more. Alternatively, objects may be photocopied or traced and the paper cut out and weighed. Several cutouts can be used to obtain a mean value and estimate likely error if it exceeds that caused by the precision of the balance. Area is found by comparison with the mass of paper of known area. Paper should be from the same stock, as water content varies.

Measuring volume

Volumes of simple regular solids can be found by determining their linear dimensions (see Table 0.26). The volume of an irregular solid can be found by displacement of a liquid. Special displacement cans with spouts to direct the overflow into a container are available (see Figure 0.33).

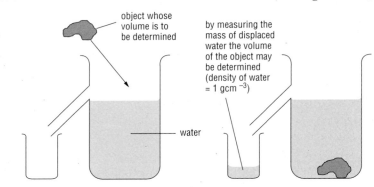

object whose volume is to be determined

by measuring the mass of displaced water the volume of the object may be determined (density of water = 1 gcm^{-3})

water

Figure 0.33 Use of a measuring can

Figure 0.34 Measuring the volumes of liquids

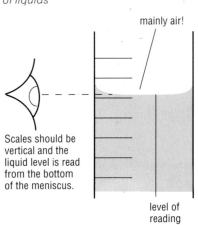

mainly air!

Scales should be vertical and the liquid level is read from the bottom of the meniscus.

level of reading

Volumes of liquids can be measured using a variety of devices. Choice depends on the precision required (see Figure 0.34). Precision depends on the diameter of the glassware where the graduation is marked. The smaller the diameter, the greater the precision.

Measuring mass

The mass of objects is most easily found by using an electronic balance. See Figure 0.35.

Figure 0.35 *Using an electronic top pan balance*

Decide on the precision that you need. Three place accuracy is seldom needed. The precision will depend on the approximate size of what you want to weigh. For example:
- up to 1kg, use a balance that reads to 0.1g
- up to 600g, 0.01g
- up to 60g, 0.001g.

Always take the following steps to ensure that your measurements are as precise as possible:
1 check balance is level
2 avoid leaning on the bench; balances are sensitive to small movements
3 use a draught screen for two or three place balances
4 use a weighing boat or piece of paper
5 pre-weigh or use *tare* if available
6 remove pan from balance to add solids. This helps to avoid spillage of corrosive materials on the balance
7 clean up any spillage immediately
8 use a spatula to transfer solids
9 reweigh boat if solid has stuck to it
10 use weighing bottles to obtain very accurate measurements of liquid quantities. Volumes can be calculated from densities if needed.

Preparing solutions of known strength

Making up a solution of known strength is an important scientific skill.
To make up a solution of known strength:
1 decide on the total volume and concentration required
2 find the mass of 1 mole of the chemical from the sum of the relative atomic masses of its constituents
3 find the mass of chemical which will give you the concentration you want in the volume you need

Methods for measuring the volumes of liquids:

increasing accuracy and precision:

measuring cylinder
volumetric flask
burette
pipette
micro-syringe

Figure 0.36 *Preparing a stock solution*

4 choose an appropriate balance and weigh out the amount of chemical you need to the precision required. If the mass is too small to give you the required precision:
   either a) make up a larger volume or make a stronger solution which you can dilute down to the required strength
   or b) weigh out the chemical and make a solution, then calculate how much you need to dilute it
5 add the chemical to a *volumetric flask* of the correct size to make your chosen volume
6 wash any left in your weighing boat into the flask
7 add slightly less water than the final amount needed, stopper the flask and shake carefully until the solid has dissolved.
8 make up the solution to the final volume required. If a volumetric flask is not available, a measuring cylinder can be used
9 transfer to a clean, dry and suitable labelled container.

Measuring current

This is shown in Figure 0.37.

Figure 0.37 *Measuring current. An ideal ammeter would have no resistance. This is not possible, so there is always a voltage drop across an ammeter which must be much smaller than that across the sample. A moving coil ammeter is usually accurate to about ± 2% of the range (full scale deflection or f.s.d.). A digital ammeter is usually better than ± 0.1% of the range.*

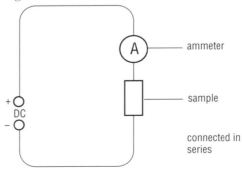

Measuring voltage
This is shown in Figure 0.38.

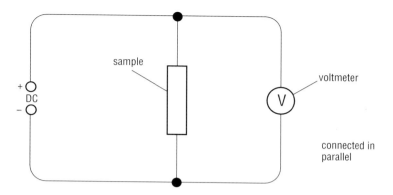

Figure 0.38 *An ideal voltmeter would have infinite resistance. Some current is always diverted from the sample, so this must have a significantly lower resistance than the voltmeter. A moving coil voltmeter is usually accurate to about ± 2% of the range. A digital voltmeter is usually better than ± 0.1% of the range.*

Other techniques
Electronic sensors and dataloggers can be used to record measurements for transfer to a data handling program in a computer. These are particularly useful for collecting large numbers of measurements in a short time or for continuous monitoring over a long period. See Table 0.27.

Table 0.27 Electronic sensors

Sensor	Useful applications
Temperature (Thermistor)	temperature changes inside and outside differently insulated rooms over the course of a day
pH	pH changes in a culture of microbes over a week
Oxygen	oxygen concentration of a pond over 24 hours
Light	two sensors can be used to detect velocity : an object cuts off light from lamps as it passes
Movement	stretching of a wire under tension, movement of a spirometer

1 | Laboratory safety and analysis of samples

Analysts are employed in many laboratories: industrial (research and quality control), forensic science, local authority, hospital pathology and others. They also work in the field, for example on geochemical or ecological investigations.

To be effective, analysts need to know how to ask the right questions in order to obtain useful data. This means they must understand the concepts and principles behind the techniques they use. The greater the knowledge and understanding you acquire, the more efficient and effective your analytical and identification work will be.

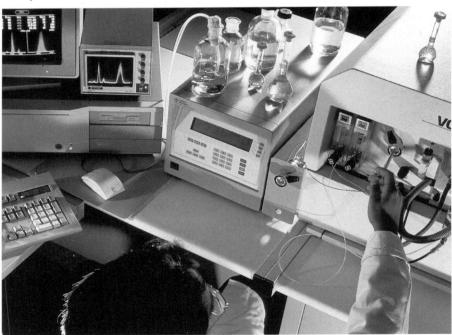

Figure 1.1 *Forensic scientists depend on a variety of analytical techniques. Here, mass spectrometry is being used to analyse a suspected drug sample.*

The Elements

Element 1.1 Investigate health and safety practices in the laboratory

Health and safety applies to all scientific work, so this element is covered in Unit 0 of your book.

▶ Safe working in the laboratory and with chemicals, page 7

Figure 1.2 Analysis is not just important on Earth. In December 1978 four American and two Russian spacecraft reached Venus. All carried a range of analytical instruments on board, including mass spectrometers, ultra-violet/visible spectrophotometers and gas chromatographs.

Element 1.2 Select analytical strategies

Your first task in any analytical problem is to decide how to tackle it. You need to:

- describe the source of the substance and explain the purpose of analysing it
- choose a sampling method and analytical technique, giving reasons for your choice.

▶ Analysing substances for a purpose, page 48

▶ Chemical formulae and structure, page 68

▶ Analytical techniques, page 50

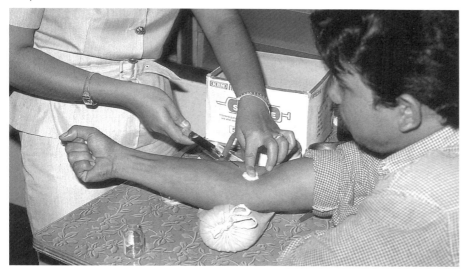

Figure 1.3 Nuclear magnetic resonance spectroscopy (nmr) can be used to investigate body fluids, such as urine and blood. Information about metabolic diseases, organ failure and drug metabolism can be obtained. Here a sample of blood is being withdrawn for analysis.

Element 1.3 Carry out analyses and evaluate results

Having chosen a method, you will now carry out the required analysis, interpreting the results and drawing conclusions. This requires you to:

- prepare the sample and use the analytical technique to collect and record the necessary observations or measurements
- if needed, carry out calculations involving measurements made during the analysis (remember to explain what you are doing)
- interpret the data gathered during the analysis and draw a valid conclusion.

▶ Experimental procedures for analyses, page 56

▶ Chemical equations and calculations, page 70

> *Qualitative analysis* is about identification. *Quantitative analysis* is about determining quantities.

> **Units for concentration:**
> standard units are mol dm^{-3}, i.e. amount of substance per unit volume of solution.
> **You may also come across:**
> - g dm^{-3}, i.e. mass per unit volume of solution
> - percentage by mass, i.e. mass in 100 g of solution.

Analysing substances for a purpose

Analyses fall into two main categories, **quantitative** and **qualitative**.

Qualitative and quantitative analyses

We analyse substances to answer questions such as:
- what components are present in a mixture?
- what is the purity of a chemical compound?
- what is the chemical structure of a new compound?

Mixtures

Qualitative analysis enables you to identify the components of a mixture. These might be elements or compounds, present in substantial or trace quantities.

Quantitative analysis enables you to determine the composition of the mixture. For a solution, the concentrations of solutes are determined.

Compounds containing trace impurities are still mixtures. Here, the purpose of quantitative analyses is to determine the purity of the major component. This is sometimes called *assaying*.

Figure 1.4 Many pharmaceuticals are manufactured using chemical reactions. Before they can be used, their purity must be checked. Trace impurities must be at an acceptably low level. Here the concentration of a solution is being determined by titration.

Compounds

Qualitative analyses enable you to identify:
- known compounds, by comparison with published data
- elements present in a compound
- ions present in an ionic compound
- functional groups present in an organic compound
- arrangement of atoms in a compound and, therefore, its *structural formula* (this usually follows the determination of empirical and molecular formulae by quantitative analysis).

Quantitative analyses enable you to determine:
- amounts of elements present in a compound and, therefore, its *empirical formula*
- molar mass of a molecular compound and, therefore, its *molecular formula*
- distance and angles between atoms and, therefore, its *chemical structure*

Having been given an analytical problem, how do you decide what needs to be done? The diagram in Figure 1.5 will help.

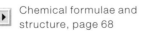 Chemical formulae and structure, page 68

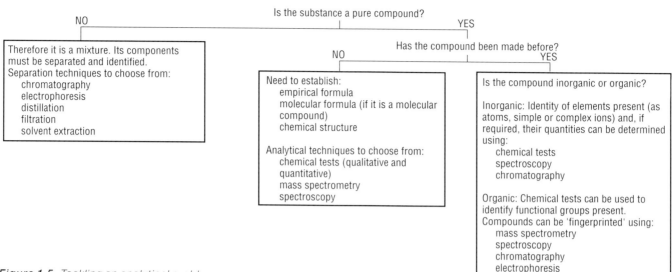

Figure 1.5 *Tackling an analytical problem*

Types of substances and their source

There are three types of substances which you may want to analyse: *inorganic compounds*, *organic compounds* and *natural products*. The last two types overlap; natural products contain organic compounds. They may be obtained from different sources. In all cases bear in mind that samples may be contaminated with pathogens: as for all practical activities, a risk assessment will be needed.

Compounds, page 14

- Samples collected from our environment (e.g. air, sea-water, rivers and lakes, rocks, soils, plants, animals, microbes). There are two main reasons for analysing such samples. One is to identify the presence of contaminants, for example, in assessing air quality or the purity of drinking water. The second is to assess naturally-occurring materials as a source of chemical substances, for example, a rock as a source of an element or a plant as a source of a therapeutic chemical compound.

- Samples collected from laboratory and industrial processes (e.g. starting materials, intermediates and products). In established processes, analysts in quality control laboratories assess whether or not substances are of an acceptable purity. In research laboratories, a new substance may be prepared. The analyst's task is to determine its chemical structure.

- Samples collected from human beings. This could be for medical diagnosis (e.g. clinical, screening) or for forensic analysis.

Q 1 Why is it important to analyse starting materials, intermediates and products in an industrial process?

Figure 1.6 *Nmr spectroscopy is a powerful technique to help determine the chemical structure of a compound.*

Analytical techniques

There are many techniques available to help you solve analytical problems. Many factors will influence your choice. What information are you trying to obtain? Is this a one-off analysis or something you will want to repeat on many occasions? Can a sample be brought to the laboratory for analysis or must it be analysed in the field?

Obtaining a sample for analysis

You will take samples of the substance you want to analyse. The sampling method used depends on the source and nature of the substance, and on what you want to know about it. An important question is 'Does the composition of a substance depend on where in the source it is taken from?' To check you should take samples from different places. This is called *random sampling*.

Figure 1.7 *The oxygen content of this river varies. It is high where the water mixes vigorously with air. Careful thought must be given to the number of samples and where to take them when measuring oxygen content.*

Q 2 A river flows through a town. How would you sample water in the river in order to monitor its purity?

For a substance which is uniform throughout (said to be *homogeneous*), a **single sample** may be taken. This is the case for all pure substances and many mixtures. Sometimes the composition of a mixture varies (it is *heterogeneous*). You will need to take a number of representative samples. If in doubt, take **representative samples** of the substance.

The preparation of a sample for analysis depends on the analytical techniques to be used.

Chemical tests

Qualitative chemical tests may be used to identify:
- elements in a chemical compound
- simple gaseous elements and compounds
- ions in an aqueous solution (often the sample under test is a solid and must be dissolved first)
- functional groups in an organic compound.

Quantitative chemical tests may be used to determine:
- quantities of components in a mixture
- amounts of elements in a compound.

Many chemical reactions give coloured solutions. The intensity of the

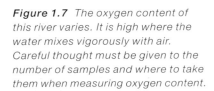

For a pure substance a single sample is taken for analysis. For a mixture one or more representative samples are taken for analysis.

Identifying anions and cations, page 56

Identifying functional groups in organic compounds, page 60

Colorimetry, page 68

colour depends on the concentration of the reactants. *Colorimetry* can be used to measure the intensity of colour and is a useful quantitative analytical technique.

Chemical tests are usually cheap and easy to carry out, though some reagents can be costly. Generally, inexpensive apparatus is required. Analysis kits which use chemical tests are often portable and can be used for fieldwork.

Mass spectrometry (ms)

Mass spectrometry can be used to determine the relative molecular mass of a compound. More powerful instruments (called high resolution mass spectrometers) measure relative molecular mass very precisely which makes it possible to determine molecular formulae.

The **mass spectrum** of a compound is unique. It can be used to identify the compound. Skilled scientists can use the mass spectrum of an unknown compound to help determine its chemical structure.

In a mass spectrometer, molecules are ionised and are broken into smaller fragments (also ionised). The mass spectrometer sorts these positive ions according to their relative masses. It also measures the relative abundances of these ions. The technique is about 1000 times more sensitive than nmr or ir spectroscopy.

Mass spectrometers are expensive but require only small samples and can yield considerable amounts of information.

Spectroscopy

Spectroscopy uses instruments which are expensive but have advantages over chemical tests. Perhaps the most important are sensitivity, accuracy and speed. Spectroscopic methods are particularly useful when many repetitive analyses are required.

Assignment trigger

Analytical instruments
Modern analytical laboratories often have very expensive instruments.

What instruments are commonly found?
What are they used for?
Why does a company invest such large sums of money by buying such instruments?

If a practical assignment is developed, it is essential that a risk assessment is made and checked by your teacher/lecturer.

Could lead to possible assignments relating to Units 1, 3 and 4.

Nuclear magnetic resonance (nmr) spectroscopy
This process can help to determine chemical structure. Known compounds can be identified from their *nmr spectra*.

The nuclei of atoms possess tiny magnetic fields. Electromagnetic radiation of appropriate energy can cause the direction of the magnetic field of some nuclei to change. Nmr spectroscopy makes use of this property to probe the environment of atoms (such as hydrogen, carbon, fluorine and phosphorus) in a compound.

Chemical substances often have at least one characteristic reaction which may be used to
• identify them (qualitative chemical test);
• determine the amount present (quantitative chemical test).

Compounds have characteristic spectra (mass spectra, nmr spectra, ir and ultraviolet/visible spectra). These 'fingerprints' can be used to identify compounds. Modern instruments are often linked to electronic databases and the search for a match is carried out automatically.

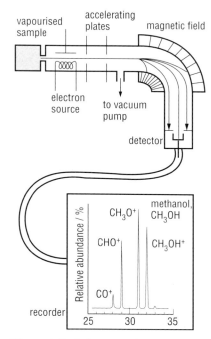

Figure 1.8 *A diagram of a mass spectrometer. The substance is vaporised and bombarded with fast moving electrons. Ions produced are deflected in a magnetic field and sorted according to their relative masses. Each ion is recorded as a peak in the mass spectrum. The height of a peak is proportional to the abundance of the ion.*

Spectroscopy involves interpreting the effect of electromagnetic radiation on substances. Qualitative, quantitative and structural data can be obtained.

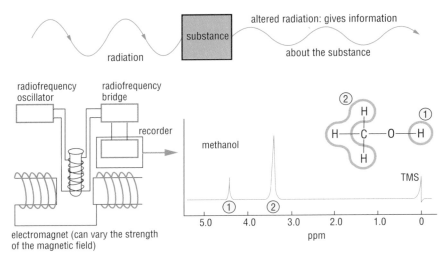

Figure 1.9 Electromagnetic radiation often changes when it passes through a substance.

Figure 1.10 Diagram of an nmr spectrometer. Electromagnetic radiation of fixed energy is passed through a substance. The strength of the magnetic field is varied. The field strength when a nucleus can absorb radiation is recorded, producing a peak in the nmr spectrum.

An absorption spectrum is obtained when the electromagnetic radiation of varying energy is passed through a substance. The spectrum is a graph of energy of radiation against the amount absorbed by the substance.

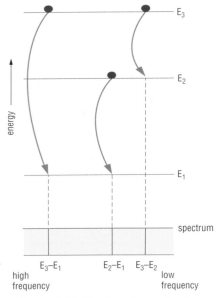

Figure 1.11 The lines in an atomic emission spectrum are due to excited electrons returning to lower energy levels.

Absorption spectroscopy

There are two important types of absorption spectroscopy: **infrared spectroscopy** and **ultraviolet/visible spectroscopy**. Both operate on the same principle. Radiation of known energy is passed through the substance. The substance is scanned by varying the energy of this radiation. Greater absorption of energy by the substance compared with a reference (usually air or the solvent the substance has been dissolved in) produces a peak in the absorption spectrum.

Colorimetry is a crude form of visible spectroscopy.

Infrared (ir) spectroscopy can be used to detect the types of bonds present in a substance, and in particular functional groups in organic compounds. The *ir spectra* of substances can be stored in a computer database. The identity of an unknown substance can be established by comparing its ir spectrum with the database.

Molecules flex, twist and vibrate. Infrared radiation is absorbed when it has sufficient energy to increase the speed of this movement. The energy of the absorbed radiation is related to the flexing, twisting and vibrating of particular bonds.

Ultraviolet/visible (uv/vis) spectroscopy is mainly used for quantitative analysis. It can provide limited evidence about chemical structure.

Electrons are in discrete energy levels in atoms and molecules. They can move between levels if given the appropriate energy. Electromagnetic radiation in the ultraviolet and visible region is of the right magnitude. Absorption of energy as electrons are promoted to higher energy levels gives rise to *uv/vis spectra*.

Colorimetry works on the principle that coloured substances absorb light from the visible region of the spectrum. It is a useful technique for quantitative measurements since the absorption is proportional to the concentration of substance in dilute solution.

The difference between colorimetry and uv/vis spectroscopy is resolution. In the latter, radiation of a very small energy range is passed through the substance. In colorimetry, it has a broad energy range.

Q 3 Scientists have isolated the active compound in a plant known to have therapeutic properties. How might they identify this compound?

Chromatography

Chromatography can be used to separate components in a mixture. Both qualitative and quantitative data can be obtained. Modern high

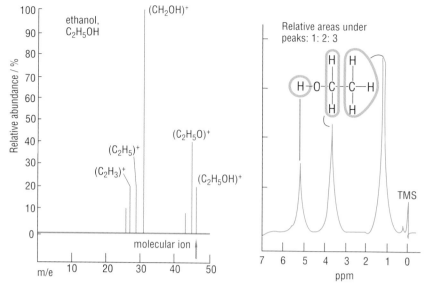

Figure 1.12 *A spectroscopic study of ethanol, C_2H_5OH. The spectra are typical of ones obtained from the techniques used, which are (from left to right) ms, nmr, ir.*

performance techniques can identify trace impurities in samples. Chromatography can also be used to separate mixtures on a large scale.

There are a range of related techniques. All work on the same principle. A delivery system supplies a **mobile phase** which is moved through a **stationary phase**. The mobile phase, which is usually a solvent, carries the substance being analysed through the stationary phase. This is called *elution*. The stationary phase often consists of a liquid supported on an inert solid. A detection system is used to monitor the separated components.

A component is attracted to both mobile and stationary phases. The relative strength of attraction for each phase is important. A component strongly attracted to the stationary phase will be held back. One strongly attracted to the mobile phase will pass through rapidly. Separation is achieved when components have different relative attractions for the two phases.

 4 Why is it difficult to separate compounds with similar chemical structures by chromatography?

The degree of separation of components in a mixture is called *resolution*. Careful selection of mobile and stationary phases will give good separation and high resolution.

> **Separation by chromatography depends on the components in a mixture having different properties such as:**
>
> • **molecular size**
> • **molecular shape**
> • **charge**
> • **solubility.**
>
> **In chromatography:**
>
> • **the mobile phase may be gas, liquid or solid**
> • **the stationary phase may be solid, liquid or gel (jelly-like medium).**
> **These two phases must be immiscible with one another. Components of the mixture must not react with either phase.**

Table 1.1 Phases in different types of chromatography

Chromatography	Mobile phase	Stationary phase
Thin-layer	liquid solvent	Al_2O_3 or SiO_2 (often bound together with $CaSO_4$ and supported on a plastic sheet or glass plate; this is called a tlc plate)
Paper	liquid solvent	H_2O (on the surface of absorbent chromatography paper and, therefore, supported by the cellulose fibres in paper)
Gas-layer	inert gas (usually N_2 or Ar)	liquid, often a silicone gum (supported on suitable solid particles and contained in a glass or metal tube)
High-performance liquid	liquid solvent	small solid particles (packed tightly in a tube, usually stainless steel)

▶ Thin layer and paper chromatography, page 64

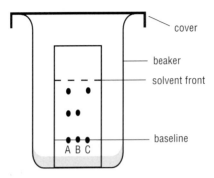

Figure 1.13 *Thin layer chromatography. The components of a mixture are separated as the solvent moves up the plate. A is a mixture of the pure substances B and C.*

Thin layer chromatography (tlc) and paper chromatography

These are both used extensively for qualitative analysis. In chemical synthesis they can be used to determine if a product is pure, to identify impurities and to monitor the course of a reaction. They are also useful in medicine and forensic science, for example for screening drugs.

Thin layer chromatography is an example of adsorption chromatography. Substances stick to the surface of the stationary phase (e.g. alumina or silica). Paper chromatography is an example of partition chromatography. Substances dissolve in the liquid which forms the stationary phase i.e. water fixed to the surface of the paper .

Paper chromatography is easy to use and cheap. However, it tends to be slow and give poor resolution. Tlc costs rather more but is much faster and gives better resolution.

Gas-liquid chromatography (glc)

This can provide both qualitative and quantitative data. Components travel through the column at different speeds. The time a component takes is called its *retention time*.

Glc equipment is expensive. Substances must be gaseous at the temperature of the oven. However, resolution is high; the components are clearly separated from one another.

Figure 1.14 *Diagram of a glc arrangement. A hypodermic syringe is used to inject the mixture through the sample port. The column (with the stationary phase) is contained in an oven. It is coiled to allow the maximum length in the least space. Detectors respond to the different components. A chart recorder plots the chromatogram.*

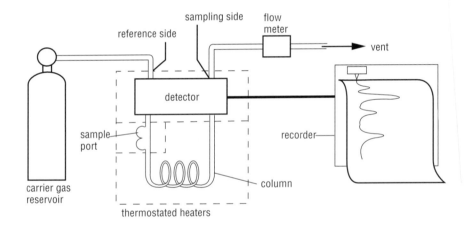

Figure 1.15 *A typical glc chromatogram. Peaks on the chart record the retention time and quantity of each component (area under the curve).*

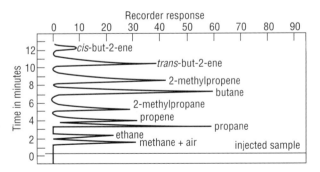

High performance liquid chromatography (hplc)

This is a powerful modern technique. Components which are very similar to one another can be separated using this technique. It provides both qualitative and quantitative data.

Equipment is very expensive but resolution is very good. The technique is fast because of the use of pressure to force the liquid solvent through.

Assignment trigger

Medicines from plants

Some medicines can be obtained from plants.

How are medicines extracted? —
How can they be identified? —
Can they be made in the laboratory? —
Commercially, would it be better to make them or
extract them from plants?
How are they tested?

*If a practical assignment is developed, it is essential that a risk assessment is
made and checked by your teacher/lecturer.*

Could lead to possible assignments relating to Unit 1.

Q 5 What factors might affect retention times in glc and hplc?

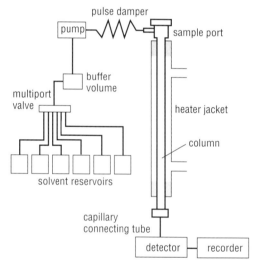

Figure 1.16 *Diagram of hplc arrangement. The substance is injected through the sample port. The pump forces the solvent or solvents (selected from the reservoirs) through the column under pressure (up to 10 MPa). Various detection systems are used, e.g. spectroscopy, fluorescence, refractive index. Separated components are sometimes collected for further study with an automatic fraction collector.*

Electrophoresis

Electrophoresis can be used to separate ions in a mixture. A sample is
placed on a suitable medium which might be paper, cellulose ethanoate or
a gel. An electric field is created by connecting electrodes to either end
and switching on a current. Positive ions (cations) move towards the
negative electrode (cathode). Negative ions (anions) move towards the
positive electrode (anode). Neutral molecules remain where they are.

As with tlc and paper chromatography, reagents can be used to stain
invisible components. Ultraviolet light or radioactive isotope labelling
might also be used.

▶ Separation of amino acids by
paper electrophoresis, page 67

**Electrophoresis is a technique used
to separate ions.
Electrophoresis is particularly
useful for biological compounds.**

$$HOOC-\underset{\underset{H}{|}}{\overset{\overset{R}{|}}{C}}-NH_2 \quad + \quad H^+ \quad \longrightarrow \quad HOOC-\underset{\underset{H}{|}}{\overset{\overset{R}{|}}{C}}-NH_3^+$$

$$HOOC-\underset{\underset{H}{|}}{\overset{\overset{R}{|}}{C}}-NH_2 \quad + \quad OH^- \quad \longrightarrow \quad {}^-OOC-\underset{\underset{H}{|}}{\overset{\overset{R}{|}}{C}}-NH_2 \quad + \quad H_2O$$

Figure 1.17 *Amino acids ionise
depending on pH*

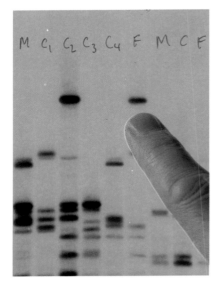

Figure 1.18 DNA fragments can be separated by electrophoresis. This makes the technique very useful to genetic engineers. Forensic scientists also use it to match body fluids left at the scene of a crime to those of the suspects (DNA fingerprinting).

'Reagent' is commonly used to describe a substance used in the laboratory, for analysis or in a chemical preparation.

Different amino acids (R = a different organic group) ionise at different values of pH. Proteins behave similarly because they also contain $-NH_2$ and $-COOH$ groups. A pH is chosen to ensure that the required amino acids ionise. The medium is maintained at that pH using a buffer solution.

Experimental procedures for analyses

Remember that all experimental procedures which you carry out in the laboratory require a risk assessment.

Identifying anions and cations

Sample preparation

You will usually be given an aqueous solution and asked to identify the ions present in solution. If the substance is a solid, your first task is to dissolve it. Using small test samples, try the following (*remember to do a risk assessment for each*):

1 water
2 dilute nitric acid (warming if necessary)
3 concentrated nitric acid (warming if necessary)

| eye protection must be worn | IRRITANT dilute nitric acid | CORROSIVE concentrated nitric acid |

Prepare about 10 cm^3 of stock solution and store in a boiling tube. Keep a sample of the original substance (things may go wrong!).

Figure 1.19 Two important techniques in qualitative analysis.

[1] A dropping pipette is used to transfer liquids. Never invert the pipette and allow liquid to get into the plastic bulb. When not in use, store it in a test tube. Some reagent bottles have dropping pipettes built in.

[2] Small samples of solution are best heated over a semi-micro Bunsen burner. If the liquid is flammable, the samples should be heated in a water bath.

Anions

In the following tests, approximately 1 cm^3 portions of the sample in solution to be tested and reagents required should be used.

Carbonates, CO_3^{2-}. Add dilute hydrochloric acid to the sample and pass any gas given off through calcium hydroxide solution ('limewater'). Formation of a white precipitate (calcium carbonate) confirms carbon dioxide and, therefore, the presence of carbonate. Solid samples can also be used.

eye protection must be worn

IRRITANT
dilute hydrochloric acid

Figure 1.20 *To identify a gas as carbon dioxide, CO_2, it is passed through limewater. If the gas is CO_2, a white precipitate of calcium carbonate forms.*

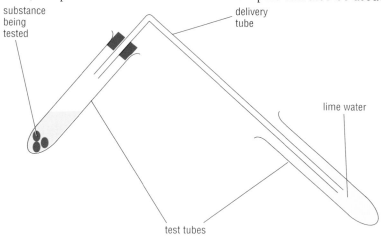

Nitrates, NO_3^- Add iron(II) sulphate solution followed by concentrated sulphuric acid to form a lower layer. If a brown ring forms between the two layers, nitrate ions are present.

IRRITANT
solid
iron(II) sulphate

CORROSIVE
concentrated
sulpuric acid

Halides, X^- (X = Cl, Br, I). Add dilute nitric acid, followed by a few drops of silver nitrate solution. Formation of a precipitate (silver halide) suggests halide ions. To decide which, note the colour of the precipitate and test its solubility, first in dilute aqueous ammonia and then concentrated aqueous ammonia.

IRRITANT
dilute
nitric acid

IRRITANT
silver nitrate
solution

1 *Chloride, Cl^-*. Silver chloride is white; readily soluble in dilute aqueous ammonia
2 *Bromide, Br^-*. Silver bromide is cream coloured; slightly soluble in excess aqueous ammonia
3 *Iodide, I^-*. Silver iodide is pale yellow in colour; insoluble in concentrated aqueous ammonia.

Sulphates, SO_4^{2-}. Add dilute hydrochloric acid followed by a few drops of barium chloride solution. A white precipitate of barium sulphate confirms the presence of sulphate.

HARMFUL
barium chloride
solution

TOXIC
sulphur dioxide
gas

CORROSIVE
dilute
sulphuric acid

Sulphites, SO$_3^{2-}$. Add dilute hydrochloric acid and warm. Hold a piece of filter paper which has been wetted with a solution of potassium manganate(VII) in dilute sulphuric acid in the mouth of the test tube. If the paper turns from purple to white, sulphur dioxide is being given off confirming the presence of sulphite.

Table 1.2 Reagents commonly used in the laboratory

(a) 'dilute' acid or alkali is about 2 mol dm^{-3};

(b) 'concentrated' acids or alkalis have the following approximate concentrations:

hydrochloric acid	12 mol dm^{-3}
sulphuric acid	18 mol dm^{-3}
nitric acid	16 mol dm^{-3}
aqueous ammonia	10 mol dm^{-3}

(c) other reagent solutions are usually about 0.1 mol dm^{-3}.

Table 1.3 The hazardous nature of acids and alkalis varies according to their concentration

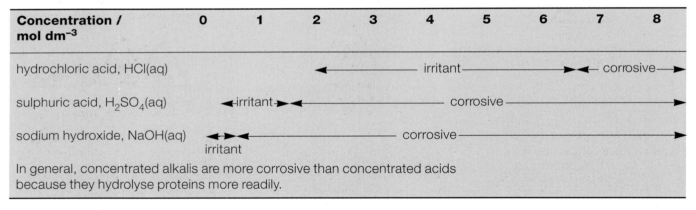

Concentration / mol dm^{-3}	0	1	2	3	4	5	6	7	8
hydrochloric acid, HCl(aq)			← irritant →				← corrosive →		
sulphuric acid, H$_2$SO$_4$(aq)	←irritant→ ← corrosive →								
sodium hydroxide, NaOH(aq)	←→← corrosive → irritant								

In general, concentrated alkalis are more corrosive than concentrated acids because they hydrolyse proteins more readily.

HARMFUL
some solutions containing copper(II)
ions, nickel(II) and chromium(III) ions

TOXIC
nickel(II) ions
and lead ions
in solution

IRRITANT
iron(III) ions
silver ions
in solution

Cations

This procedure will enable you to identify the following cations in solution: ammonium (NH$_4^+$), calcium (Ca^{2+}), sodium (Na$^+$), potassium (K$^+$), zinc (Zn^{2+}), aluminium (Al^{3+}), silver (Ag$^+$), lead (Pb^{2+}), copper(II) (Cu^{2+}), nickel(II) (Ni^{2+}), chromium(III) (Cr^{3+}), iron(II) (Fe^{2+}), iron(III) (Fe^{3+}), manganese(II) (Mn^{2+}).

Figure 1.21 *The pH can be tested by withdrawing a drop on the end of a glass rod and touching it on indicator paper.*

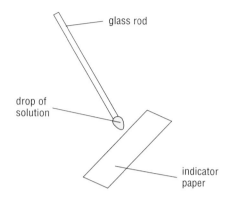

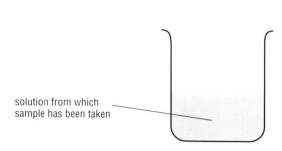

solution from which
sample has been taken

eye protection
must be worn

[1] If the solution is acidic, add dilute sodium hydroxide to 1 cm³ solution of the sample until it is neutral. Use indicator paper to check.

CORROSIVE
dilute sodium hydroxide
concentrated hydrochloric acid

- White precipitate: go to [2]
- Coloured precipitate: go to [4]
- No precipitate: add a further 1 cm³ dilute sodium hydroxide and warm carefully. Hold a piece of moist indicator paper in the mouth of the test tube (avoiding contact with the sides). If the paper turns blue, ammonia is being given off, indicating the presence of ammonium ions.
  If no ammonia is indicated, place a small sample of the original solid on a watch glass. Using a dropping pipette, add a few drops of concentrated hydrochloric acid. Moisten a piece of Nichrome wire with the mixture and hold it in a Bunsen flame. It is essential that the wire is cleaned between tests.
- Bright yellow flame indicates sodium ions.

- Lilac flame (still visible through blue glass) indicates potassium ions.

[2] Add a further 2–3 cm³ dilute sodium hydroxide. Precipitate does not dissolve: go to [3]
  Precipitate dissolves: take a fresh 1 cm³ sample of solution and add dilute aqueous ammonia. A white precipitate should form immediately. Add a further 3–4 cm³ dilute aqueous ammonia. If precipitate
- dissolves: indicates zinc ions;
- does not dissolve: indicates aluminium ions.

IRRITANT
ammonia solution
dilute hydrochloric acid

[3] Take a fresh 1 cm³ sample. Add 1 cm³ dilute hydrochloric acid. If a white precipitate forms, add dilute aqueous ammonia. If precipitate
- dissolves: indicates silver ions;
- does not dissolve: indicates lead ions.

[4] The colour of the precipitate suggests the hydroxide which has formed.
  Blue or green precipitate. Add dilute aqueous ammonia. If precipitate dissolves to give:
- deep blue solution: indicates copper(II) ions;
- lavender solution: indicates

nickel(II) ions;
- yellow solution: indicates chromium(III) ions.

- White-green precipitate. Leave to stand for 15 minutes, occasionally shaking the mixture. If precipitate slowly changes to a rusty-brown: indicates iron(II) ions.

- Rusty-brown precipitate. Add dilute hydrochloric acid until precipitate just dissolves, followed by 2 drops of ammonium thiocyanate solution. Intense red solution: indicates iron(III) ions.

HARMFUL
ammonium thiocyanate

- Very pale pink precipitate. Add concentrated nitric acid and a little sodium bismuthate. Warm gently.
- Intense purple solution: indicates manganese(II) ions.

CORROSIVE
concentrated nitric acid

Figure 1.22 *Flame tests can be used to identify sodium (Figure 1.22a) and potassium (Figure 1.22b).*

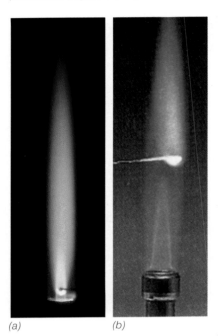

(a) (b)

 6 What could usefully form part of a portable analytical kit for geologists to use in the field? How might it be used?

Assignment trigger

Drinking water

A major problem for most people in the world is the lack of an adequate supply of drinkable water.

What makes water undrinkable?
Who tests that it is safe to drink?
How do they test it?
What do they test for?

If a practical assignment is developed, it is essential that a risk assessment is made and checked by your teacher/lecturer.

Could lead to possible assignments relating to Unit 1.

Identifying functional groups in organic compounds

Table 1.4 Classes of organic compound and functional groups

Class of compound	Functional group
Alkene	$>C=C<$
Alcohol	$-OH$
Carboxylic acid	$-C\underset{OH}{\overset{O}{<}}$
Aldehyde	$-C\underset{H}{\overset{O}{<}}$
Ketone	$>C=O$
Amine	$-NH_2$

Solubilities can give you some preliminary idea about the class of organic compound (Table 1.5).

Table 1.5 Solubility of organic compounds in water, acids and alkalis

Class of compound	Solubility
Alkenes	insoluble in water, dilute hydrochloric acid and dilute sodium hydroxide
Alcohols	alcohols with low molar masses dissolve in water to give a neutral solution; solubility decreases with increasing molar mass
Carboxylic acids	carboxylic acids with low molar masses dissolve in water to give acidic solutions; solubility decreases with increasing molar mass; all carboxylic acids dissolve in dilute sodium hydroxide and the water-insoluble ones may be precipitated from these solutions by the addition of dilute hydrochloric acid
Aldehydes and ketones	aldehydes and ketones have similar solubility properties to alcohols; generally, however, they are rather less soluble in water
Amine	aliphatic amines dissolve in water to give an alkaline solution; aromatic amines are insoluble in water but dissolve in dilute hydrochloric acid, from which they may be recovered by the addition of dilute sodium hydroxide

The following tests may be used to suggest the presence of the following functional groups in an organic compound: alkene, alcohol, carboxylic acid, aldehyde, ketone, amine. The scale of analysis and experimental techniques used are similar to those used for anions and cations.

eye protection
must be worn

Alkenes

Add 1 drop of the substance to 1 cm³ solution of bromine in hexane. Shake gently. If the solution changes from red-brown to colourless, substance is probably an alkene. If sample is a gas, add the bromine in hexane to a test tube containing the gas, stopper and shake.

HARMFUL
bromine solution in hexane

HIGHLY FLAMMABLE
bromine solution in hexane

Alcohols

Both of the following tests must prove positive:
(a) Add 1 drop of the substance to 1 cm³ distilled water, followed by 1 drop of Universal indicator solution. The solution (if one forms) should be neutral if the substance is an alcohol.
(b) Add a small quantity of phosphorus pentachloride to a 0.5 cm³ sample of the substance. Hold a piece of moist indicator paper in the mouth of the test tube. If it turns red (indicating an acidic gas is given off), the substance may be an alcohol.

CORROSIVE
phosphorus pentachloride

Carboxylic acids

Add a small quantity of the substance to 1 cm³ dilute sodium carbonate solution. Pass any gas given off through calcium hydroxide solution. Formation of a white precipitate (calcium carbonate) confirms the gas as carbon dioxide, and indicates that the substance is an acid.

FLAMMABLE
typical aldehydes and ketones

HIGHLY FLAMMABLE
methanol

HARMFUL
typical aldehydes and ketones

Aldehydes and ketones

Dissolve a small quantity of the substance in the minimum quantity of methanol. Add about 1 cm³ of 2,4-dinitrophenylhydrazine solution. Formation of yellow/orange/red crystalline precipitates indicates that the substance is an aldehyde or a ketone.

TOXIC
methanol

TOXIC
2, 4-dinitrophenylhydrazine

Aldehydes and ketones may be distinguished by their reaction with Benedict's solution. Add a small quantity of the substance to 2 cm³ of Benedict's solution. Warm in a water bath at about 80 °C for several minutes. Formation of a red-brown precipitate indicates that the substance is an aldehyde.

Amines

Warm a small quantity of the substance in a test tube and hold a glass rod with a drop of concentrated hydrochloric acid on it in the vapour. Formation of a dense white cloud indicates that the substance is an amine.

CORROSIVE
concentrated hydrochloric acid

Urine tests

Doctors sometimes carry out urine tests to assess the health of a patient.

What substances are they checking for?
How do the tests work?
What does it tell them?

If a practical assignment is developed, it is essential that a risk assessment is made and checked by your teacher/lecturer.

Could lead to possible assignments relating to Units 1 and 7.

7 Some sugars are said to be reducing; they give a red precipitate with Benedict's solution. Others are non-reducing. What is the difference in their chemical structures?

Quantitative chemical tests

Volumetric analysis is quantitative analysis which uses measurement of volumes. It is sometimes called titrimetric analysis because it involves titrations.

Figure 1.23 *A general method for volumetric analysis*

[1] Sample preparation: dissolve a measured quantity of substance and make up to a known volume of solution in a volumetric flask. It is essential to transfer all of the substance.

[2] Transfer a fixed volume sample of the solution (called an aliquot) by pipette, using a safety filler, to a conical flask. Allow the solution to run out freely and then touch the solution in the flask with the pipette tip. Do not blow out the pipette unless the instructions tell you to do so.

[3] After addition of a suitable indicator (if required) titrate the aliquot with a reagent of known concentration from a burette. Such a solution is called a standard solution. You can identify the end-point for the titration (the point at which sufficient reagent has been added) by a change in colour. First carry out a rough titration. Subsequently, the reagent can be added from the burette 1 cm^3 at a time until the 1–2 cm^3 from the end point. The reagent should then be added drop by drop, mixing the contents of the flask thoroughly between additions.

Acid-base titrations

The concentration of an acid can be determined by titrating against an alkali of known concentration, and vice versa. A suitable acid-base indicator is needed. Carbonates and hydrogencarbonates can also be titrated against acids.

> **A standard solution is one whose concentration is known accurately. The term is used to describe solutions which are required for volumetric analysis.**

Titration of 20.0 cm^3 portions of sodium hydroxide solution against 0.100 mol dm^{-3} hydrochloric acid

Titration	1	2	3
1st burette reading	1.00	22.15	0.00
2nd burette reading	22.15	43.00	20.80
difference	21.15 (rough)	20.85	20.80

Average (of 2 and 3) titration $= \frac{20.85 + 20.80}{2} = 20.8$

Figure 1.24 *A typical page from an analytical notebook recording the results of a volumetric analysis. Notice that the average has been rounded off to the nearest 0.1 cm^3.*

Redox titrations

These are titrations which involve oxidation-reduction reactions. You will probably use two important types:

Manganate(VII) titrations. Any substance which reduces manganate(VII) ions can be determined by titration with standard potassium manganate(VII) solution. In acid solutions, purple manganate(VII) ions are reduced to pale pink manganese(II) ions.

Assignment trigger

Vitamin C

Vitamin C is found in many foodstuffs. You need it for good health.

What is vitamin C?
Why is vitamin C an important ingredient of food?
How does its content vary between different foodstuffs?
How is it affected by cooking?
How much do you need?
How is it manufactured?

If a practical assignment is developed, it is essential that a risk assessment is made and checked by your teacher/lecturer.

Could lead to possible assignments relating to Units 1, 4 and 7.

Iodine-thiosulphate titrations. Iodine is produced when a suitable oxidising agent is added to a solution of iodide ions. The presence of iodine can be determined by titration against a standard solution of thiosulphate ions. Starch forms an intense black colour with iodine. The change from black to white is used to indicate the end point of an iodine-thiosulphate titration. The starch solution is usually added when the iodine colour has diminished to a pale straw colour. The equation for this is as follows.

$$I_2(aq) + 2S_2O_3^{2-}(aq) \rightarrow 2I^-(aq) + S_4O_6^{2-}(aq)$$

Figure 1.25 *No indicator is needed in a manganate(VII) titration. The colour change when just sufficient potassium manganate(VII) solution has been added is easily observed. The pale pink colour persists in solution at the end point.*

Thin-layer and paper chromatography

You will probably use thin-layer and paper chromatography to identify components in mixtures. It is often trial and error to find the best solvent for a particular mixture. Scientists learn by experience which solvents are best for which kinds of mixtures.

Method

The method described here for tlc can also be used for paper chromatography.

Figure 1.26 *Marking a tlc plate. Several small samples of solution may be added one after the other. Each must be allowed to dry before adding the next.*

[1] Dissolve a small quantity of the substance to be investigated in a solvent.

[2] Draw a baseline, using a graphite pencil, on the plate (Figure 1.26). It should be just above the level that will be reached by the solvent in the jar. Apply the solution to the plate using a finely drawn out glass tube. The spot formed by the solution should be as small as possible. This is because components that do not separate well will tend to overlap if large spots are made.

[3] Put the solvent in the jar and cover with a lid. Leave for 10 minutes to allow the atmosphere to saturate. Stand the plate in the jar and replace the lid.
  When the solvent front is near the top of the plate, remove the plate. Mark the position of the solvent front.

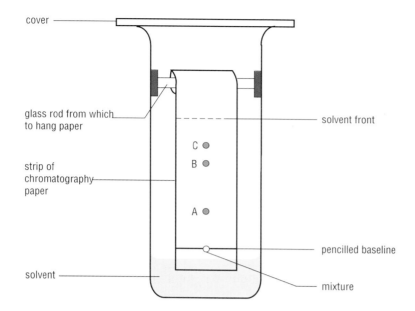

cover

glass rod from which to hang paper

solvent front

strip of chromatography paper

C ●
B ●

A ●

pencilled baseline

solvent

mixture

Figure 1.27 Ascending paper chromatography is often used. It is a cheap and effective way to separate some mixtures.

Two-way chromatography

A technique which often improves separation is two-way paper chromatography. A square sheet of paper is used and a single sample placed in one corner. A chromatogram is run in the usual way. It is then dried and rotated through 90°, so that the spots lie on a new baseline. A second solvent is used to run the chromatogram again in the new direction.

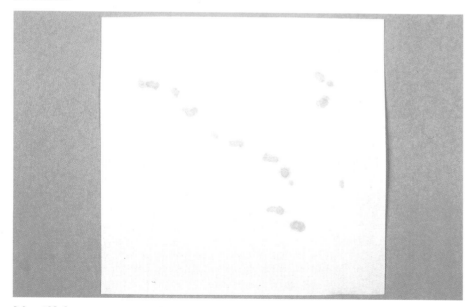

Figure 1.28 Two-way paper chromatography can be used to separate mixtures of amino acids. The colourless amino acids are 'seen' by spraying the paper with ninhydrin. This reagent reveals the amino acids as purple spots.

Identifying components

Coloured components will be visible. Often, however, they are not. A variety of techniques can be used to 'see' them:

- Specially pre-treated plates, when exposed to ultraviolet light, reveal substances as pale purple spots (*appropriate safety precautions need to be taken when using ultra-violet light*).
- Exposure of plates to 'developers' (such as iodine vapour or chemical reagents which are sprayed on the plate after separation).

- Radioactive isotopes can be used as tracers (*appropriate safety precautions need to be taken when using radioactive isotopes*). X-ray film is placed over the plate for a period of time. The positions of the components show up as dark spots when the film is developed. The degree of darkness indicates the amount of radiation and, therefore, the concentration of the component.

Quantitative measurement is possible by scraping the spot from the plate. The component is extracted from the stationary phase. A suitable analytical technique can then be used to determine quantity.

R_f values

The distance a component moves relative to the solvent front is called its R_f (Relative to the *front*) value.

$$R_f = \frac{\text{distance moved by component}}{\text{distance moved by solvent front}}$$

For a given substance, R_f depends on the nature of the mobile and stationary phases. In a given combination of mobile and stationary phases, at a particular temperature, the R_f value for a substance is always the same. Therefore, no matter what mixture a substance is in, determination of R_f values allows a substance to be identified.

Repeating the separation using different solvents allows you to check the identification. Another important method for cross-checking is to run known substances alongside the mixture to compare the spots that separate out.

Q 8 Use a ruler to determine the R_f values of A, B and C in Figure 1.29

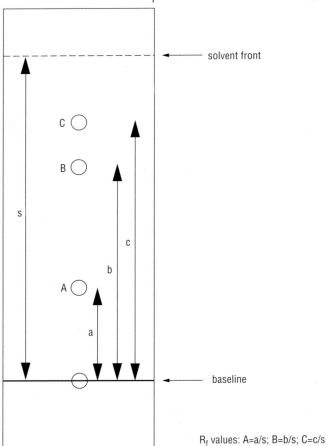

Figure 1.29 *Calculating R_f values*

R_f values: A=a/s; B=b/s; C=c/s

Separation of amino acids by paper electrophoresis

This method illustrates the use of paper electrophoresis. You may have the opportunity to try some other techniques.

[1] Cut a piece of filter paper to fit the electrophoresis tank. Rule a pencil line across the centre of the paper, at right angles to the ends that will be dipped into the electrode compartments. Mark and label origins on the pencil line, at least 1 cm apart and from the edge of the paper. **Warning:** sweat contains amino acids so wash your hands and wear gloves when handling the filter paper.

[2] Apply samples in the same way as tlc or paper chromatography.

[3] Add the chosen buffer to the electrode compartments and set up the electrodes ready to switch on. *If you use a voltage greater than 20V dc the electrodes must be enclosed.*

electrical hazard

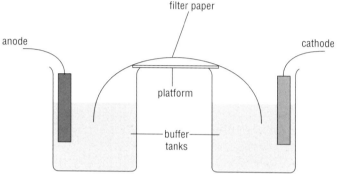

Figure 1.30 *For electrophoresis, a stable dc source which supplies about 5 to 8 V cm^{-1} is best. 5 V cm^{-1} means 5 V potential difference per cm of distance between the electrodes. Above 10 V cm^{-1} causes excessive heating and, consequently, evaporation and possible breakdown of compounds. More sophisticated apparatus incorporates cooling devices.*

[4] Wet each end of the paper with buffer to within about 2 cm of the origin. Put the paper in position, cover the tank and switch on the current immediately. The rest of the paper will be wetted by capillary action. This method causes the least spreading of the samples.

[5] Leave for about 3 hours at 8 V cm^{-1} (lower voltages will take longer). Switch off current before touching the apparatus. Remove the paper using tongs or gloves and dry in an oven at 110°C or a warm fume cupboard (depending on the buffer used).

[6] Develop by dipping in freshly prepared ninhydrin solution (200 mg in 100 cm^3 propanone) until thoroughly soaked.

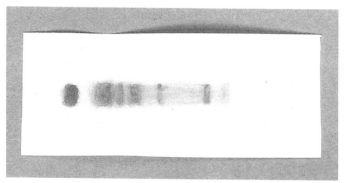

Figure 1.31 *The person who carried out this electrophoresis on amino acids did not wear gloves. What's more, we could identify the culprit from the fingerprint they left behind.*

Safety: *ninhydrin solution is harmful. Wear gloves and use only in a fume cupboard. Avoid skin contact and inhaling the fumes. Carry out the procedure as quickly as possible. Should you get any on your skin, wash with plenty of water immediately.*

[7] Dry thoroughly in a fume cupboard and look for the stained amino acids. Heat for a few minutes in an oven to intensify the colours if necessary.

| protective gloves | fume cupboard | HARMFUL ninhydrin solution | HIGHLY FLAMMABLE propanone |

Assignment trigger

Sweeteners

Fruit juices contain amino acids. It is illegal to add to fruit juices some sweeteners which are made from amino acids.

How can you test for their presence?

How can you determine the quantities present?

What other materials contain amino acids?

If a practical assignment is developed, it is essential that a risk assessment is made and checked by your teacher/lecturer.

Could lead to possible assignments relating to Unit 1.

Colorimetry

You use a colorimeter to measure transmission or absorbance of light. Solutions which contain coloured substances present in reasonable concentration can be used as these absorb specific wavelengths of visible light. The substance itself may be coloured (e.g. haemoglobin in blood) or a reagent may be added (e.g. starch suspension to which iodine dissolved in potassium iodide solution has been added).

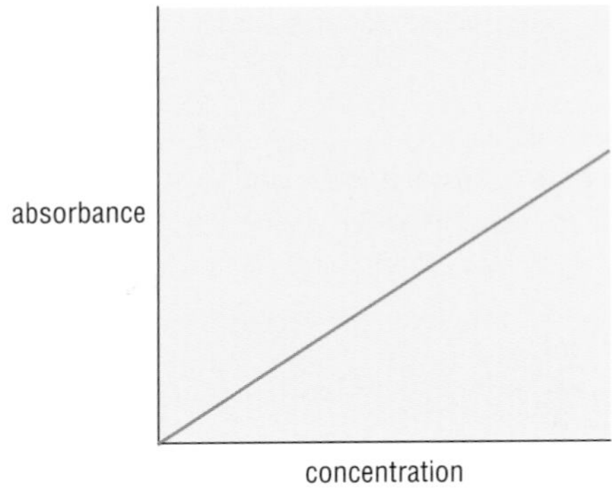

Figure 1.32 A calibration curve of absorbance against concentration must be constructed using a known dilution series of the substance being measured. If there is a straight line relationship, concentration is directly proportional to absorbance (this is called the Beer-Lambert relationship).

Here is the sequence for using a colorimeter:

[1] Switch on about 10 minutes before use. This allows the lamp to warm up and stabilise.

[2] Choose an appropriate coloured filter. This should be a complementary colour to that of the substance under investigation. For example, a blue filter is used for red solutions.

[3] Select appropriate sample tubes. These must be matched to give the same transmittance of light when placed in the correct orientation (usually indicated by a mark). Alternatively the same tube can be used repeatedly. Avoid touching the sides of the sample tubes and keep them dry.

[4] Zero using the solvent (sometimes called the blank solution).

[5] Adjust sensitivity using a sample tube containing a known quantity of test substance. (Not all colorimeters allow this).

[6] Decide whether to use absorbance or transmittance scale, take readings. Absorbance is usually preferred if the Beer-Lambert relationships applies.

[7] Check for reproducibility by using a standard solution to take repeated readings at regular intervals and by duplicating test solutions.

[8] Plot a calibration curve by preparing a dilution series of solutions.

Chemical formulae and structure

Elements combine to form chemical compounds. Chemical formulae tell us how many atoms of the elements combine and something about their arrangement. There are different kinds of chemical formulae, giving different kinds of information.

Empirical formulae

The empirical formula of a compound shows the ratio of atoms present in the compound. This ratio is the stoichiometry of the compound. For example, sodium sulphate has the empirical formula Na_2SO_4. The subscripts tell us that sodium, sulphur and oxygen atoms are present in a 2:1:4 ratio. The ratio of carbon, hydrogen, nitrogen and oxygen atoms in glycine is 2:5:1:2. Therefore, its empirical formula is $C_2H_5NO_2$.

 9 What type of analytical data is needed to be able to determine the empirical formula of a compound?

Molecular formulae

In compounds with molecular structures, the molecular formula gives the number of atoms of each element present in one molecule of the compound. Butane has the empirical formula C_2H_5. However, a molecule of butane has four carbon atoms and ten hydrogen atoms, and so the molecular formula is C_4H_{10}. Another example is glucose. Its empirical formula is CH_2O but molecular formula is $C_6H_{12}O_6$.

Q 10 What type of analytical data is needed to be able to determine the molecular formula of a compound?

The molecular formula does not, however, tell us how the atoms are arranged in the molecule. So, although we know that there are 4 carbon and 10 hydrogen atoms in a butane molecule we do not know how they are arranged in the molecule.

Structural formulae

Molecular compounds

For a molecule, the structural formula indicates how its atoms are arranged. There are two types of structural formulae: full and semi-structural. The full structural formula shows all the bonds present in a molecule. The semi-structural formula is chemical shorthand for the full structural formula.

compound	molecular formula	full-structural formula	semi-structural formula
butane	C_4H_{10}	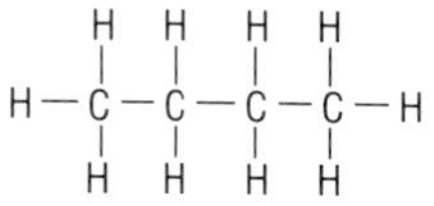	$CH_3CH_2CH_2CH_3$
propene	C_3H_6	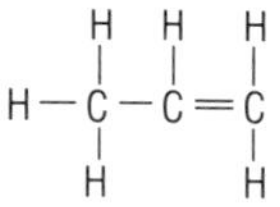	CH_3CHCH_2
ethanoic acid	$C_2H_4O_2$	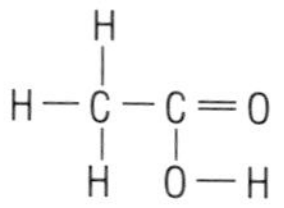	CH_3COOH

Compounds with the same molecular formula but different structural formulae are called *isomers*. For example, two compounds have the molecular formula C_2H_6O but different structural formulae are shown in Figure 1.34.

compound	full-structural formula	semi-structural formula
ethanol	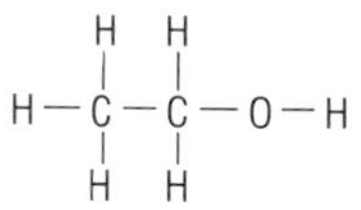	CH_3CH_2OH
methoxymethane	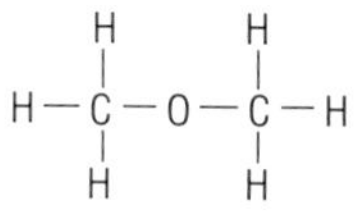	CH_3OCH_3

As well as the empirical formula, data on relative molecular mass or molar mass is needed to determine molecular formula. However, high resolution mass spectroscopy can be used to give the molecular formula of a compound directly.

Empirical, molecular and structural formulae are used and give increasing information about the compound.
Empirical formula: indicates the simplest ratio in which atoms combine in a compound (its stoichiometry).
Molecular formula: indicates the actual numbers of atoms present in a molecule.
Structural formula: indicates the arrangement of atoms within a molecule.

Figure 1.33 Some examples of chemical formulae

Figure 1.34 Isomers with the molecular formula C_2H_6O.

Chemical structure

Structural formulae indicate the three-dimensional chemical structure of a compound. A range of techniques are available which allow the distances and angles between atoms in a compound to be determined. A full chemical structure would indicate all this information.

each C is in a
tetrahedral
environment

all bond angles 109.5°

C — C bond length   154 pm

C — H bond length   109 pm

—— indicates bond in the plane of the page

······· indicates bond going into the plane of the page

◄— indicates bond coming out of the plane of the page

Figure 1.35 The chemical structure of ethane

Chemical equations and calculations

Balanced chemical equations

Balanced chemical equations are the key to calculating:
- quantities and yields in chemical reactions
- results from volumetric analyses.

Balanced chemical equations are the scientist's shorthand for conveying information about reactants and products involved in chemical reactions.

A balanced equation tells us:
- the reactant and products involved
- the amounts of reactants involved and products formed
- their **states of matter** (gas, liquid, solid, or aqueous solution).

Some examples will help to illustrate this:

$$2Al(s) + 3Cl_2(g) \rightarrow 2AlCl_3(s)$$

This means two moles of solid aluminium reacts with three moles gaseous chlorine to give two moles solid aluminium chloride.

$$2C_2H_6(g) + 7O_2(g) \rightarrow 4CO_2(g) + 6H_2O(l)$$

This means two moles of gaseous ethane react with seven moles of gaseous oxygen to give four moles of gaseous carbon dioxide and six moles of water.

$$CaCO_3(s) + 2HCl(aq) \rightarrow CaCl_2(aq) + CO_2(g) + H_2O(l)$$

This means one mole of solid calcium carbonate reacts with two moles of aqueous hydrochloric acid to give one mole of aqueous calcium chloride, one mole of gaseous carbon dioxide and two moles of water.

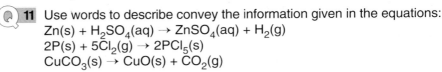 **11** Use words to describe convey the information given in the equations:
$$Zn(s) + H_2SO_4(aq) \rightarrow ZnSO_4(aq) + H_2(g)$$
$$2P(s) + 5Cl_2(g) \rightarrow 2PCl_5(s)$$
$$CuCO_3(s) \rightarrow CuO(s) + CO_2(g)$$

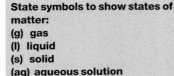

State symbols to show states of matter:
(g) gas
(l) liquid
(s) solid
(aq) aqueous solution

Calculations using balanced equations

Once we have a balanced chemical equation we can use it to work out the quantities of chemicals reacting. This is very useful because it tells you the quantities that you need to measure out.

The following sequence can usually be used:
1 Write the balanced equation for the reaction.
2 Convert known quantities of reactants or products (masses or volumes) into amounts of substance (moles).
3 Use the equation to work out the amounts of the other subtances involved.
4 Convert back from amounts of substance to quantity.
   An example will help you.

Calculate the mass of magnesium oxide that could be formed from 2.4 g magnesium ($M[Mg] = 24$ g mol^{-1}; $M[O] = 16$ g mol^{-1}).

1   Equation for the reaction:
   $$2Mg(s) + O_2(g) \rightarrow 2MgO(s)$$

2   Using $n = \dfrac{m}{M}$, amount of Mg atoms $= \dfrac{2.4}{24} = 0.1$ mol

3   From the equation, 2 mol Mg gives 2 mol MgO (a 1:1 mole ratio).

   Therefore, 0.1 mol Mg yields 0.1 mol MgO

4   $M[MgO] = 24 + 16 = 40$. Using $m = nM$
   mass of MgO $= 0.1 \times 40 = 4$ g

   Therefore, 2.4 g Mg can give 4 g MgO.

Q **12** Calculate the quantities (by mass) of the following: 1 mol CuO, 0.5 mol SO_2, 6 mol NaCl, 0.001 mol $KMnO_4$, 0.05 mol $NiSO_4.5H_2O$.

Q **13** Calculate the amount of substance in each of the following: 10 g $CaCO_3$, 22 g CO_2, 2.4 g CH_4, 2.5 g $CuSO_4.5H_2O$

Calculations for volumetric analysis

We can use similar methods to work out the results of a titration. The balanced equation for the titration reaction must be known. The calculation sequence is the same as that used above.

Consider the following acid-base titration. You have been given a solution of sodium hydroxide and asked to determine its concentration. You do a titration and find that 25.0 cm^3 of the solution requires 15.0 cm^3 of 0.10 mol dm^{-3} hydrochloric acid for complete reaction.

1 Equation for the reaction:
   $$HCl(aq) + NaOH(aq) \rightarrow NaCl(aq) + H_2O(l)$$

2 15.0 cm^3 of 0.10 mol dm^{-3} HCl(aq) contains

   $\dfrac{15}{1000} \times 0.1$ mol HCl $= 1.5 \times 10^{-3}$ mol

3 Using the equation, 1 mol HCl reacts with 1 mol NaOH

   Therefore, 1.5×10^{-3} mol HCl reacts with 1.5×10^{-3} mol NaOH

4 Therefore, 25.0 cm^3 NaOH(aq) contains 1.5×10^{-3} mol NaOH

   and 1 dm^3 NaOH(aq) contains $1.5 \times 10^{-3} \times \dfrac{1000}{25}$ mol NaOH

   $= 0.060$ mol

Therefore, concentration of NaOH(aq) is 0.060 mol dm^{-3}.

Converting quantities and amounts:
$$n = \frac{\text{amount of substance}}{\text{mol}}$$
$$m = \frac{\text{mass of substance}}{\text{g}}$$
$$M = \frac{\text{molar mass}}{\text{g mol}^{-1}}$$
$$n = \frac{m}{M} \qquad m = nM$$

You will either be given a solution and asked to determine the concentration of one or more of the solutes, or you will be given a solid and asked to determine its composition.

14 20.0 cm³ H_2SO_4(aq) reacted completely with 16.0 cm³ of 0.15 mol dm⁻³ KOH(aq). What is the concentration of the sulphuric acid?

15 25.0 cm³ NH_3(aq) reacted completely with 26.8 cm³ of 0.01 mol dm⁻³ H_2SO_4(aq). What is the concentration of the ammonia solution and what mass of ammonia would be present in 1 dm³ of this solution?

16 2 g $CaCO_3$(s) was added to 50 cm³ of 1 mol dm⁻³ HCl(aq). When reaction was complete the solution was titrated against 0.5 mol dm⁻³ NaOH(aq). What volume of the sodium hydroxide solution would be required?

A second example. You are given a sample of 'iron tablets' and asked to calculate the percentage of iron present, assuming it is all present as iron(II). 0.312 g of the crushed tablets was dissolved in 20 cm³ distilled water and 5 cm³ dilute sulphuric acid added. 20.1 cm³ of 0.0100 mol dm⁻³ potassium manganate(VII) solution was added to give a permanent pink colour to the solution.

$M[Fe^{2+}] = 55.8$ g mol⁻¹

1 Equation for the reaction:

$$5Fe^{2+}(aq) + MnO_4^-(aq) + 8H^+(aq) \rightarrow 5Fe^{3+}(aq) + Mn^{2+}(aq) + 4H_2O(l)$$

2 20.1 cm³ of 0.0100 mol dm⁻³ $KMnO_4$(aq) contains

$$\frac{20.1}{1000} \times 0.0100 \text{ mol } MnO_4^-(aq)$$

$$= 2.01 \times 10^{-4} \text{ mol}$$

3 Using the equation, 1 mol MnO_4^-(aq) reacts with 5 mol Fe^{2+}(aq).

Therefore, 2.01×10^{-4} mol MnO_4^-(aq) react with 1.005×10^{-3} mol Fe^{2+}(aq).

4 0.312 g of the tablets contained 1.005×10^{-3} mol Fe^{2+}.

Since $M[Fe^{2+}] = 55.8$ g mol⁻¹; using $m = nM$

mass of $Fe^{2+} = 1.005 \times 10^{-3} \times 55.8$ g $= 0.0561$ g

Therefore, percentage by mass of iron in the iron tablets
$$= \frac{0.0561}{0.312} \times 100 = 18.0\%$$

17 Hydrogen peroxide (H_2O_2) can be bought in the pharmacist's. A solution of H_2O_2(aq) was diluted 20 fold and 25.0 cm³ of this solution required 21.3 cm³ of 0.0100 mol dm⁻³ $KMnO_4$(aq) for complete reaction. Calculate the percentage by mass of hydrogen peroxide in the original solution.

Case study

PAINKILLER FROM A POISONOUS FROG

Many useful chemicals are extracted from naturally-occurring materials. Plants and animals have proved to be valuable sources of therapeutic drugs, for example. Morphine is an analgesic, sedative and hypnotic that has been used for centuries. It is obtained from the opium poppy, *Papaver somniferum*. Alternatively it may be synthesised from simpler chemicals. It is widely used to relieve short-term acute pain and to reduce suffering in the latter stages of terminal illnesses such as cancer.

Morphine and the two related compounds, codeine and heroin, are often called narcotics. As analgesics they have a number of disadvantages; they produce depression of breathing, constipation and sedation. They are also addictive.

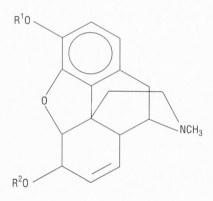

morphine	$R^1 = R^2 = H$
codeine	$R^1 = CH_3, R^2 = H$
heroin	$R^1 = R^2 = CH_3-C\overset{O}{<}$

Illustration 1 The chemical structures of the narcotic analgesics morphine, codeine and heroin.

In 1992 a group of researchers reported the extraction of a compound, epibatidine, from the skin of a South American frog. They found that it was a painkiller 200 times as potent as morphine. The following extract was taken from *New Scientist*, 30 May 1992. The approach used to isolate epibatidine and to establish its chemical identity is commonly used to investigate other naturally-occurring materials as sources of chemicals.

Potent painkiller from poisonous frog

A CHEMICAL extracted from the skin of an Ecuadorian frog has turned out to be a painkiller 200 times as potent as morphine. The chemical, dubbed epibatidine after the frog (*Epipedobates tricolor*), seems to work in a different way to current painkillers, blocking hitherto unknown receptors in the brain.

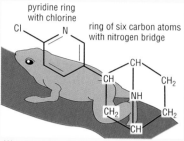

Illustration 2 The chemical structure of epibatidine.

John Daly and his colleagues at the National Institutes of Health of Betheseda, Maryland, extracted 60 milligrams of material from a total of 750 frogs. They purified this using chromatography to obtain 24 milligrams of the new chemical. Analysis by mass spectrometry indicated that the compound had a chemical formula $C_{11}H_{13}N_2Cl$.

When Daly's team subjected the compound to infrared and nuclear magnetic resonance spectrocopy (NMR), they found that it consists of a pyridine ring with a chlorine atom attached (see diagram). This ring is joined to another ring of six carbon atoms, with a nitrogen bridge across the middle (*Journal of the American Chemical Society*, vol 114, p 3745).

Epibatidine is unusual for three reasons. It is a member of an entirely new class of alkaloids; it is an organo-chlorine compound, which is rarely found in animals; and it is a powerful painkiller. Alkaloids are a class of natural compounds which behave somewhat like alkalis. They are extracted mostly from plants, and include nicotine, morphine and cocaine.

One of the characteristic features of epibatidine's structure is the chlorine atom which is attracted to its pyridine group. The chemists predict that if this atom is involved in the compound's powerful analgesic behaviour, the non-chlorine form of the molecule will not function as a painkiller. They believe that by adding other chemical groups to the molecule, it may be possible to make other analgesics.

Questions

1 What methods can be used to extract chemicals from naturally-occurring materials?

2 Why was chromatography used by the research team and what form of chromatography was it likely to have been?

3 What was the percentage yield of epibatidine from the extracted material?

4 How might the purity of the product be assessed?

5 What was the purpose of the analysis undertaken by Daly's team?

6 The empirical formula of an organic compound can be determined by chemical analysis. A weighed sample is combusted in excess oxygen, in the presence of a catalyst, to ensure complete oxidation of the compound. The products of combustion are carbon dioxide, CO_2, and water, H_2O. What masses of CO_2 and H_2O would be obtained if 0.0100 g of epibatidine were analysed in this way?

7 Explain why the empirical formula and the molecular formula of epibatidine are the same.

8 What techniques were used to establish the chemical structure of epibatidine?

9 What information may be obtained from the different analytical techniques employed?

Case study

HOW ACID IS YOUR FOOD?

Fish and chips without vinegar just wouldn't be the same. The sharp or sour taste of many foods is due to the presence of organic acids such as ethanoic acid (in vinegar), citric acid (in citrus fruits) and lactic acid (in sour milk). Some are also useful food preservatives, for example benzoic acid (which is E210 if you look at the labels on some foods).

Illustration 1 Pancakes without sugar and the contrasting sharp taste of lemon juice doesn't seem right. It is the citric acid in lemons which is responsible for this sharpness. For many years fruit juices were the only commercial sources of citric acid. Nowadays it is produced by fermentation of sucrose.

Vinegar is a solution of ethanoic acid, CH_3COOH, in water, often with some colouring such as caramel added. The concentration of the ethanoic acid is usually about 4% w/v, in other words about 4 g in 100 cm^3 of solution. You can buy various types of vinegar in the supermarket or food store. It is straightforward to determine the ethanoic acid content.

Required: 0.100 mol dm^{-3} sodium hydroxide solution
phenolphthalein indicator solution
50 cm^3 burette, stand and white tile
20 cm^3 pipette
10 cm^3 pipette
pipette filler
100 cm^3 volumetric flask
250 cm^3 conical flasks
sample of vinegar to be analysed

IRRITANT
sodium
hydroxide
solution

Method:
1. Use a pipette to transfer 10.0 cm^3 vinegar into a 100 cm^3 volumetric flask. Make the solution up to 100 cm^3 with distilled water.
2. Place the 0.100 mol dm^{-3} sodium hydroxide in the burette.
3. Pipette 20 cm^3 of the diluted vinegar solution into a conical flask and add 2–3 drops of phenolphthalein.
4. Titrate against the sodium hydroxide solution to a permanent pink colour.
5. Using the equation

$$CH_3COOH(aq) + NaOH(aq) \rightarrow CH_3COONa(aq) + H_2O(l)$$

calculate the concentration of ethanoic acid in the diluted sample and, therefore, in the original vinegar sample.

This general method can be adapted to determine the acid content of various foodstuffs. For example, citric acid can be determined, though it is important

to know that this is a tribasic acid, so one mole reacts with three moles of sodium hydroxide.

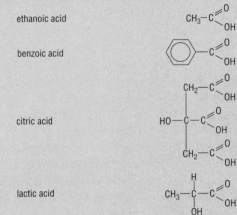

ethanoic acid

benzoic acid

citric acid

lactic acid

Illustration 2 The structures of some organic acids found in foodstuffs

Fizzy drinks contain carbon dioxide, which makes them weakly acidic. The carbon dioxide content can be determined by a similar method as organic acids except that methyl orange solution should be used as the indicator. The relevant reaction is:

$$CO_2(aq) + NaOH(aq) \rightarrow NaHCO_3(aq)$$

Since the solubility of carbon dioxide decreases as the temperature increases, it is advisable to cool the drink in a refrigerator before analysis. It is also important to recognise that some fizzy drinks also contain other acids, such as citric acid or tartaric acid, to give them flavour.

Questions

1 Using the method described above, a 20.0 cm^3 diluted sample of white vinegar required exactly 13.8 cm^3 of 0.100 mol dm^{-3} sodium hydroxide for complete reaction. Calculate the concentration (w/v) of ethanoic acid in the undiluted vinegar.

2 Wine contains a variety of acids such as ethanoic acid, citric acid, tartaric acid and sulphurous acid. However, the acid content is often given as 'ethanoic equivalent'. Devise a method for comparing the acidity of different wines.

3 Lemons and oranges contain citric acid. Devise a method for determining how the acid content of these fruits varies during the ripening process.

4 Lemonade contains dissolved carbon dioxide and citric acid. Devise a method to determine the concentration of both. (Hint: Carbon dioxide can be removed from solution by boiling for a prolonged period, while citric acid is involatile. Citric acid forms insoluble salts with a number of metal ions.)

For questions 2-4 describe the method, giving details of apparatus and reagents, and explain how you would use the data collected to calculate the required information.

2 | Investigate materials and their use

Most living things survive by adapting to their environment. As the environment changes, they have to change as well in order to survive generation after generation.

Human beings can be said to do the opposite. We often adapt our environment to make it more comfortable or productive. In order to do this, we need an abundant supply of appropriate materials. Scientists can identify those properties which a material must have for a particular use. They can measure those properties and work out how the structure of the material can be adapted to make it more useful.

Figure 2.1 These overhead electricity cables will only be effective if they are made of a suitably conductive material. The pylons needed to support them also need to meet particular design requirements, e.g. strength and weather resistance.

The Elements

Element 2.1 Identify the properties of materials for particular uses

Objects can only perform their function satisfactorily if the materials from which they are made have appropriate properties.

To select a material for a particular use, you need to:

- identify the purpose for which a material is needed and the conditions under which it must perform
- describe what properties a suitable material must have
- select a material and explain why you chose it.

 Materials and their use, page 78

Experimental methods for determining properties, page 93

Structure of materials, page 111

Figure 2.2 Modern advances in information technology are dependent on semiconductors. This silicon chip has been made so that it has just the right properties for its purpose.

Element 2.2 Determine the properties of a material

Scientists must be able to measure useful properties of materials. Your task is to write reports on the measurement of four different properties of materials. At least one report must include an account of how the property is determined in an industrial laboratory.

The task has four distinct stages for each property which you measure:
- describe the property to be determined
- make appropriate measurements safely and use them to determine the property.

You will also need to:
- relate the properties of a material to its structure
- describe how properties are measured in an industrial laboratory.

Figure 2.3 The properties of polythene can be modified by the method of production. Both low-density polythene (LDPE) and high-density polythene (HDPE) find extensive use; for example LDPE is used for food wrapping and HDPE is used for plastic boxes and milk crates.

Element 2.3 Modify materials to make them more useful

A material can often be made more useful by modifying its structure. To modify a property of a material you need to:
- describe suitable methods to modify a material
- modify a material.

You will also need to:
- explain changes in properties in terms of the material's structure
- describe how properties are modified in an industrial process.

Modifying the properties of a material, page 104

Structure of materials, page 111

Materials and their use

The objects which we use are all made out of materials. Each object is designed to do something specific. It will only accomplish that task if the material has been correctly chosen.

For example, a table has to act as a stable platform for food, books and computers. An object can only perform its function if it is made from a material with the right set of properties. Tables can be made from almost any material, but they are unlikely to be satisfactory if they are made from rubber or cement!

Purpose

Materials which are used to make objects will have one or more purposes. Here are some examples.

Support

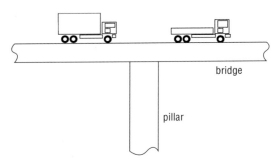

Look at Figure 2.4. The pillar is supporting part of the bridge. Its function is to keep the road surface in the same place as traffic moves over it. For the pillar to accomplish this function, its material must have an appropriate mix of properties.

The pillar must have a high compressive strength, so that there is no danger of it crumbling under the weight of the road and traffic. It must have a low elasticity so that the road does not move up and down as the amount of traffic varies. A low density would be useful, so that the pillar has a low weight. Also, the pillar has to be chemically resistant to traffic fumes, water, air and salt (used for melting ice). Finally, a low cost will be important.

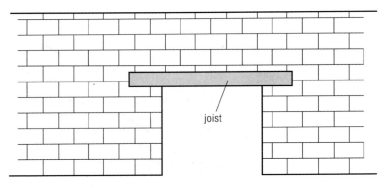

A different type of support is shown in Figure 2.5. The joist supports the wall above the door. The weight of the wall will compress the top surface of the joist and stretch its bottom surface. So the joist material needs to have a high tensile strength. A certain degree of toughness would be a useful safety feature; this will prevent catastrophic failure of the joist.

Materials are needed to provide support and protection. Their thermal and electrical conductivities are also important properties for many applications.

 What's available, page 81

 Physical properties of materials, page 85

Figure 2.4 A pillar which is supporting part of a bridge must have a high compressive strength, a low elasticity and be chemically resistant.

Figure 2.5 A joist in a brick wall must be tough and have a high tensile strength.

Protection

Figure 2.6 shows the construction of a length of domestic electrical connecting cable. It contains two materials; one for the outer protective cladding, the other for the electrical core.

The outer cladding has to be an electrical insulator, so it must have a low value of electrical conductivity. It also needs to be wear-resistant and waterproof. The whole cable must be flexible, so the cladding will have to made from a tough material.

Figure 2.6 *A domestic electricity cable.*

Assignment trigger

Protective clothing

People who work in industry are often supplied with special clothing by their employers.

Why do employers do this?
What properties must the clothing have?
What materials are used?

If a practical assignment is developed, it is essential that a risk assessment is made and checked by your teacher/lecturer.

Could lead to possible assignments relating to Unit 2.

Electrical conduction

The core of an electrical cable must have a very high value for electrical conductivity. So it has to be made from a metal. That metal must be resistant to oxidation, otherwise screw connections between lengths of cable will become unreliable. Copper is the usual choice.

The flexibility can be achieved by using lots of strands rather than a single rod. So the core must be made from a ductile material that is easily drawn out into a wire.

Heat conduction

Any fibrous material which has small pockets of air is a poor conductor of heat. Such materials are widely used to slow down the rate at which heat energy passes from one place to another (see Figure 2.7).

Figure 2.7 *Materials which are poor conductors of heat energy help us to keep heat energy where it is needed.*

Metals are good conductors of heat. They are used whenever it is important for heat energy to be quickly transferred from one place to another. For example, the food inside a copper saucepan can be heated quickly over a gas flame. A glass saucepan is not as good at conducting heat energy, needing more energy to keep the water boiling.

Conditions of use

You can start to decide which material is best for an object by asking questions about the **conditions which that material will have to endure**.

Stress and strain

Think about the various forces which the object will be exposed to. Where will they act? Will they compress the object or stretch it? In what direction? Will they be constant or will they fluctuate? How large will they be? How rigid must the object be?

Wear

Think about how the shape of the object will change with time. Does the object involve moving parts? Moving parts will eventually show signs of wear and fail. How much wear is acceptable? Which parts of the object will get the most wear from bashing other objects? Will it come into contact with sharp objects or rough objects? How hard must the material be for it to resist bumps and scratches?

Temperature

What are the maximum and minimum temperatures to which the material will be exposed in normal use? What properties must it have at those temperatures? Does it matter if it becomes brittle or soft? Suppose that the material is exposed to temperatures outside this range; does it matter if it burns or melts?

Chemical environment

Think about the corrosive chemicals with which the object will come into contact. Does the material have to be resistant to attack by acids or alkalis? Must it be waterproof? Does it matter if the material dissolves or softens or changes shape in water? Does it matter if the material reacts with oxygen in the air? Is long-term oxidation of the surface going to be a problem? Is the material likely to burn under normal conditions of use?

> ## Assignment trigger
>
> ### Chemical plants
> Laboratory preparations are often carried out in simple glassware. Industrial plant often uses different apparatus made of other materials.
>
> What operations are carried out in chemical plants?
> What properties must the materials have and why?
> What materials are used?
> What happens when a plant is scrapped?
>
> *If a practical assignment is developed, it is essential that a risk assessment is made and checked by your teacher/lecturer.*
>
> *Could lead to possible assignments relating to Units 2 and 6.*

> **The important conditions which a material may have to endure are stress, strain, wear, temperature and corrosive chemicals.**

 What's available, page 81

 Physical properties of materials, page 85

What's available

Materials fall into four distinct classes. Each class of material has its own characteristic set of properties.

Metals

Metals have several useful properties, some of which are not shared by any other class of material. Table 2.1 gives values of these properties for four metals in common use.

Materials may be metals, polymers, ceramics (including glasses and semiconductors) or composites. Each type of material has its own special set of properties.

▶ Structure of materials, page 111

Table 2.1 Properties of some metals

Property	Copper	Aluminium	Iron	Gold
Electrical conductivity/$\Omega^{-1}m^{-1}$	6×10^7	4×10^7	1×10^7	5×10^7
Young modulus/Nm^{-2}	13×10^{10}	7×10^{10}	21×10^{10}	8×10^{10}
Tensile strength/Nm^{-2}	30×10^7	5×10^7	21×10^7	12×10^7
Density/kgm^{-3}	8 900	2 700	7 900	19 300
Melting point/K	1 356	932	1 812	1 336

Metals are all excellent electrical conductors. Their *electrical conductivity* is high. This means that they are widely used to transfer electrical energy from one place to another.

Metals are also *ductile*. They can permanently change their shape when sufficient pressure is applied. For example, a bar of steel can be hammered, rolled and pressed until it becomes the completely different shape of a car body panel (see Figure 2.8). Many metals melt at low enough temperatures for them to be shaped by casting into moulds (see Figure 2.9).

Figure 2.8 A large hydraulic press at a car factory. Steel sheets are stamped into a mould to make them into body panels for cars.

Many metals are *strong*. They can withstand high *tensile* and *compressive stress* before they are plastically deformed. Their *Young Modulus* is large, so they don't change shape readily when they are subjected to forces.

Figure 2.9 *Hot metal being poured into a mould*

Metals are vulnerable to chemical attack. They are liable to react with oxygen in the air as well as with water. For example, iron is converted into rust when exposed to air and water. It is for this reason that many metals need a protective coating of paint.

Assignment trigger

Fuses

Electrical appliances usually have fuses in them.

Why are they there?
What properties must they have?
What materials can they be made from?
How can you measure the properties of these materials?

If a practical assignment is developed, it is essential that a risk assessment is made and checked by your teacher/lecturer.

Could lead to possible assignments relating to Unit 2.

Polymers

A polymer is made from molecules which are very long. They are generally tough and low density and cheap. Table 2.2 gives values for the useful properties of some polymers in common use.

Table 2.2 Properties of some polymers

Property	Polythene	Perspex	Polystyrene
Density/kgm^{-3}	960	1 180	1 050
Electrical conductivity/$\Omega^{-1}m^{-1}$	10^{-14}	10^{-13}	10^{-11}
Tensile strength/Nm^{-2}	29×10^6	60×10^6	40×10^6
Young modulus/Nm^{-2}	1×10^9	3×10^9	35×10^9

Polymers are very good electrical insulators. They are also often transparent and many can be easily moulded into shape when heated to relatively low temperatures. Polymers which can be moulded in this way are called *thermoplastics. Thermosetting* polymers undergo a chemical reaction when they are heated; this makes them stronger, but also means that they cannot be softened by heating.

The only drawback of polymers is their tendency to creep when tensile forces are applied. They slowly get steadily longer and longer when they are stretched. Polymers which have this behaviour are called *plastics*.

Polymers are highly resistant to attack by chemical attack by air and water. Furthermore, they are waterproof. However, polymers are not usually very hard. They are easily scratched and are not very wear resistant.

Ceramics

Glasses, semiconductors and pure ceramics have many properties in common.

Pure ceramics

Ceramics are made by baking mixtures of metal oxides or other minerals at high temperatures. Their properties are, in many ways, exactly opposite to those of metals. Table 2.3 should make this clear.

Ceramics are hard. They have a very high *compressive strength*, being able to withstand large compressive stress before fracturing (see Figure 2.10).

Figure 2.10 Ceramics can be very strong in compression. This car is being held up by four china teacups.

Ceramics are strong but they are also brittle. The value of their Young Modulus is quite high, but they are liable to crack if the tensile stress is too great.

Ceramics are excellent *insulators*. Their electrical conductivity is so low that it is often decided by the amount of water they contain.

Table 2.3 Properties of some ceramics

Property	China	Porcelain	Brick	Cement
Electrical conductivity/$\Omega^{-1}m^{-1}$	10^{-10}	10^{-11}		
Young modulus/Nm^{-2}	90×10^9	70×10^9	7×10^9	40×10^9
Compressive strength/Nm^{-2}	110×10^6	100×10^6	2×10^6	20×10^6
Density/kgm^{-3}	2 800	2 500	$\approx 1\ 600$	2 300
Softening temperature/K	1 800	1 800		

Ceramics often start off as mixtures of finely powdered minerals suspended in water. This slurry can be poured into moulds, then heated to drive off the water and let chemical bonds form between the minerals. (Cement is different because it does not need heating. There is a direct chemical reaction between the minerals and water to bond the particles together.) There is no other practical way of moulding ceramics into set shapes. They are too brittle to be hammered or cut precisely and melt at too high a temperature to be cast into moulds.

Although ceramics are resistant to chemical attack by air and water, they are *porous*. The gaps (or pores) in their structure allow water to get into them; they are not very waterproof.

Glasses

Glasses have many properties in common with ceramics, but one vital difference. They are transparent, whereas ceramics are opaque. It is often the optical properties of glasses which make them useful. Table 2.4 gives some values for useful properties of some glasses.

Table 2.4 Properties of some types of glass

Property	Silica glass	Window glass	Pyrex glass
Young modulus/Nm^{-2}	7×10^{10}	7×10^{10}	7×10^{10}
Density/kgm^{-3}	2 200	2 500	2 250
Softening temperature/K	1 940	1 000	1 090

Glasses are chemically inert as far as air and water are concerned. Unlike ceramics, they are waterproof. Glasses are hard and brittle.

Semiconductors

Most materials are either metals or non-metals. They are normally distinguished by the value of their electrical conductivity. Metals have a very high value ($\approx 10^7 \, \Omega^{-1}m^{-1}$) and non-metals have very low values ($\approx 10^{-12} \, \Omega^{-1}m^{-1}$). Semiconductors are materials whose value of conductivity falls between these two extremes. This property, above all others, is what makes semiconductors useful.

The conductivity of a piece of semiconductor is highly sensitive to its environment. Semiconductors are therefore widely used as sensors of light and temperature (see Figure 2.11).

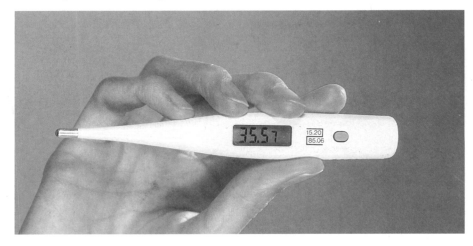

Figure 2.11 An electronic thermometer. The temperature sensor in the tip is a semiconductor. The integrated circuit which processes the information from the sensor and drives the liquid crystal display is also a semiconductor.

Modern electronic switches are made of layers of different semiconductors; the conductivity of one layer is strongly affected by the voltage of an adjacent layer (see Figure 2.12). All solid-state electronic components use semiconducting materials to achieve their function.

Composites

A composite material is a mixture of two other materials, taking advantage of the best qualities of each material. The basic structure of a composite is shown in Figure 2.13. It generally consists of fibres of a hard, strong material embedded in a matrix of another material which is plastic and tough. The result is a material which has the strength of the fibre, with the toughness of the matrix.

The materials used to make a number of composites are shown in Table 2.5. In each case, the outcome is a material which is strong without being brittle.

Table 2.5 Types of composite

Composite	Fibre	Matrix
fibreglass	glass	polymer
concrete	steel	cement
cermet	ceramic	metal
wood	cellulose	lignin

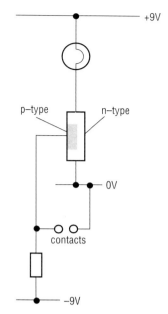

Figure 2.12 *A field effect transistor (FET) switch. If the p-type insert is at a much lower voltage than the n-type slab, there is no current in the bulb. A finger placed across the contacts raises the voltage of the p-type insert, allowing electrons to flow through the n-type slab, causing the bulb to glow.*

Assignment trigger

Concrete

The important ingredient in all concrete materials is cement. Other materials are added.

What is cement?
What are concrete materials used for?
What conditions must they withstand?
What materials are added to cement?
Why are they added?
How do they affect the strength of cement?

If a practical assignment is developed, it is essential that a risk assessment is made and checked by your teacher/lecturer.

Could lead to possible assignments relating to Unit 2.

Physical properties of materials

Mechanical properties

All solid materials have a number of mechanical **properties**. These can be used to decide how suitable the material is for a particular application.

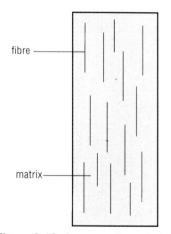

Figure 2.13 *A composite material has fibres of one material embedded in a matrix of a different material.*

The important properties of materials are Young modulus, yield stress, breaking stress, wear resistance, density, conductivity (thermal and electrical) and chemical resistance.

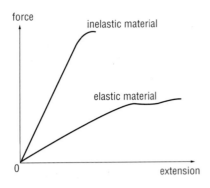

Figure 2.14 *Typical force-extension curves for elastic and inelastic materials. Note that both curves are straight lines close to the origin.*

Elasticity and stiffness

The *elasticity* of a material tells you by how much it is going to stretch when you apply forces to it. An elastic material stretches much more than an inelastic one. Figure 2.14 shows what happens to a sample of material when a force is applied to it; the extension always increases as the force increases. The Young modulus of the sample is given by the gradient of the straight line portion of the graph near the origin.

$$\text{extension (m)} = \frac{\text{force (N)} \times \text{length (m)}}{\text{area (m}^2) \times \text{Young modulus (Nm}^{-2})}$$

$$x = \frac{Fl}{AE}$$

A large value for the Young modulus means that the sample has a relatively small extension. So materials with a large value for the Young modulus are not very elastic. They are stiff.

1 A girl weighs 700 N. She hangs from the end of a 25 m long nylon rope. The diameter of the rope is 1.0 cm and the Young modulus of nylon is 2.0×10^9 Nm^{-2}. Show that the rope is extended by 11 cm.

Yield stress

Any force applied to a material will deform it. If the force is large enough, the material will become plastic. It will remain deformed when the force is removed.

It is the stress placed on the material which decides whether or not it will be plastically deformed. The stress on a material is the force per unit area.

$$\text{stress (Nm}^{-2} \text{ or Pa)} = \frac{\text{force (N)}}{\text{area (m}^2)} \qquad \sigma = \frac{F}{A}$$

Any stress whose value is greater than the yield stress will permanently deform a material. It will not regain its original shape when the stress is removed.

The yield strain is often quoted instead of the yield stress. Strain is a measure of how much a sample of material has been extended when it is squashed or stretched.

$$\text{strain} = \frac{\text{extension (m)}}{\text{original length (m)}} \qquad \varepsilon = \frac{x}{l}$$

2 The yield stress of steel is 2.5×10^8 Nm^{-2}. Show that a force of at least 4 900 N is needed to plastically stretch a steel rod of diameter 5.0 mm.

Breaking stress

Should the stress on a material exceed the *breaking stress*, then it will break. Most materials are stronger in compression than tension, so they have two values for the breaking stress. The compressive strength tells you how strong the material is when you are squeezing it. The tensile strength is the maximum stress the material can take when you stretch it.

3 The compressive strength of a typical brick is about 5×10^7 Nm^{-2}. Show that a single 10 cm × 6 cm × 21 cm brick can support a weight of up to 1 MN.

Toughness

A material is tough if it is difficult to break. Such materials are able to suffer large extensions before they snap. A stress-strain curve for a typical tough material is shown in Figure 2.15. Once the material has passed the elastic limit it is permanently deformed; the strain remains when the stress is removed.

Metals and polymers are tough; ceramics and glasses are not.

Hardness

A *hard* material resists changing its shape when large pressures are applied. It is difficult to dent a hard material. Ceramics are very hard. Most metals are not hard.

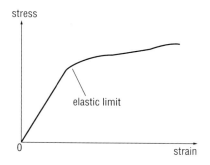

Figure 2.15 Typical stress-strain curve for a tough material.

Assignment trigger

Spare parts

Artificial limbs, contact lenses, heart valves and dental fillings are all aids to or replacements for parts of the human body.

Under what conditions must they perform?
What materials are they made of?
What properties should they possess?
What materials are most likely to have these properties?

If a practical assignment is developed, it is essential that a risk assessment is made and checked by your teacher/lecturer.

Could lead to possible assignments relating to Units 2 and 7.

Brittleness

A *brittle* material breaks easily into two parts when it is stretched. Figure 2.16 shows a typical stress-strain curve for such a material. Brittle materials extend very little when they are subjected to tensile forces; they are very stiff. However, they are very weak under tension. Microscopic cracks in their structure can grow catastrophically when they are stretched, leading quickly to shattering.

Glasses, ceramics and stone are all examples of brittle materials.

Wear resistance

Whenever two objects move past each other, there is the possibility of *wear*. The surfaces of the object may gradually change shape as material is removed from them. Lubricants such as grease or oil are widely used to keep such moving surfaces apart from each other and reduce wear to a minimum.

Ductility

A *ductile* material can be stretched into a very long strand without the need to heat it up beforehand (see Figure 2.17). The material appears to flow when a sufficiently large tensile force is applied.

Flexibility

A *flexible* material is easy to bend when forces are applied. Almost any material can be made flexible by making it into thin strands or sheets.

A common method of assessing the flexibility of an object is to bend it back on itself until it snaps (see Figure 2.18). The radius of the smallest circle which the material can be bent around is proportional to the thickness of the material. So thin fibres of glass are very flexible indeed, whereas thick rods of glass are not.

Figure 2.16 Typical stress-strain curve for a brittle material.

Figure 2.17 Copper wires are made by drawing the metal through a succession of holes, each smaller than the previous one.

Figure 2.18 Thin strands of glass fibre which are used for telecommunications are very flexible.

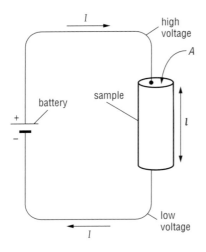

Figure 2.19 Electric current I flows through the sample from high voltage to low voltage. The value of I depends on the length of the sample l, its cross-section area A, the p.d. of the battery V and the conductivity of the material .

A tough material will be more flexible, for the same thickness, than a material which is brittle.

Malleability

A *malleable* material can be squeezed into almost any shape when sufficient compressive force is applied. Many materials become sufficiently soft to do this when they are hot enough, but malleable materials can be hammered and pressed into different shapes without any heating.

Density

The *density* of a material is its mass to volume ratio. High density materials have a larger mass for a given volume than low density materials.

$$\text{density (kgm}^{-3}) = \frac{\text{mass (kg)}}{\text{volume (m}^3)} \qquad D = \frac{m}{V}$$

Density is an important property when selecting a construction material. Given two materials which have the same strength, the one with the lower density will be able to support more. A high density material might even have difficulty standing up under its own weight!

Q 4 Oak has a density of 720 kgm^{-3}. Show that an oak plank which is 15 cm × 2 cm × 3 m will have a mass of 6.5 kg.

Electrical conductivity

The electrical conductivity of a material is a measure of how easily it lets an electric current flow through it.

When there is a potential difference (p.d. or voltage) across the ends of a material then an electric current flows through it (Figure 2.19). The resistance of the material (in ohms (Ω)) is defined as follows.

$$\text{resistance } (\Omega) = \frac{\text{voltage (V)}}{\text{current (A)}} \qquad R = \frac{V}{I}$$

The resistance of an object depends on its length, cross-section area and the resistivity of the material it is made from.

$$\text{resistance } (\Omega) = \frac{\text{resistivity } (\Omega\text{m}) \times \text{length (m)}}{\text{area (m}^2)}$$

A material's conductivity is the reciprocal of its resistivity.

$$\text{resistance } (\Omega) = \frac{\text{length (m)}}{\text{conductivity } (\Omega^{-1}\text{m}^{-1}) \times \text{area (m}^2)} \qquad R = \frac{l}{\sigma A}$$

A material with a high value for conductivity lets electric current flow through it relatively easily.

Q 5 The resistivity of copper is 1.56×10^{-8} Ω m. Show that a copper wire of length 25 m and diameter 1.0 mm has a resistance of only 0.5 Ω.

Assignment trigger

Electrical safety

Electrical products on sale in shops must be safe.

What might make them unsafe?
How can the correct design and choice of materials make them safe?

If a practical assignment is developed, it is essential that a risk assessment is made and checked by your teacher/lecturer.

Could lead to possible assignments relating to Unit 2.

Thermal conductivity

The rate at which heat energy is conducted through a material depends on its thermal conductivity.

$$P = \frac{kA\Delta T}{x}$$

P is the rate at which heat energy is transferred across the sample (W).
k is the thermal conductivity of the sample ($Wm^{-1}K^{-1}$).
A is the area of the sample through which the heat energy is being conducted (m^2).
ΔT is the temperature drop across the sample (K).
x is the thickness of the sample (m).

Good conductors of heat have large values for thermal conductivity. So copper ($400\ Wm^{-1}K^{-1}$) is one of the best conductors available. Wood ($0.15\ Wm^{-1}K^{-1}$) is a poor conductor (and therefore a good insulator).

Q 6 A single-skin brick wall on the side of a house is 5 m high and 8 m long. The bricks are 12 cm thick and have a thermal conductivity of $1.2\ Wm^{-1}K^{-1}$. If the inside of the house is at 20 °C when the outside is at 5 °C, show that heat energy passes through the wall at a rate of 6 kW.

Chemical resistance

No material is chemically inert. So when you specify the chemical resistance of a material, you have to specify which chemicals it has to be resistant to! A petrol tank has to withstand chemical attack by petrol, but it doesn't matter if it dissolves in sulphuric acid!

The chemical environment of most objects is normal atmospheric conditions. This means air and water. The main active ingredient in air is oxygen. It reacts with most metals to form a layer of metal oxide on their surfaces. In the case of aluminium, this oxide layer seals off the rest of the metal from chemical attack. However, in the case of iron, surface oxidation (rusting) can seriously weaken its structure (see Figure 2.20).

Figure 2.20 Rusting seriously weakens structures made from steel.

Water tends to dissolve materials. Rainwater is often acidic, particularly when there is a lot of pollution in the air (see Figure 2.21).

Figure 2.21 *Erosion of stonework caused by acidic gases present in polluted air*

Some materials are not waterproof. Water can get into them through pores in their surface. Ceramics are particularly porous. This may not only affect their density and electrical conductivity, but it may also eventually weaken the material. Substances can slowly dissolve in the water and be removed when the water flows out of the material.

Coming to a decision

How do you decide which material is the best one to use for a particular purpose?

For example, spoons are designed to help in preparing food. What material should a spoon be made of? Ceramic, polymer, composite or metal? Metals are poor for dealing with hot food because they conduct heat very well. On the other hand, metal spoons are easier to clean. Nor do they warp, discolour or crack with age. But one composite (wood) is cheaper than metal. Polymer is even cheaper than wood, but often melts at fairly low temperatures. Decisions, decisions!

Listing properties

One way forward is to list all of the important properties which the material must have. You have to think about the conditions of use. Then you can use Table 2.6 to decide on the classes of materials which are likely to be useful.

For example, a spoon needs to be resistant to chemical attack, a poor conductor of heat, wear resistant, tough and quite strong. If you inspect Table 2.6 carefully, you will see that no material is good for all of these properties. So a spoon can be made from a number of different materials. Some examples are shown in Figure 2.22.

Deciding on the best choice for a material involves considering the conditions of use, cost, availability, ease of fabrication, environmental factors and fashion.

Figure 2.22 *Spoons can be made from a number of different materials.*

Table 2.6 Properties of materials. This table gives the general rules. There are exceptions!

Property	Metal	Ceramic	Glass	Polymer	Composite
Transparent	no	no	yes	often	no
Brittle	no	yes	yes	no	no
Chemically resistant	not often	often	yes	yes	often
Electrical conduction	yes	no	no	no	sometimes
Heat conduction	yes	sometimes	moderate	no	not often
Dense	usually	moderate	moderate	no	not often
Ductile	often	no	no	no	no
Elastic	no	no	no	can be	no
Flexible	yes	no	no	can be	no
Hard	not often	yes	yes	no	can be
Strong	yes	yes	yes	can be	yes
Tough	yes	no	no	yes	yes
Wear resistance	moderate	high	moderate	poor	variable

Cost

The cost of a material is often all-important. There may be several materials which have the right physical properties for a particular purpose. The one which gets used is usually the one with the lowest cost.

When considering the cost of a material you need to consider three factors. There is the cost of the raw material itself, the cost of transporting it to where it is needed and the cost of getting it into the right shape.

Occasionally the cost of a material is not the crucial factor. This may be because only the best will do. Many uses of materials for aviation, defence and space fall into this category (see Figure 2.23). In the case of a humble spoon, however, cost is all important.

Figure 2.23 Sometimes the cost of a material is the least important factor.

The cost of a material is linked to its availability. Rare materials are expensive. Availability of a material is usually a serious consideration for very large engineering projects. For example, you don't specify that a dam has to be made from granite blocks unless the local terrain is also made of granite!

For many people who live in developing countries, the availability of a material is crucial. There is no point in deciding to make stainless steel spoons if the only raw materials at your disposal are wood and rock.

Ease of fabrication

How easy will it be to make the object out of your chosen class of material? This really depends on the shape of the object. Intricate shapes are difficult to achieve with composite materials. Polymers can be moulded easily into simple shapes. Metals can be pressed and carved into any shape you like.

Environmental factors

There are several environmental factors which you may need to bear in mind when selecting a material. Can the material be easily recycled once the object has worn out or ceased to be useful? If the material can't be recycled, is it biodegradable? Does the manufacture of the material involve lots of energy? Is a lot of toxic waste produced when the material is manufactured? Is the material likely to pose a health hazard to its users? Does the extraction of the raw materials pose an unacceptable hazard?

In the case of a spoon, the use of wood from rainforests might be seen as environmentally unacceptable. Composite materials are very difficult to recycle. Polymers are not biodegradable, and thermosetting ones cannot be recycled.

Aesthetic considerations

In developed countries, aesthetic considerations are very important. Nobody is going to buy a spoon unless it looks good and feels right for the task. This is the reason why so many spoons are made out of metal, even though metals are good conductors of heat.

The final choice of material for an object is nearly always a compromise. It is rare for there only to be one material which can do the job at a given price. Fashion often has the last word!

Experimental methods for determining properties

This section describes how you could measure four different properties of a material in the laboratory. It will help you to appreciate the techniques and apparatus which are used to measure these properties by professional scientists.

Young modulus

To find a value for the Young modulus of a material you need data on how its strain depends on its stress. Reliable data is difficult to obtain because the strain is often quite small for even large stresses.

Here is a procedure which you can use in a laboratory to find the Young modulus of a material. It gets around the main sources of error which beset this type of measurement.

▶ Physical properties of materials, page 85

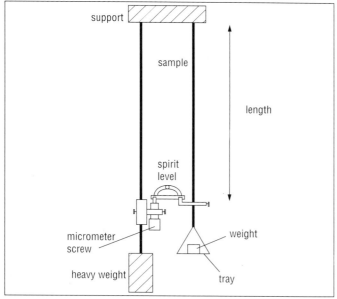

Figure 2.24 *Apparatus which can be used to measure the Young modulus of a sample of wire*

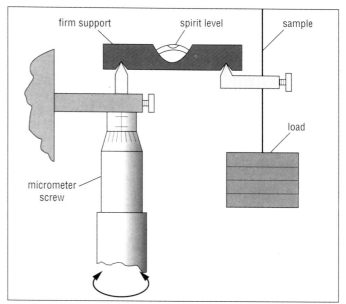

Figure 2.25 *The arrangement of micrometer screw and spirit level*

Apparatus

The apparatus is shown in Figure 2.24. The sample is a long thin wire which is hung from a firm support. The stress is supplied by the weight of the mass hung from the end of the wire. A thin wire will have a larger stress than a thick one for the same weights on the end. Similarly, a long wire will have a greater extension than a short one for the same stress. The extension is measured by a micrometer screw. This allows measurements with a precision of ±0.005 mm. As you can see from Figure 2.25, a spirit level is used to indicate when the end of the micrometer is level with the end of the sample.

The micrometer is suspended from the same support as the sample, on a length of the same material. This is to prevent any thermal expansion of the sample being misread as a change of strain. Any change of temperature during the measurement process will result in an identical movement of the micrometer and the lower end of the sample.

Procedure

The first step is to measure the diameter of the sample with a micrometer screw gauge. Several measurements at various places along the sample are much better than just one. You also need to have a value for the unstretched length of the sample.

Ensure that the sample has no kinks and bends which could straighten out when it is stressed. Then place the smallest weight in the tray which will make the wire hang straight. Adjust the micrometer until the spirit level is horizontal. Note its reading.

Increase the weight on the end of the sample by adding a known weight to the tray. Note the new reading of the micrometer.

Repeat by adding another weight to the tray. The wire should extend the same amount each time a fixed weight is added.

Continue until the extension stops going up by the same amount each time the extra weight is added to the tray.

eye
protection
must be worn

Data analysis

Use your data to plot a graph of the weight on the end of the sample against the micrometer reading. An example is shown in Figure 2.26.

For small stresses, the sample will obey the following equation.

$$\text{Young modulus} = E = \frac{\text{stress}}{\text{strain}} = \frac{\sigma}{\varepsilon}$$

The stress is given by the weight on the end of the sample F and its cross-section area A.

$$\text{stress} = \sigma = \frac{F}{A}$$

The strain is given by the extension x of the sample and its original unstretched length l.

$$\text{strain} = \varepsilon = \frac{x}{l}$$

If you combine these three pieces of algebra you obtain the following expression.

$$\frac{F}{x} = E\left(\frac{A}{l}\right)$$

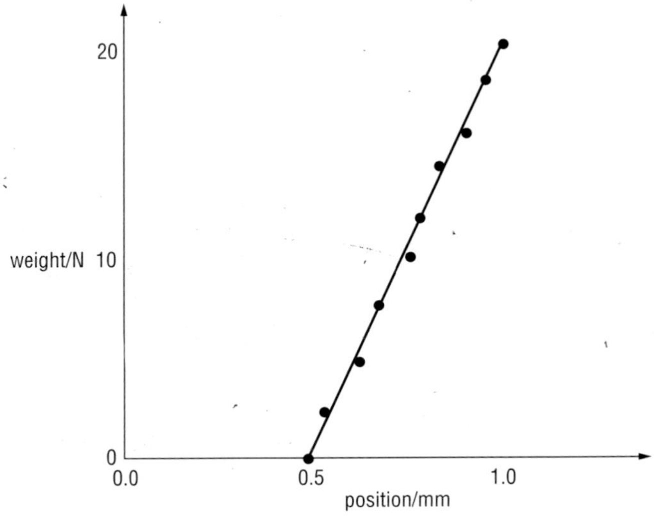

Figure 2.26 *A graph showing how the position of the micrometer screw depends on the weight in the tray.*

The quantity F/x is the gradient of the graph in Figure 2.26. In this case, its value is $4.11 \times 10^4 \, \text{Nm}^{-1}$. The value of A can be calculated from the diameter of the wire d as follows.

$$A = \pi \left(\frac{d}{2}\right)^2 = \pi \left(\frac{0.63 \times 10^{-3}}{2}\right)^2 = 3.12 \times 10^{-7} \, \text{m}^2$$

Since the unstretched length of the sample in this case is 1.52 m, a value for the Young modulus E is easily calculated.

$$\frac{F}{x} = E\left(\frac{A}{l}\right)$$

therefore $\quad 4.11 \times 10^4 = E\left(\frac{3.12 \times 10^{-7}}{1.52}\right)$

or $\qquad E = \dfrac{4.11 \times 10^4}{2.05 \times 10^{-7}}$

or $\qquad E = 2.00 \times 10^{11} \, \text{Nm}^{-2}.$

Likely error

Your final value for the Young modulus is the combination of four different measurements. The precision of each measurement depends on the instrument you used. This is summarised in Table 2.7. (The value quoted is the largest one measured.)

▶ Measurement: accuracy, precision and errors, page 31

Table 2.7 Precision of measurements

Quantity	Instrument	Value	Precision	%error
Force	spring balance	20.0 N	±0.05 N	0.25
Extension	micrometer	0.50 mm	±0.005 mm	1.00
Length	metre rule	1.52 m	±0.005 m	1.00
Diameter	micrometer	0.63 mm	±0.005 mm	0.80

The next step is to write down the equation for calculating the Young modulus from the basic measurements. These are the force F, the extension x, the length l and the diameter d.

$$E = \frac{\sigma}{\varepsilon}, \, \sigma = \frac{F}{A}, \, \varepsilon = \frac{x}{l}, \, A = \frac{\pi d^2}{4}$$

therefore $E = \dfrac{4Fl}{\pi d^2 x}$

The equation tells you that the percentage error for the diameter is doubled when you calculate the total percentage error in E. This is because you square the diameter when you calculate a value for the Young modulus. Total % error $= 0.25 + 1.00 + (2 \times 1.00) + 0.80 \approx 4$.

So the likely error in the value for the Young modulus will be

$$2.00 \times 10^{11} \times \left(\tfrac{4}{100}\right) = 0.08 \times 10^{11} \, \text{Nm}^{-2}.$$

Therefore, being pessimistic, $E = 2.0 \pm 0.1 \times 10^{11} \, \text{Nm}^{-2}$ for the sample.

7 The table gives data for a copper wire of length 95 cm and diameter 0.80 mm. Use it to show that the Young modulus of copper is 1.3×10^{11} Nm^{-2}.

Weight in tray/N	0.0	9.8	19.6	29.4	39.2
Micrometer reading/mm	5.42	5.56	5.71	5.86	5.95

Refractive index

Transparent materials can alter the direction of light which enters and leaves them. Figure 2.27 shows what happens to a ray of light as it travels through a transparent block. The effect is called refraction.

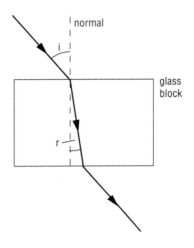

Figure 2.27 *A beam of light changes direction as it enters and leaves a block of transparent material.*

On its way from air into the material the light ray changes direction. The direction is always measured with respect to the normal. This is a construction line drawn at right angles to the surface of the material.

Snell's Law relates the angle of incidence (i) to the angle of refraction (r) via the refractive index (n) of the material.

$$\text{refractive index} = n = \frac{\sin(i)}{\sin(r)}$$

A large value for the refractive index means that there is a large change of direction as light enters and leaves the material.

Here is a method of measuring the refractive index of a rectangular block of material. It can give accurate results if you make enough measurements and use a sharp pencil!

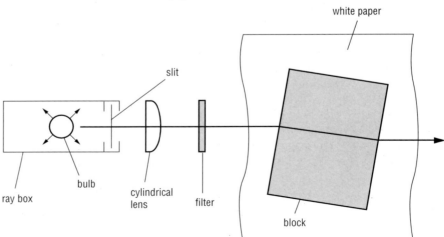

Figure 2.28 *Apparatus for measuring the refractive index of a glass block*

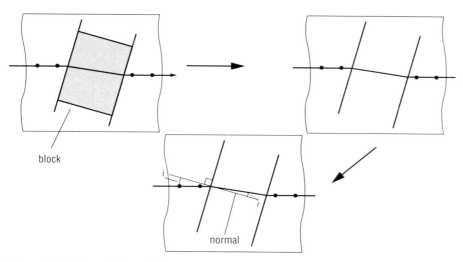

block

i

normal

r

Figure 2.29 *Draw dots on the beam of light. Draw along the two faces of the block. Remove the block and use the lines and dots to draw the path of the beam. Finally, draw in a normal and measure the angles i and r.*

Apparatus

Figure 2.28 shows you the apparatus. You need a large rectangular block of the substance whose value of n you need to find. The cylindrical lens and slit produce a single thin beam of light from the ray box. That ray passes through the block. The filter defines the colour and wavelength of the light being used. (The value of the refractive index always depends on the colour of the light being used.)

Procedure

The technique is straightforward. The sequence of Figure 2.29 shows you what to do.

Place the block on white paper so that the path followed by the beam of light can be recorded as a series of pencil dots. Draw a line around the block before it is removed.

The paper now has enough information on it for you to be able to measure the angles of incidence and refraction with a protractor.

Data analysis

A single measurement will not give you a very precise value. You really need to repeat the measurements many times for different values of the angle of incidence. A graph is the best way to combine the results of many measurements. The two angles i and r fit this formula.

$$n = \frac{\sin i}{\sin r}$$

This is the same as $\sin i = n \times \sin r$. So a graph of $\sin i$ against $\sin r$ should be a straight line, with a gradient of n. An example is shown in figure 2.30. Most of the points lie close to a straight line whose gradient is 1.45. Two points are way off, indicating that those measurements are probably faulty and need to be made again!

Likely error

Each measurement that you make will contain a fairly large random error. Even if you draw very carefully on your sheet of paper, you are unlikely to be able to measure the angles with a precision of better than $\pm 1°$. For an angle of $45°$, a precision of $\pm 1°$ gives an error of ± 0.01 in the value of $\sin 45 = 0.71$.

So the percentage error in $\sin i$ and $\sin r$ will be about $\left(\frac{0.01}{0.71}\right) \times 100 = 1.4\%$. Therefore the overall percentage error in a single measurement of n will be about 3%.

▶ Using graphs, page 37

▶ Measurement: accuracy, precision and errors, page 31

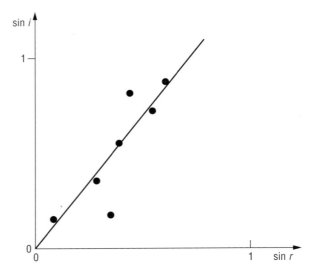

Figure 2.30 *Typical results for the experiment. Note that two points have probably been badly measured!*

Of course, the influence of random errors can be reduced by making lots of measurements. The graph of Figure 2.30 contains five reasonable measurements. Their values are given in Table 2.8.

Table 2.8

						Average
Incidence angle _i_	16	34	44	57	72	
Refraction angle _r_	11	23	29	34	41	
Refractive index _n_	1.44	1.43	1.43	1.50	1.45	1.45
Deviation	−0.01	−0.02	−0.02	+0.05	0.00	0.00
Deviation^2	0.0001	0.0004	0.0004	0.0025	0.0000	0.0009

▶ Measurement: accuracy, precision and errors, page 31

The likely error is the standard deviation. This is $\sqrt{0.0009} = 0.03$. The result of the five measurements is therefore 1.45 ± 0.03. Fifty measurements could possibly reduce the likely error to ± 0.01!

Q **8** Here are some data for a glass block. Use them to show that its refractive index is 1.55.

_i_/°	10	26	42	64	73
_r_/°	5	17	24	35	38

Electrical conductivity

The conductivity of a sample indicates how easily electric current can flow through it. This can be obtained by finding the resistance R of wire samples which have known cross-sectional area A and length l.

▶ Physical properties of materials, page 85

$$R = \sigma \left(\frac{l}{A}\right)$$

You measure the resistance of a sample by measuring the current I which flows through it when a voltage V is placed across it.

$$R = \frac{V}{I}$$

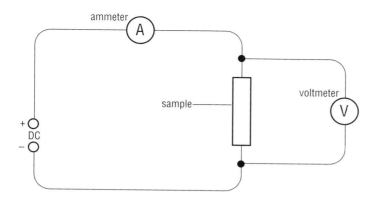

Apparatus and procedure

Figure 2.31 gives a circuit diagram of an arrangement suitable for a conductor. The sample needs to have a resistance which is much larger than the connecting wires or contacts. It should therefore be a long, thin wire.

The voltmeter must have a high input impedance, so that it diverts as little current as possible from the sample. A typical electronic voltmeter will divert 1μ A per volt. Provided that the current measured by the ammeter is much larger than this, you can assume that all of the current which goes through the ammeter also goes through the sample.

Table 2.9 gives some data for a steel wire.

Table 2.9

Length	53 cm
Diameter	0.21 mm
Voltage drop	1.49 V
Current	0.97 A

The first step is to calculate the resistance of the sample.

$R = ?\,\Omega$ $R = V/I$
$V = 1.49$ V
$I = 0.97$ A

$$R = \frac{1.49}{0.97} = 1.54\ \Omega$$

Then you calculate the conductivity.

$R = 1.54\ \Omega$
$l = 0.53$ m
$\sigma = ?\ \Omega^{-1}\mathrm{m}^{-1}$

$$A = \pi \times \left(\frac{0.21 \times 10^{-3}}{2}\right)^2 = 3.46 \times 10^{-8}\ \mathrm{m}^2$$

$$R = \frac{l}{\sigma A}$$

so $1.54 = \dfrac{0.53}{\sigma \times 3.46 \times 10^{-8}}$

therefore $\sigma = \dfrac{0.53}{1.54 \times 3.46 \times 10^{-8}}$

or $\sigma = 9.95 \times 10^6\ \Omega^{-1}\mathrm{m}^{-1}$

Using graphs, page 37

Data analysis

A straight line graph is the easiest way of combining the results of several experiments to obtain a best value for the conductivity of a material. The aim is to draw a graph whose gradient is equal to the conductivity.

For each sample, you will have measured the resistance R, length l and cross-sectional area A. These three quantities are linked with the conductivity by this formula.

$$R = \frac{l}{\sigma A}$$

Here is an alternative form of the equation.

$$\frac{l}{A} = \sigma R$$

So a graph of $\frac{l}{A}$ against R will have a gradient of σ (see Figure 2.32). Any resistance r in the circuit which is not due to the samples will show up as an intercept; it will not affect the value of the gradient.

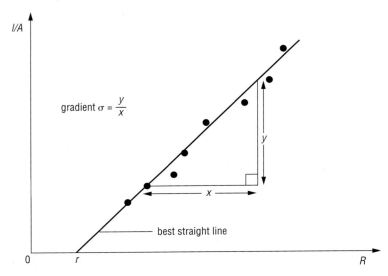

Figure 2.32 A graph to combine the results of measurements made on several different samples of the same material.

Measurement: accuracy, precision and errors, page 31

Likely error

The error in the measurement described above is going to be quite large. Table 2.10 takes you through the calculation.

Table 2.10

Quantity	Value	Precision	%error
Current	0.97 A	±0.005 A	0.5
Voltage	1.49 V	±0.005 V	0.3
Diameter	0.21 mm	±0.005 mm	2.4
Length	53 cm	±0.5 cm	0.9
	total % error	0.5 + 0.3 + 2 (2.4) + 0.9 = 6.5	

So the likely error in the conductivity value is
$$9.95 \times 10^6 \times (\tfrac{6.5}{100}) \approx 0.7 \times 10^6 \, \Omega^{-1} \, m^{-1}.$$

The final value is therefore $10.0 \pm 0.7 \times 10^6 \ \Omega^{-1}m^{-1}$.

Another source of error is variation in temperature. The conductivity of a metal changes with temperature and the current through the sample will give it heat energy.

Q 9 Here are some results of measurements made on three samples of copper wire. Use them to show that the conductivity of copper is $6.4 \times 10^7 \ \Omega^{-1}m^{-1}$.

Diameter/mm	0.13	0.08	0.20
Length/cm	89.0	151.0	194.0
Voltage/V	1.31	1.42	1.29
Current/A	1.02	0.29	1.20

Specific heating capacity

Give an object some heat energy and its temperature will go up. The temperature rise ΔT is fixed by the quantity of energy added E, the mass of the object m and the specific heating capacity c of the object.

heat energy transferred (J)
= mass (kg)
  $\times$ specific heating capacity (Jkg^{-1}K^{-1})
  $\times$ temperature rise (K)

$E = mc\Delta T$

Notice that the units of temperature here are Kelvin (K). You will normally measure temperature changes in degrees celsius (°C). A change in temperature of 1 °C is exactly the same as 1 K. The zero points are different: 0 °C is the same temperature as 273 K.

To measure the specific heating capacity (s.h.c.) of an object you need to measure the temperature rise when a known quantity of heat energy is added. The difficulty lies in ensuring that all of the heat energy you dump in the object stays there!

Assignment trigger

Burnt tongues

When you eat a hot jam tart you may burn your tongue on the jam but not on the pastry.

Why do some foods stay hotter longer?
How could you measure the heat energy content of the food?
What other factors are involved?

If a practical assignment is developed, it is essential that a risk assessment is made and checked by your teacher/lecturer.

Could lead to possible assignments relating to Unit 2.

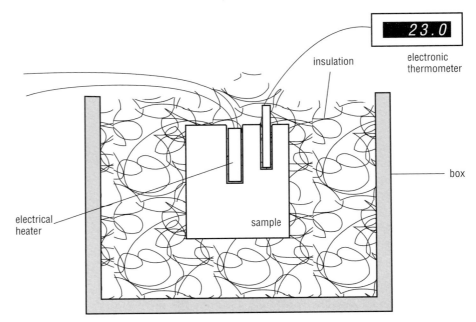

Figure 2.33 *Apparatus for measur-ing the s.h.c. of a sample of material.*

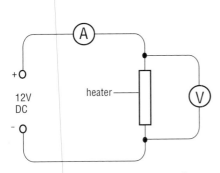

Figure 2.34 *The arrangement of meters needed to measure the power of the heater.*

Using graphs, page 37

Apparatus

Figure 2.33 illustrates some apparatus which you can use to measure the s.h.c. of a solid sample.

The sample is enclosed in a large box which contains a fluffy material such as expanded polystyrene or cotton wool. This is to cut down the rate at which heat energy leaves or enters the sample from the outside world. An electrical heater is embedded in the sample, with a small amount of oil to give good thermal contact across the gap between sample and heater. The probe of an electronic thermometer is also embedded in the sample.

The heater converts electrical energy into heat energy. The amount of electrical energy delivered to the sample is measured with a voltmeter, an ammeter and a stopwatch.

electrical energy transferred (J)
= voltage (V) × current (A) × time (s)
$E = VIt$

The arrangement of meters is shown in Figure 2.34.

Procedure

Start off by placing the sample in a deep freeze, so that it goes well below room temperature. Then place it in the insu-lated box with the heater and ther-mometer attached. Measure the temper-ature of the room.

Switch on the heater, start the stop-watch and measure the temperature at regular intervals until the sample is as far above room temperature as it was below at the start. Using a data logger will make these measurements less tedious!

You will also need to record the current in the heater and the voltage across it when the sample reached room temperature.

Data analysis

Figure 2.35 is a graph of some results obtained in an experiment to measure the s.h.c. of aluminium. Room temperature was 16 °C. As you can see, the sample started off at –2 °C and ended up at +33 °C. You can also see that although the heater was delivering heat energy to the sample at a steady rate, the temperature did not rise steadily.

While the sample was below 16 °C, it was gaining heat from the rest of the room. When it was above 16 °C, it was losing heat to the rest of the room. Only when it was at 16 °C did the sample not exchange heat energy with its surroundings.

The gradient of the graph at 16 °C is 3.6 °C per minute. Table 2.11 contains the rest of the data you need to calculate the s.h.c.

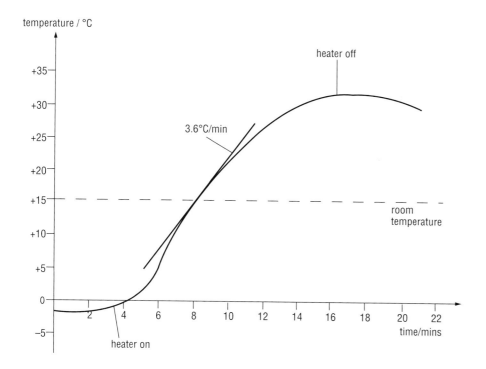

Figure 2.35 A graph showing how the temperature of the sample changed with time during the experiment.

Table 2.11

Voltage	12.2 V
Current	4.7 A
Mass	1.012 kg

You first calculate how much heat energy the heater dumped in the sample during one minute.

$$E = VIt$$

so $\quad E = 12.2 \times 4.7 \times 60 = 3.44 \times 10^3 \text{ J}$

Then you calculate the s.h.c.

$$E = mc\Delta T$$

so $3.44 \times 10^3 = 1.012 \times c \times 3.6$

or $3.44 \times 10^3 = 3.64 \times c$

therefore $c = \dfrac{3.44 \times 10^3}{3.64} = 945 \text{ Jkg}^{-1}\text{K}^{-1}$

Error compensation

The procedure outlined above should eliminate most of the errors caused by transfer of heat energy between the sample and its surroundings. It doesn't, however, take any account of the heat energy given to the thermometer probe and the heater. You need to another experiment to take account of that!

The second experiment is exactly the same as the first one, except that the mass of the sample has to be different. When a sample of mass 1.982 kg was used, the rate of temperature rise at 16 °C was 1.9 °C per minute.

Suppose that the combined heating capacity of the thermometer and

▶ Measurement: accuracy, precision and errors, page 31

heater is h JK^{-1}. This is the heat energy needed to raise their temperatures by 1K. Then the first experiment (described above) gives this equation.

$$3.44 \times 10^3 = h \times 3.6 + 1.012 \times c \times 3.6$$

The second experiment gives this equation.

$$3.44 \times 10^3 = h \times 1.9 + 1.982 \times c \times 1.9$$

You now need to eliminate h from these equations. The easiest way is to rewrite each equation so that it only has h on the right hand side.

$$\left(\frac{3.44 \times 10^3}{3.6}\right) - (1.012 \times c) = h$$

$$\left(\frac{3.44 \times 10^3}{1.9}\right) - (1.982 \times c) = h$$

Then you can eliminate h by putting the last two equations equal to each other.

$$\left(\frac{3.44 \times 10^3}{3.6}\right) - (1.012 \times c) = \left(\frac{3.44 \times 10^3}{1.9}\right) - (1.982 \times c)$$

$$\text{or} \quad 956 - 1.012c = 1810 - 1.982c$$

$$\text{so} \quad (1.982 - 1.012)c = 1810 - 956$$

$$\text{therefore} \quad c = \frac{854}{0.970} = 880 \text{ Jkg}^{-1}\text{K}^{-1}$$

Of course, the final answer is only as precise as the least precise measurement. This is the measurement of temperature. The percentage error in that measurement is $\left(\frac{0.05}{1.9}\right) \times 100 = 2.6\%$.

So the final value for $c = 880 \pm 25$ Jkg^{-1}K^{-1}.

Q 10 This table contains some data for a 2.12 kg block of iron being heated in a room at 20 °C.

Temperature/°C	11.5	17.0	19.8	24.3	27.4
Time/minutes	2.0	3.0	4.0	5.0	6.0

The experiment was repeated with a 0.95 kg block of iron. Some of the measurements are given in this table.

Temperature/°C	1.6	11.2	20.0	27.9	35.1
Time/minutes	1.0	2.0	3.0	4.0	5.0

In both experiments the heater voltage and current were 13.0 V and 4.9 A. Use the data to show that the s.h.c. of iron is 440 Jkg^{-1}K^{-1}.

Modifying the properties of a material

The useful properties of many materials can be improved dramatically with appropriate treatment. For example, the tensile strength of iron can be raised from 350 MNm^{-2} to over 900 MNm^{-2}. All you have to do is add 0.8% carbon so the iron becomes mild steel, heat the sample to 750 °C and cool it very rapidly.

Each material has its own set of techniques for improving its important properties. Some techniques involve heat treatments. Some involve mixing in large or small amounts of other materials. Many of them were discovered by trial and error.

Scientists now have a good understanding of how these modifications affect the structure of a material. They use this knowledge to devise industrial processes for modifying materials. These processes aim to be economical, reliable and to deliver a modified material which meets the customer's requirements.

Metals

There are two main ways in which the mechanical properties of metals are improved. They can be mixed with other metals to form **alloys**. Various forms of heat treatment can also be applied.

Heat treatment

Pure metals are usually soft and ductile. They can be hammered, squeezed and pulled into new shapes by applying large enough stresses at room temperature. This cold working of a metal makes it stronger and more brittle. This effect is called work hardening.

 Annealing a metal makes it softer and more ductile. Alloys of metals are stronger than pure metals.

Metals, page 112

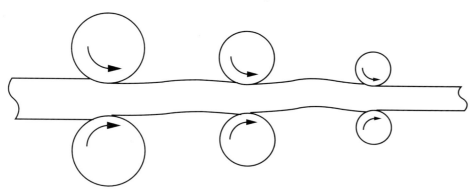

Figure 2.36 *Reducing the thickness of a metal strip by passing it between a series of rollers.*

Table 2.12 contains data for a cold worked copper strip which has been reduced in thickness by rolling (see Figure 2.36). Although the sample becomes stronger each time that the thickness is reduced, it also becomes more brittle.

Table 2.12

Final thickness/%	Tensile strength/MNm^{-2}	Maximum strain
100	210	0.58
90	240	0.38
80	270	0.23
60	330	0.10
20	410	0.05

Annealing

The ductility of work-hardened metals can be improved by **annealing** them. The sample is heated to slightly above the recrystallisation temperature and then allowed to cool.

Table 2.13 gives approximate values for the recrystallisation temperature of some commonly used metals (the value drops as the hardness of the sample increases).

 Annealing, page 113

Table 2.13 Recrystallisation temperatures of some metals

Metal	Recrystallisation temperature/°C
Tungsten	1200
Nickel	600
Iron	450
Copper	190
Aluminium	150

The length of time that the sample spends above the recrystallisation temperature affects its final hardness.

A long annealing time gives a sample back its original ductility, but reduces its strength. This is ideal for allowing further cold working of the sample. Industrial processes which cold work metals involve annealing stages to keep the metal ductile as its shape changes (Figure 2.37).

Figure 2.37 *Copper wire is annealed in order to improve its ductility.*

A short annealing time results in a sample which is tougher (less brittle) than before, but almost as strong. It is therefore used as the final stage in cold working.

Alloying

Alloying, page 113

Pure metals are rarely used for structural applications. This is because their mechanical properties can always be improved by alloying them with other metals.

An alloy is a metal which has other metals mixed with it. For example, brass is copper which contains some zinc. Table 2.14 shows how the strength and brittleness of copper are improved by the presence of zinc.

Table 2.14 Improving characteristics of copper

Copper:zinc ratio	Tensile strength/MNm^{-2}	Maximum strain
100:0	210	0.58
90:10	260	0.63
80:20	300	0.67
70:30	330	0.70
60:40	360	0.85

Glasses

The important properties of glass for most applications are its refractive index and its transparency. Both can be modified by altering the amount and type of impurity in the glass. Glass can also be toughened by heat treatment.

Impurities

Long thin fibres of glass are used to transmit pulses of light from one place to another. These pulses can carry all sorts of information, including telephone conversations and television pictures. Weight for weight, these optical fibres can carry far more information than metal cables.

A useful optical fibre for long-distance communications must have one important property. It must be very transparent. The secret of making optical fibres is the removal of impurities from the glass.

The usual technique for purifying glass is called zone refining. It is illustrated in figure 2.38.

Heat treatment

The glass used for windows can be toughened by **heat treatment**. This is how it works. While the plate of glass is still hot, its outside layers are cooled by jets of cold air, so the outside layers cool down rapidly, shrinking in the process, while the middle is still hot and flexible. The middle section cools slowly, shrinking and compressing the outer solid layers at the same time. The result is a pane of glass whose outer layers are in a permanent state of compression. This prevents surface cracks opening up when the glass is flexed. This makes it less likely that cracks will propagate through the pane, snapping it in two.

Semiconductors

Most semiconductors are useless in their pure state. This is especially true of silicon. The marvels of modern electronics are only possible because scientists can modify the conductivity of silicon by adding controlled amounts of other elements.

Doping

All silicon-based electronic components start off as thin slabs of pure silicon. The conductivity of pure silicon is quite low at room temperature ($\approx 0.02\ \Omega^{-1}\text{m}^{-1}$). It can be raised a lot by **doping** the silicon. Atoms of other elements are inserted into the silicon. This increases the number of

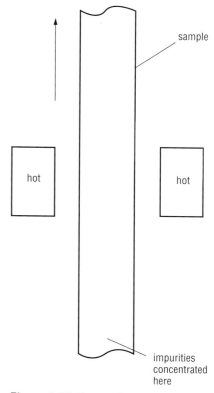

Figure 2.38 Zone refining. The glass rod is slowly drawn through a hot region. The impurities tend to migrate down the rod, staying in the hot region. When all of the rod has passed through the oven, the bottom (which is now rich in impurities) is cut off and discarded. The process is then repeated as often as necessary to achieve the desired purity.

The optical properties of glass are decided by the amount and type of chemical impurities in it. Heat treatment can toughen glass.

▶ Semiconductors, page 115

Doping a pure semiconductor with other atoms will convert it into a material with positive or negative mobile charges.

mobile charge carriers.

Silicon can be doped in two ways. If it is doped with phosphorus, the extra charge carriers will be negative. The silicon ends up as an n-type semiconductor. On the other hand, if the silicon is doped with boron, the extra charge carriers are positive. The silicon becomes a p-type semiconductor.

Etching silicon

Figure 2.39 shows the stages involved in converting a slab of pure silicon into a field effect transistor (FET).

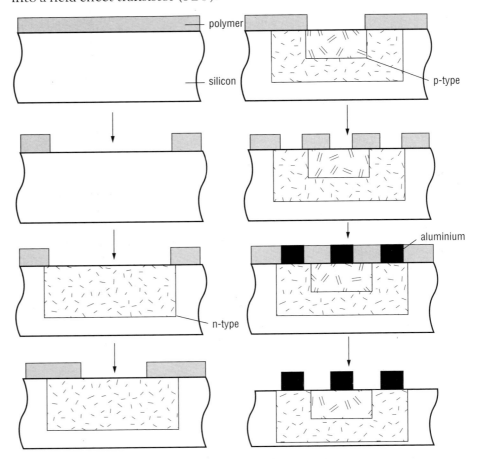

Figure 2.39 *Stages in the manufacture of a field effect transistor. A thin film of light-sensitive polymer is spread over the surface of the silicon. Parts of the film are exposed to light. This weakens the polymer, so that it can be dissolved in alkali. This etching leaves parts of the silicon exposed.*

The silicon is then heated and immersed in a gas of phosphorus atoms. These diffuse into the exposed parts of the silicon, creating a region of n-type semiconductor. The remaining polymer is removed by exposing it to light and dissolving it in alkali.

A fresh pattern of polymer is now etched onto the silicon. It is then immersed in a gas of boron atoms. A region of p-type semiconductor is thus built into the silicon.

A third pattern is etched on to the silicon. The cold silicon is then immersed in a gas of aluminium atoms. These do not diffuse into the silicon, but build up a thin layer on its surface. These metallic deposits act as connecting pads for the FET.

> The strength of a polymer is increased by cross-linking and cold drawing.

▶ Polymers, page 114

Polymers

There are a number of techniques for modifying the properties of polymers. Their stiffness and strength can be increased by **cross-linking**. Their strength can also be increased by **cold drawing**.

Cross-linking

Many polymers in their pure state are fairly soft. They lack rigidity and strength. If a thermosetting polymer is heated, there is a chemical reaction forming links between the molecules which makes the sample much stiffer and harder. The process is known as cross-linking and it cannot be reversed.

Melamine-methanal is a good example of a thermosetting plastic. The starting material is a viscous liquid. Once it has been heated it turns into a hard, heat-resistant and water-resistant solid. It is widely used to make kitchen utensils, crockery and bathroom furniture.

Epoxy and polyester resins are cold setting plastics. The polymer is a sticky liquid. When it is mixed with a hardening agent, cross-linking takes place over a few hours at room temperature. The final product is a tough solid.

Assignment trigger

Nylon

Nylon has numerous uses. It is found in many different products.

What is nylon?
What products are made of nylon?
How is nylon manufactured?
Can you make it in the laboratory?
How is it processed to produce different forms with different properties?

If a practical assignment is developed, it is essential that a risk assessment is made and checked by your teacher/lecturer.

Could lead to possible assignments relating to Units 2, 3 and 6.

Cold drawing

The strength of many polymers can be increased by stretching them past their elastic limit. The following experiment will show you this effect clearly.

Grasp a rubber band and stretch it as far as you can. To start with, the band is very easy to stretch; it has a low value for its Young modulus. Once the band has been extended a lot, it becomes much stiffer; its Young modulus has got larger. So stretching a polymer makes it stiffer. Rubber, of course, is an elastic polymer. It returns to its original shape when you let go of it. Polymers which are plastic become stiffer when they are stretched well past their elastic limit. This technique is called cold drawing.

Composites

A **composite** is really a material which has already been modified by mixing it with another material. Its properties depend on the proportions of its constituents.

Composites can have their properties altered by changing the proportions of matrix and fibre.

Ceramics

The only way of modifying the properties of pure ceramics is to make them into composite materials. They are often mixed with metals, since metals possess the toughness which ceramics lack.

 Ceramics, page 113

Reinforced concrete

Figure 2.40 illustrates what happens when a heavy load is placed on a concrete beam. The beam cracks because cement, like most ceramics, has a relatively low tensile strength.

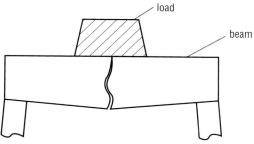

Figure 2.40 Cracks open up on the bottom of a concrete beam when it is loaded from the top.

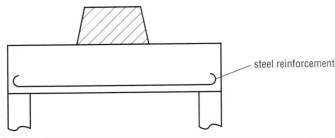

steel reinforcement

Figure 2.41 A steel reinforcement along the bottom of the beam can prevent cracks in the concrete from opening up.

A steel reinforcement has been included in the beam shown in Figure 2.41. Steel rods are placed in the concrete while it is setting. Steel is tough and has a high tensile strength. This prevents the concrete beam from failing catastrophically when it is loaded. It doesn't, however, stop cracks forming in the concrete where it is placed in tension.

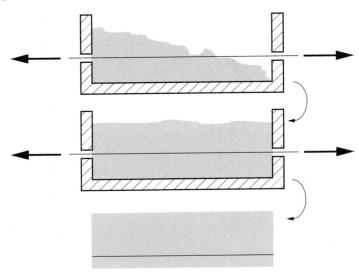

Figure 2.42 Stages in the manufacture of pre-stressed reinforced concrete

Pre-stressed reinforcement is illustrated in Figure 2.42. The steel bars inserted into the setting concrete are stretched. Once the concrete has set hard, the ends of the bars are released, so that the whole beam is compressed. The concrete remains compressed when a load is placed on the beam. Cracks do not appear on the bottom surface as it is never in tension.

Cermets

Composites which are made by mixing ceramics with metals are called *cermets*. They have the hardness of a ceramic with the toughness of a metal.

A cermet is made by mixing finely ground powders of the ceramic and metal. The mixture is cold welded by compressing it in a mould. The metal particles are joined to each other by this process. The sample is then sintered by raising it above the recrystallisation temperature of the metal. The final product consists of fine hard particles suspended in a tough matrix.

Tungsten carbide bonded with cobalt is an example of a cermet. It is used to make tools for cutting metals, glasses and ceramics.

The properties of a cermet can be modified by altering the proportions of metal to ceramic. A cermet which needs to be hard at high temperatures will contain a lot of ceramic. A cermet which needs to be tough and have a high tensile strength contains a lot of metal.

Glasses

Fibreglass is a useful composite material. It consists of a cold-setting thermoplastic reinforced by mats of woven glass fibres (Figure 2.43). The resulting material has the strength and hardness of the glass combined with the toughness and shock resistance of the polymer.

Figure 2.43 The properties of fibre-glass are useful in building things which need to combine toughness and resistance to wear.

Polymers

Fibrous material which is added to a polymer to modify its properties or reduce its cost is called a *filler*.

Cheap materials such as paper, sawdust and cotton are often added to polymers to reduce their cost. They act as bulking agents.

Some hard thermoplastics are too brittle to be useful on their own. The addition of fibrous material before the thermosetting stage makes them much tougher. For example, bakelite (used for electrical fittings) contains sawdust, paper or rags.

Changing proportions

The mechanical properties of a composite can be finely tuned by altering the proportions of its constituents.

The matrix of a composite material has to be tough, but it often isn't very strong. The fibre provides the strength, but it also tends to be brittle. So a composite which is mostly made of the matrix material will be tough, but not very strong. On the other hand, if it is mostly made of the fibre, it will be strong but brittle. By altering the proportions of filler and matrix, you can tailor the strength and toughness of the composite to its application.

Structure of materials

Finding out how to modify the properties of a material by trial-and-error is a tiresome business. It takes a long time and isn't often a very effective way of making real progress.

Understanding the structure of a material enables scientists to suggest which methods and techniques are likely to produce the desired outcome.

The ions in a metal are bound in a lattice by the electrons which are free to move between them. Planes of ions can slip past each other easily. Slip only occurs easily in grains, so the size of grain affects the mechanical properties of a sample. The size of grain can be altered by work hardening and annealing.

Figure 2.44 *Typical arrangement of atoms in a solid metal*

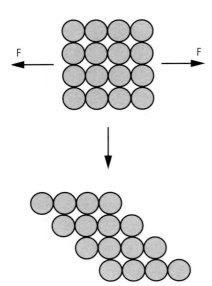

Figure 2.45 *Planes of atoms slip over other planes if sufficiently large forces are applied.*

Figure 2.46 *Grains. The lines in each grain show the direction of the slip plane.*

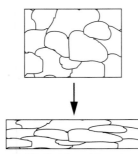

Figure 2.47 *Cold working changes the shape of the grains.*

Metals

Atoms in a solid metal sit in a regular pattern as shown in Figure 2.44. This regular three-dimensional pattern is known as a **lattice**.

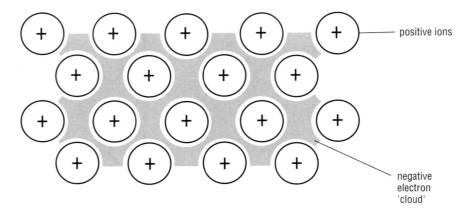

positive ions

negative electron 'cloud'

Metallic bonding

Each atom in a solid metal loses one or more electrons to become a positive ion. The mobile electrons can move freely in the spaces between the ions. Each ion repels all of the surrounding ions, because they all have the same type of electric charge. On the other hand, each ion is attracted to the mobile electrons because they have different types of electric charge.

So each ion is firmly held in place by the other ions and the mobile electrons around it. The pattern of ions is regular; solid metals are crystals. Their atoms sit in a lattice structure, bonded tightly together.

Slip

Metals are ductile because planes of ions in the crystals can slip over each other easily. Look at Figure 2.45. When sufficiently large forces are applied to the crystal, whole planes of ions move. They can do this because the mobile electrons which provide the attraction between the planes are able to move along with them. When the stress is removed, the electrons can bind the ions together in their new position.

Grains

When a liquid metal turns into a solid, it starts to crystallise in many places at the same time. These crystals (or *grains*) grow until there is no liquid metal left. The result is a jumble of small crystals interlocked with each other (see Figure 2.46). Each grain will have its *slip planes* pointing in different directions.

Brittleness

Figure 2.47 shows what happens to the grains when a sample of metal is cold worked. Planes of ions in the grains slip past each other. This changes the shapes of the grains as well as breaking them up into smaller grains.

Making the grains smaller makes the sample more brittle. The forces which hold the grains to each other at the grain boundaries are smaller than the forces which hold ions in place within the grains themselves. So each grain boundary is a line of weakness. Enough tension will overcome the forces which bind the grains to each other. As the grains become smaller, there are more and more lines of weakness, making it easier to pull the sample apart, so the sample becomes more brittle.

Work hardening

A reduction in grain size also reduces the ductility of the sample. Slip can only occur inside a grain, where there is a regular crystal structure. Furthermore, it takes place most easily if the slip planes are in the same direction as the force. So when a sample of metal is stressed, slip occurs first in those grains which have their slip planes in the ideal orientation. Once all of this slip has occurred, it then happens in other grains whose slip planes are less ideally oriented. This requires a larger stress than before.

The result is that as the sample is deformed, you need to apply a progressively larger stress to obtain any further deformation. The sample's strength increases as it is stretched.

Annealing

A sample of work hardened metal is annealed by holding it at a high enough temperature for recrystallisation to take place. New grains start to grow in the metal, starting at sites on the grain boundaries. The new grains take material from the old grains around them, growing larger as time goes on (see Figure 2.48).

Large grains can change their shape more when stressed than small grains can. Slip can only take place within a grain. It stops at grain boundaries. So a sample of metal with large grains will be far more ductile than a sample with small grains. Small grains make the metal harder but more brittle.

Alloying

An alloy consists of one metal mixed with another. When a liquid alloy solidifies, each metal tends to form grains separately. The final solid alloy therefore has a fine-grained structure, and is much harder than either of the pure metals.

Ceramics

Ceramics are strong because each atom in them is firmly bonded to all of the other atoms. Their brittleness arises because the atoms are only strongly bonded if they are arranged in **giant lattices**.

Giant lattices

The bonding between the atoms in many ceramics is ionic. The atoms become either positive ions or negative ions. They arrange themselves in regular patterns (see Figure 2.49) or lattices. Each ion is firmly locked in place by its neighbours. Ionic crystals are very hard, with no possibility of slip. So ceramics are very hard indeed.

Other ceramics are examples of giant covalent lattices. Each atom is firmly bound to its neighbours by covalent bonds. These bonds involve the sharing of electrons between the atoms and they act in a fixed direction. This means that they also force the atoms to sit in a fixed lattice structure.

Cracks

Any sample of ceramic contains imperfections. It will not have a regular crystal structure throughout. There will be microscopic cracks, places

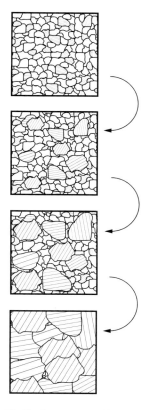

Figure 2.48 *During recrystallisation, new crystals form at grain boundaries and grow.*

The atoms in ceramics are arranged in giant ionic or covalent lattices. This makes it very hard to change the shape of a ceramic, but also makes them susceptible to cracks.

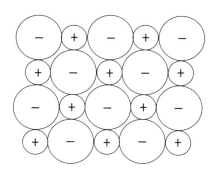

Figure 2.49 *Typical arrangement of ions in an ionic solid*

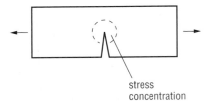

Figure 2.50 *The stress in a bar under tension is much larger at the tip of a crack than anywhere else.*

Atoms in polymers are bound to each other in long flexible chains by covalent forces. The strength of a polymer is increased by aligning these molecules (cold drawing) or arranging for extra bonds between them (cross-linking).

where the forces between atoms are relatively weak. Any of these cracks at the surface of the sample can, under the right circumstances, grow rapidly and allow the sample to split into two. Cracks make ceramics brittle.

Consider the ceramic illustrated in Figure 2.50. It has been subjected to tensile stress. The stress will be same throughout the sample except near the crack. There is stress concentration at the tip of the crack, because the material on either side of the crack is not stressed at all. So a moderate stress applied to the whole sample can easily result in enough stress at the crack tip to open it up further. Once this process starts, the crack tip moves through the sample at the speed of sound. The sample fails very suddenly.

Metals do not tend to fail this way because slip usually occurs first.

Polymers

Polymers have very long molecules. They are made by joining together large numbers of small molecules (*monomers*) in long chains. Figure 2.51 illustrates the formation of polyethylene (polythene) from ethene. Each atom in a polymer is bound to its neighbours by strong **covalent** bonds. These allow a small amount of bending of the polymer molecule, but they also make it difficult to snap a polymer molecule in two.

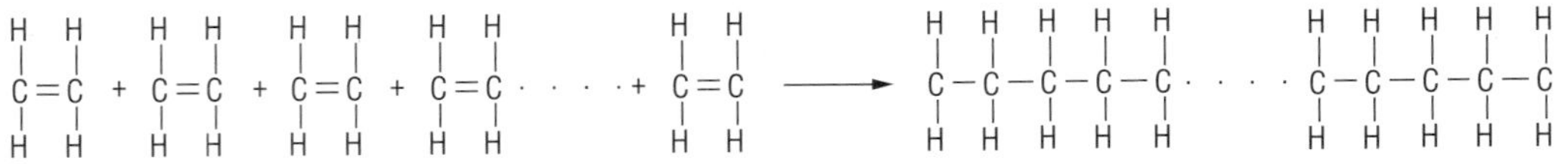

$$
\begin{array}{c}
\underset{\underset{H}{|}}{\overset{\overset{H}{|}}{C}}=\underset{\underset{H}{|}}{\overset{\overset{H}{|}}{C}} + \cdots
\end{array}
$$

Figure 2.51 *A large polymer molecule can be made by joining together large numbers of small molecules.*

Cross-linking

Although the bonds linking the atoms in a polymer are very strong, the forces between polymers are often relatively weak. The molecules can slide past one another easily. Such polymers are *plastic*. They have large permanent strains for relatively small stresses.

Some polymers have molecules which, under the right circumstances, can form strong covalent bonds with each other. It may require heat, the addition of a catalyst or an extra molecule, but the end result is the same. The long chain molecules are no longer able to slide freely past each other. The cross-linking has locked them firmly in three dimensions into a rigid mass (see Figure 2.52).

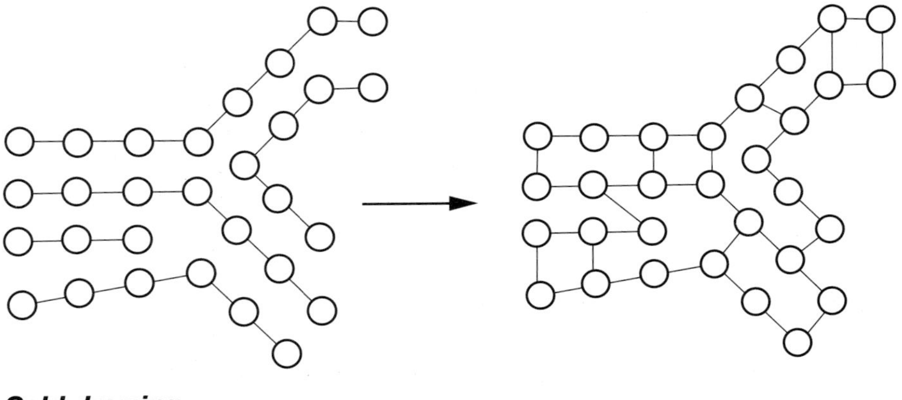

Figure 2.52 *Cross-links between long polymer molecules make a sample much stiffer.*

Cold drawing

Normally, a solid polymer has its molecules tangled together, all pointing in different directions. The process of cold drawing leaves the molecules all pointing in roughly the same direction. This increases the stiffness of the materials quite dramatically.

Cold drawing works because the force needed to straighten out a polymer molecule is much smaller than the force needed to snap it in two. As the tensile stress on a sample is increased, the polymers straighten out and become less tangled with each other, until all of them are aligned roughly parallel to each other. At a low enough temperature, this process is irreversible. The sample now has a relatively large Young modulus because applied stress will be attempting to snap a molecule in two rather than just straightening it out.

Semiconductors

Although silicon is not the only useful semiconductor, it is the most widely used. The concepts and ideas explained below apply to all semiconductors.

Holes

The structure of pure silicon is represented in Figure 2.53. An atom of silicon has four electrons in its outer shell. Each electron is shared with an electron from a neighbouring atom, making a strong covalent bond. Every atom is therefore firmly bonded to its neighbours, making a rigid structure.

Since none of the electrons are free to move from atom to atom, the sample should not be able to conduct electricity. It contains no mobile charges.

However, there is a small chance that an electron can obtain enough energy to escape from an atom. That energy comes from the random thermal vibrations of the atoms (the sample's heat energy). The negative electron will wander away through the sample, leaving behind a positive ion (a hole).

The sequence of Figure 2.54 shows how a hole can move around the sample. If an electron in an atom next to the hole gets enough energy, it can fall into the hole. The hole moves in the opposite direction to the electron.

So pure semiconductors contain equal numbers of positive and negative mobile charges. Their conductivity rises rapidly with temperature, as more and more heat energy is available to let electrons escape from the atoms.

Band theory

A semiconductor can only conduct electricity because some electrons get enough thermal energy to escape from atoms. Electrons in a semiconductor which are mobile are said to be in the conduction band. Electrons in the valence band are bound to their atoms. The energy needed for an electron to get from the valence band to the conduction band is called the band-gap energy.

Figure 2.55 is a series of energy level diagrams for electrons in a semiconductor at various temperatures. At 0 K (absolute zero) the conduction band is empty and the valence band is full. As the temperature rises, more and more electrons are transferred into the conduction band, leaving holes in the valence band.

The number of electrons in the conduction band rises rapidly as the temperature goes up (Figure 2.56). As the thermal energy in the solid increases, each electron in the valence band stands more chance of getting enough energy to jump into the conduction band. Nevertheless, at

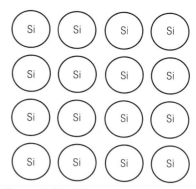

Figure 2.53 *Silicon atoms sitting in a lattice*

The conductivity of a semiconductor is controlled by the amount of acceptor or donor impurity present in the lattice. The presence of these impurities make it easy for electrons jump out of the valence band at room temperature.

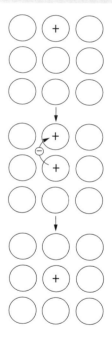

Figure 2.54 *How a hole can drift through a semiconductor*

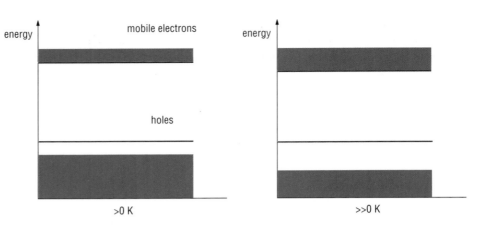

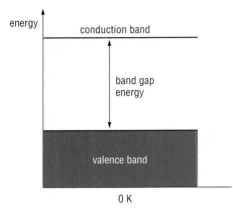

Figure 2.55 *Energy levels in a semi-conductor. At 0 K, there are no electrons in the conduction band. As the temperature increases, more and more electrons find the energy to jump from the valence band to the conduction band. The gaps in the valence band act like holes.*

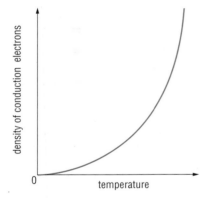

Figure 2.56 *The number of electrons in the conduction band rises steeply with increasing temperature.*

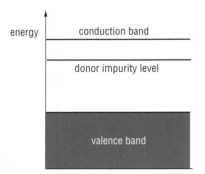

Figure 2.58 *The phosphorus atoms create a thin band of electrons above the valence band. All of these electrons can jump from the donor impurity level to the conduction band at relatively low temperatures.*

room temperature (≈ 300 K) only 1 in about 2×10^9 atoms in the lattice will have given an electron to the conduction band!

n-type semiconductors

Figure 2.57 represents the structure of a sample of silicon which has been doped with a small amount of phosphorus. The result is an n-type semiconductor.

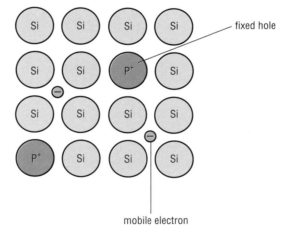

Figure 2.57 *The phosphorus impurity makes the silicon into an n-type semiconductor*

A phosphorus atom has five electrons in its outer shell. Four of these form covalent bonds with neighbouring silicon atoms. The fifth needs very little energy to escape and wander freely through the sample.

The doping has created a material which contains mobile negative charges (electrons) and fixed positive holes (the phosphorus ions). Furthermore, the density of these charges is fixed by the amount of phosphorus, so the conductivity is independent of temperature.

Donor impurity levels

Figure 2.58 shows how the energy levels in the **semiconductor** are changed by the presence of the donor impurities. Electrons in the donor impurity level will need relatively little energy to get into the conduction band. So although an n-type semiconductor is an insulator at 0 K, all of the donor impurity electrons will be in the conduction band at room temperature.

p-type semiconductors

The structure of a sample of silicon which has been doped with a small amount of boron is shown in Figure 2.59. The result is a p-type semiconductor.

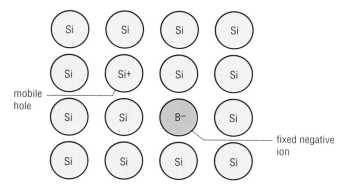

Figure 2.59 *The boron impurity makes the silicon into a p-type semiconductor.*

A boron atom has only three electrons in its outer shell. A fourth electron is captured from a neighbouring silicon atom, so that the boron atom can make four covalent bonds with its neighbours. The boron atom becomes a fixed negative ion, and one of its neighbours becomes a positively charged hole. As explained above, the hole can wander freely through the sample.

So a p-type semiconductor contains mobile positive charges (the holes) and fixed negative charges (the boron ions).

Acceptor impurity levels

The band theory explanation of p-type semiconductors is shown in Figure 2.60. The acceptor impurity level allows electrons to leave the valence band at relatively low temperatures. Electrons which end up in the acceptor impurity level are stuck, but the holes they leave behind in the valence band are mobile.

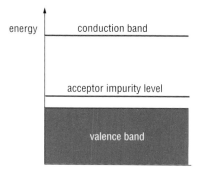

Figure 2.60 *The boron atoms introduce a new energy level, just above the valence band. At relatively low temperatures, this acceptor impurity level gets filled with electrons from the valence band, leaving a number of mobile holes behind.*

Case study

BEAMS AND ARCHES

People have built themselves structures from the earliest recorded history. Indeed, their religious structures are often the only remaining tangible evidence of their existence (Illustration 1). Until very recently, the styles of such large-scale constructions were limited by the need to use stone.

Illustration 1

Stone is durable

Three building materials were available to early communities. Mud bricks, stone and wood. Of these, only stone is sufficiently durable to allow a structure to last for more than a few generations. Mud bricks are eventually washed away by rain and need continual maintenance if the building is to survive. Wood is susceptible to attack by insects and fungi. If kept dry, it can last hundreds of years. Stone is the only material which allows a building to survive for thousands of years.

Stone is an excellent building material, provided that you always avoid tension. Like all crystalline materials, stone is very susceptible to cracks. If a small crack opens up near the surface of a stone block, it will spread through the block at the speed of sound. To avoid the possibility of this catastrophic failure, all parts of a stone construction need to be in compression.

Stone beams are bad

Building a large structure out of stone is not very difficult. You simply cut it into identical regular-shaped blocks and pile them on top of one another. Provided the foundations are strong enough to take the load, the result can be quite stable and durable. Each block compresses the blocks below it, so gravity keeps the structure firmly together.

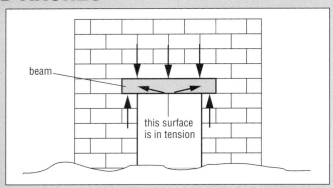

Illustration 2

The big problem is how to put gaps into the structure. How do you insert windows and doors? The earliest monument makers solved this by using stone beams. Illustration 2 shows the forces which act in a beam which is supported at either end. Those forces exist because of the weight of the beam itself. The top of the beam is in compression, but the bottom of the beam is in tension. This is inevitable. The downwards tug of gravity must be balanced by an upwards force of equal magnitude, otherwise the beam is going to plummet downwards. That balancing force comes from the vertical component of the tension in the lower part of the flexed beam.

Illustration 3

Although the ancients used stone beams (Illustration 3), they have their limitations. Large spans are impossible, particularly if the beam has to hold up more than its own weight. A thick beam is much stronger than a thin one, but unfortunately it is also heavier. For a given span, there is a limit to how thick you can make the beam before it breaks under its own weight! Large spans were only made possible by the invention of the arch.

Arches take the strain

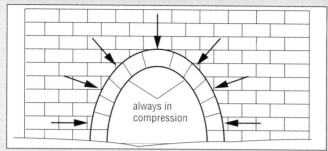

Illustration 4

An arch is a beam which has been shaped so that when it is loaded the bottom surface is compressed instead of extended. Look at Illustration 4. The weight of the wall exerts a downwards force on each block in the arch, squeezing it between the neighbouring blocks. The result is a very strong form of construction, provided that there is enough horizontal push at the base of the arch. This is no problem in Illustration 4, because the weight of the wall on either side of the arch ensures that friction with the foundations will be sufficient.

Buttresses fly to the rescue

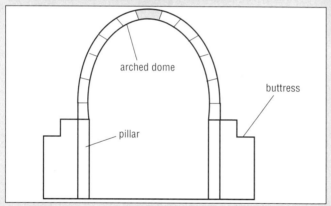

Illustration 5

Illustration 5 shows a cross-section through a typical large mediaeval cathedral. The object is to create as large and tall a space as possible at the centre of the cathedral. The roof is therefore an arched dome which rests on massive pillars. The pillars support the weight of the dome, but cannot, of themselves, provide any inwards push on the base of the dome. This comes from buttresses. These are basically heavy columns of stone which are leaning inwards on the pillars. Each pillar is therefore pushed outwards by the dome and inwards by the buttresses. If the architect gets his sums right, the result is a stable structure with none of the stone blocks in tension. If

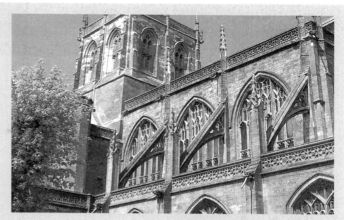

Illustration 6

the sums are wrong, the structure will collapse!

The buttresses need to lean against the top of the pillars, since this is where the dome exerts its outwards push. A flying buttress is an elegant alternative to the massive pile of rock leaning against the pillar. As you can see from Illustration 6, it is another arch, compressed at one end by the dome and at the other end by a free-standing buttress. The result is an extremely beautiful structure, a testimony in stone to the patience and ingenuity of those early engineers whose faith in the next life drove them to construct durable monuments in this one.

Questions

1. List the materials which can be used to build modern houses. Contrast this with a list of materials which were actually used to build a particular house. Explain why each material was probably chosen.

2. What materials would be used to build a large cathedral today? What advantages would they have over stone? Would different materials be used in different parts of the building?

3. Clothes have changed over the centuries. This change has partly arisen because of the availability of different materials. What properties must a material have for use in clothing? In what ways do those properties limit the style of clothes which can be made? Find out what materials were available 2000 years ago. Contrast this with a list of materials available today.

4. There is a limit to how long a vertical metal cable can be before it snaps under its own weight. The table below contains data for two widely used alloys: mild steel and aluminium alloy. Calculate the maximum length of each material that can dangle vertically.

Material	Tensile strength /MNm^{-2}	Density /kgm^{-3}
Mild steel	300	7700
Aluminium alloy	240	2800

Case study

SIZE AND SHAPE

Bone is very strong because it is a composite material. It contains hard crystals of calcium phosphate embedded in a matrix of collagen. Its properties compare favourably with other composites such as reinforced concrete and fibreglass.

Collagen is a long-chain protein molecule, so it has many of the properties of polymers. The long chains get tangled up with each other, making collagen hard and difficult to distort. It lacks a crystal structure, so cracks cannot propagate through it easily. Instead of snapping when subjected to large stresses, collagen simply changes shape. It is tough, elastic and flexible. Many fish have skeletons made only from collagen. As cartilage it is strong enough to support organisms which spend their lives underwater. Sharks, for example, have skeletons made entirely from cartilage. They can get away without having bones because most of their weight is supported by the water around them.

Hollow strength

Illustration 1

Take a look at the two animals in Illustration 1. Although they appear the same size in the photographs, you can instantly tell which one is large and which one is small. The thickness of their legs relative to their length gives them away. This case study is going to show you how the science of materials can be used to show why the shape of an animal is fixed by its size.

Tensile strength

Mammals use bones to support themselves and provide a network of levers for their muscles to pull on. Bone is a remarkable material which has evolved over millions of years, honed to perfection by the need for survival. Table 1 compares its tensile strength with that of other similar materials.

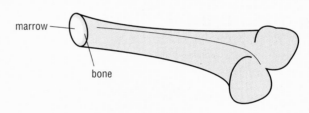

Illustration 2

Illustration 2 shows a bone in cross-section. Notice that it is hollow. This gives extra strength. Of course, the maximum force F which you can put along the length of a bone only depends on its cross-sectional area A and its tensile strength σ_u. In fact, $F = \sigma_u A$. If a hollow bone contains the same mass of bone as a solid one, why does the hollowness confer extra strength?

Table 1

Material	Tensile strength/MNm^{-2}
Bone	140
Wood	100
Glass	50
Concrete	6
Brick	5

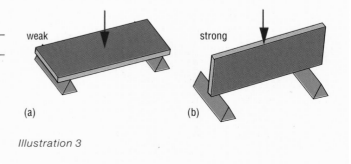

Illustration 3

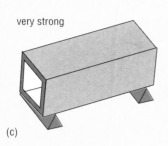

very strong

(c)

Illustration 3 (continued)

Suppose that you have a plank of wood. If you suspend it between two supports as shown in Illustration 3a, it is very flexible and easy to break. However, if you support the same plank as shown in Illustration 3b, with the short side downwards, it becomes much stiffer and difficult to break. A box girder is much stronger that a solid beam of the same weight (Illustration 3c). You can think of a bone as a box girder which has a circular cross-section. By concentrating the stress-resistant material around the outside of a soft tube of marrow, a bone increases its ability to resist flexing forces.

Scaling up and down

The stress on your leg bones can be estimated as follows. The diameter of the femur is about 4 cm, and your weight is about 800 N. If the weight is shared evenly between both legs, the stress will be $\frac{400}{(\pi 0.02^2)}$ = 320 kNm^{-2}. Since the tensile strength of bone is 140 000 kNm^{-2}, this gives a safety margin of $\frac{140\,000}{320}$ = 440. You are most unlikely to break your legs by standing on them! However, there are other activities (such as jumping and running) which place much larger stresses on your leg bones.

It is reasonable to suppose that humans have evolved so that they have a safety margin which is adequate but not over-generous. After all, building bones and moving them around takes a great deal of energy. Any animal which spent more energy on its bones than it really needed to would soon be extinct. So we can safely assume that all mammals have roughly the same safety margin.

Suppose that we made a giant copy of you at twice the normal scale, with the same safety margin. The weight of an object is proportional to its volume, so the giant will have a weight of 800×2^3 = 6 400 N. If the stress on each leg bone is still only 320 kNm^{-2}, its radius r can be calculated as follows.

$$320 \times 10^3 = \frac{6\,400}{(\pi r^2)}$$

so $\quad r^2 = \dfrac{6\,400}{(\pi \times 320 \times 10^3)}$

$\qquad\qquad = 0.0064$

or $\quad r = 0.08$ m

So the diameter of the giant's leg bone will be 16 cm. This is four times larger than your own, even though the giant is only supposed to be twice as large! If his bones are comparatively thicker than yours, the giant cannot have the same shape as you. An animal's shape depends on its size.

The tensile strength of bone places an upper limit on the size of human which can stalk our planet. This can be estimated by considering your own thigh. Its overall diameter is about 16 cm, about 4 times larger than the bone down its centre. A giant who is twice your size, will have thighs 32 cm across, containing bones of diameter 16 cm. A super-giant who is twice as large again, would have thighs 64 cm across, but the bones would also have a diameter of 64 cm. This doesn't leave any room for muscles! Large animals, such as elephants, have smaller safety margins for their bones than we do. This allows some room for muscle as well as bone in their limbs. However, they cannot run and jump as we do without risking broken bones.

Questions

1 Why is calcium phosphate hard but brittle? Why is collagen tough? Why is bone hard and tough?

2 Teeth are made from layers of different materials. Describe the structure of a tooth. Explain the important properties of the materials which occur in each layer of the tooth.

3 Describe the structure of a modern suspension bridge. State and explain what materials are used for each part of the bridge. Contrast the materials used in a modern suspension bridge with those used in an ancient bridge.

4 Ancient barns were built from wood. Find out how *tie beams* were used to support the heavy roofs of these barns. Why were the same techniques not used for the ancient cathedrals?

5 What properties should materials used in building aircraft have? How do they compare with the actual properties used to build large aircraft today? Why are different materials used for small aeroplanes?

6 Insects have exoskeletons made from a composite called *chitin*. Explain why there is a limit to the size to which an insect can grow before there is no room for muscles inside its skeleton.

Case study

STEEL

Steel is the wonder material of the twentieth century. Its combination of tensile strength, toughness and cheapness has made possible structures such as those featured in Illustration 1.

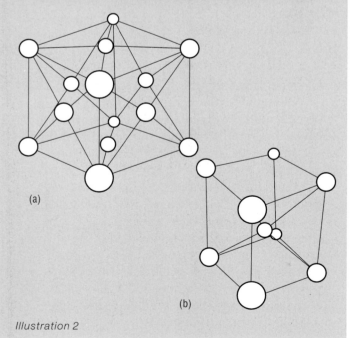

Illustration 1

Heat treatment

Steel is a composite material made from iron and a small amount of carbon. The iron is often alloyed with small amounts of other metals (such as manganese, nickel and chromium). The important mechanical properties of steel (hardness and toughness) can be adjusted by appropriate heat treatment.

For example, the tensile strength of a fully annealed sample of steel which contains 0.4% of carbon is about 600 MNm^{-2}. If the sample is raised above 850 °C and then rapidly plunged into cold water, its tensile strength rises to about 900 MNm^{-2}.

Phases

The very special properties of steel arise from the fact that there are two sorts of solid iron. It exists in two phases. Pure iron melts at 1527 °C. Solid iron above 910 °C has its ions arranged in a face-centred cubic (or f.c.c.) structure (Illustration 2a).

(a)

(b)

Illustration 2

Below 910 °C the ions are arranged in a body-centred cubic (or b.c.c.) structure (Illustration 2b).

The two forms (or phases) of solid iron can absorb different amounts of carbon. This is shown in Table 1. The amount of carbon dissolved in the iron alters the transition temperature between the two phases. This is shown in the graph of Illustration 3.

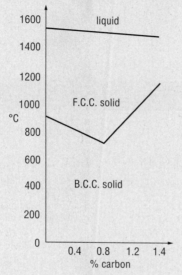

Illustration 3

Table 1

Phase	Carbon
f.c.c.	1.70%
b.c.c.	0.03%

Strength

Consider a sample of steel which contains 0.8% carbon. If it is heated above 723°C, all of that carbon will be dissolved in the f.c.c. phase.

As the sample cools, the b.c.c. phase takes over from the f.c.c. phase. The b.c.c. phase contains almost no carbon at all. So the carbon is deposited as iron carbide (FeC_3). The result is grains which consist of layers of hard iron carbide in a tough matrix of pure iron. These grains of pearlite are shown in Illustration 4.

Illustration 4

If the original steel contains more than 0.8% carbon, the final result is grains of pearlite bonded together by a matrix of iron carbide. Since iron carbide is not ductile (its structure is similar to that of a ceramic), high carbon steels are very hard but brittle. Should the steel have less than 0.8% carbon, the result is grains of pearlite bonded together by a matrix of pure iron. So low-carbon steels are quite hard (because of the pearlite grains) but tough (because of the ductile iron matrix).

Quenching

The hardness of a steel, like all metals, depends on the size of its grains. Small grains make the metal hard. If a steel is cooled slowly, there is plenty of time for grains of iron carbide to grow alongside grains of pure iron. However, if the steel is cooled quickly (quenched) from its f.c.c. form to its b.c.c. form there is no time for this to happen. Instead, the carbon is left as small imperfections inside the grains of pure iron. The carbon distorts the regular crystal structure of the iron, making slip very difficult. So quenched steel is very hard and strong.

Alloys

Quenching only increases the hardness of the sample if it cools rapidly enough. So a thick sample may only be hardened near the surface. (The temperature of its interior may fall too slowly when the sample is plunged into the coolant.) Alloying the iron with small amounts of other metals reduces the rate at which the steel has to be cooled for quenching to take place. So alloy steels allow much larger samples to be quenched.

Tempering

A quenched steel is very hard, but it is also relatively brittle. This is useful for devices which need to be very hard, but not tough. The toughness of quenched steel can be improved by a second heating process.

A quenched sample doesn't spend much time above the recrystallisation temperature, so the grains are very small. Tempering the sample gives some of the carbon locked in the pure iron a chance to form very small grains of iron carbide. The end product has a structure similar to that of a cermet. The hard particles of iron carbide are held in a strong, tough matrix of finely grained iron.

Quenched steel is tempered by raising its temperature to between 200 °C and 600 °C and letting it cool slowly. The higher the temperature, the less brittle the steel becomes, but there is also a loss of hardness. Table 2 contains data for 0.45% carbon steel which has been quenched.

Table 2

Temperature/°C	Tensile strength /MNm^{-2}	Maximum strain
No tempering	980	0.12
200	980	0.15
300	960	0.17
400	900	0.21
500	780	0.25
600	680	0.28

Steel for making cutting tools needs to be hard, so it is tempered at about 250 °C. On the other hand, steel for springs and saws needs to be flexible, so it is tempered at 600 °C.

Case-hardening

A hard piece of quenched steel will be brittle. It will not be tough. Yet there are many applications which require a material which is both hard and tough. Gear wheels, for example, need to be hard and wear-resistant, yet also strong and shock resistant. Case-hardening allows the surface of a steel component to be hard and its interior to be tough.

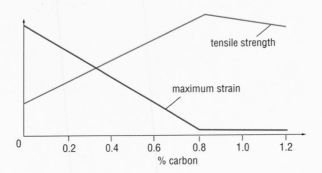

Illustration 5

The toughness and hardness of a steel depend on the amount of carbon it contains. This is illustrated in the graph of Illustration 5. A low carbon steel (0.2%) is tough but not hard. A high carbon steel (0.8%) is hard but not tough. So if a component is made from mild steel, it will be tough and shock resistant. Its surface can then be hardened by carburising (dissolving more carbon) and quenching.

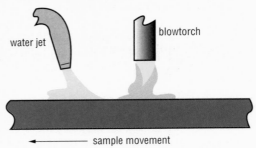

Illustration 6

The commonest method of carburising is to heat the component in methane at 900 °C for a few hours. The aim is to increase the amount of carbon in the surface layer to 0.8%. The component at 900 °C is then quenched by plunging it into cold water. This leaves a tough core. The surface steel is then given a separate quenching at 750 °C, often with a blow-pipe and water jet as shown in Illustration 6. This produces a much stronger, harder surface. Finally, the whole component is tempered at 200 °C to make the surface less brittle.

Questions

1. What is a composite material? Give some examples. Explain why composite materials are useful.

2. Explain the meaning of the following terms: *hardness*, *toughness* and *brittleness*. Describe how each of these characteristics can be modified in metals.

3. What is annealing? Explain why it improves the ductility of metals. Why is it necessary at all?

4. Why are metals tough and ceramics brittle?

5. Explain the meaning of the terms *tensile strength* and *strain*.

6. Steel is routinely used in the construction of bridges because it has a high tensile strength. Yet the early bridges made of iron were designed so that no part of them was in tension. Why?

Case study

MATERIALS AND MEDICINE

The following article from *New Scientist* describes a potential medical application of a material developed in the space industry.

SHUTTLE INSULATION PATCHES UP BROKEN BONES

THE MATERIAL that stops US space shuttles from burning up when they re-enter the Earth's atmosphere may soon be used to repair broken or degenerating bones. Researchers at NASA's Ames Research Center in California have joined forces with industrialists and academics in Texas to adapt reusable surface insulation, or RSI, for use in bones.

The ceramic insulation material is a blend of silica, aluminium fibre and borosilicate glass, and the researchers have already shown that it is not rejected when implanted in monkeys and rats. They intend to use slivers of the material as "scaffolding" for rebuilding bones that are damaged or worn, because its mechanical properties and structure are similar to that of bone.

Casey Fox of BioMedical Enterprises, a small company in San Antonio, Texas, wants to use the material together with implants such as metal pins, wires, plates and screws to help bone fractures and breaks to heal.

"What we hope will happen is that bone cells grow into the pores in the material, so the result is fibre-reinforced bone," says Howard Goldstein, the senior staff scientist at Ames and the project leader. "However, at the moment the pores of the ceramic material are a few microns across, and the cells that could grow into them are larger. So we need to increase pore size."

Working with Fox and with Thomas Aufdemorte of the Health Science Center at the University of Texas in San Antonio, Goldstein hopes to do this by putting in larger fibres of silicon or by firing the ceramic at higher temperatures.

"We hope to modify the surface structure somewhat, and vary the porosity and strength of RSI," says Goldstein. "It will probably be weaker than bone even after we've modified it, but it should gain strength as bone grows into it."

Fox says that the idea of using shuttle insulation material in medical applications developed from a long-standing collaboration between NASA and the University of Texas to investigate how bones degenerate in low-gravity conditions.

Andy Coghlan
30 October 1993

Questions

1 What is the purpose of RSI in the space shuttle and what conditions must it withstand?

2 Summarise the properties of RSI and explain why it was chosen.

3 How could the specific heat capacity of a sample of RSI be determined?

4 What are the attractions of using RSI to rebuild bones? In what ways must the properties of the material be modified for this use?

5 How could the strength of RSI, and any modified forms of the material, be determined and compared with bone?

6 What parts of the human body can be replaced, repaired or improved (when they are not functioning properly) by the use of artificial materials? In each case, summarise the desirable properties of the materials.

3 | Obtain new substances

Thousands of scientists are engaged in obtaining new substances either from chemical reactions or by extraction from natural sources. The growth in our understanding of chemical reactions and the discovery of new reactions, coupled with the skilful application of experimental techniques, enables scientists to obtain more and more new substances. These include consumer products (e.g. medicines, detergents, food preservatives, pesticides, fertilisers, plastics) and new technologies (e.g. organic semiconductors, advanced materials). In the past fifty years the range of chemical techniques has grown so much that in many situations it is possible to have a chemical compound with properties made to order.

Figure 3.1 *Small scale reactions between gases and solids can be carried out in the laboratory with little difficulty. However, industrial chemical reactors are often huge, complex and sophisticated.*

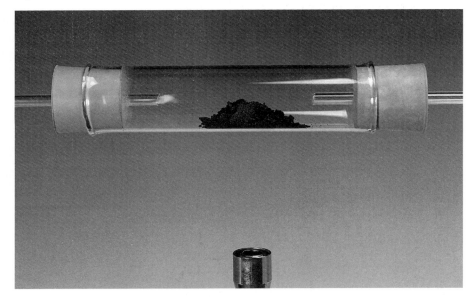

The Elements

Element 3.1 Plan the preparation of substances
Having been told what substance to make, or having identified it yourself, you need to decide how to prepare it. You need to:
- explain why the substance is needed

Planning a preparation, page 128

- find possible preparative routes, carry out a risk assessment for each and select the most suitable one
- list the requirements, such as apparatus and reagents, for the preparative route you chose to use.

▶ Preparative methods, page 132

Element 3.2 Prepare quantities of substances

To prepare a particular quantity of a substance you need to:
- calculate the quantities of reactants needed to prepare the required quantity of substance
- prepare the substance, taking the necessary safety precautions.

You will also be asked to think about preparing the substance on an industrial scale. You need to:
- identify factors, such as equipment or disposal of co-products, which should be considered when scaling up a laboratory reaction.

▶ Quantities, yields and scaling up, page 143

Element 3.3 Extract and determine yield of substances

In any reaction you will have to: extract a substance from a reaction mixture or natural source; purify it and determine purity; calculate the yield. You need to:
- select a suitable extraction method
- extract the substance, taking the necessary safety precautions
- check the purity of the extracted substance
- determine the yield of product.

▶ Chemical equations and calculations, page 70

Figure 3.2 *This chemical reactor is used to make compounds for perfumes. Small quantities are needed and so a batch process is used. This is basically a straightforward scale-up of laboratory apparatus.*

Planning a preparation

Substances can be prepared by chemical reaction or obtained by extraction from a natural source, such as plants. Sometimes both methods can be used for a particular substance. If the substance is to be obtained commercially, the choice between preparation and extraction is often decided by economic factors.

Figure 3.3 Although indigo can be obtained by extraction from this plant, it is cheaper to synthesise it in the laboratory. Therefore, chemical reaction is the method chosen for this industrial preparation.

> **Preparative route: a sequence of chemical reactions by which a required substance is made from available starting materials.**

The preparation of a substance involves converting one substance into another by one or more chemical reactions. The original substance and other reagents you need are called the **starting materials**. More than one reaction may be needed. For a chosen method, the necessary reactions are carried out in sequence. This is called the **preparative route**.

Reasons for obtaining a substance

Improved products

Substances are made by the chemical and pharmaceutical industries to meet particular demands. New and improved products are constantly being sought for things like treatments for asthma in medicine, or plastics in packaging that can be recycled.

Given a problem, researchers identify a range of compounds which may prove useful. These are called *candidate compounds*.

For example in asthma, adrenaline is released during the early stages of an attack. It causes the air ways to contract. By finding compounds such as ephedrine which block the receptor for adrenaline, relief from an asthma attack can be given. Notice the similarity between the two compounds (see Figure 3.4).

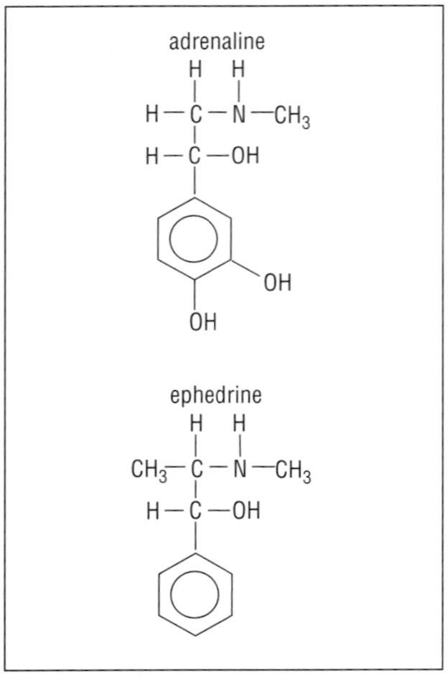

Scientists apply their knowledge and experience to choose the most promising compounds for further study. Modern technology, in particular electronic databases and computer-aided molecular design, plays a big part. Selected compounds are prepared in the laboratory and tested to assess their effectiveness for the job at hand.

Process economics

In an industrial process involving chemical reactions, *co-products* are often formed alongside the *main product*. The process becomes more economical if a use can be found for one or more of the co-products. Otherwise, the company is simply faced with the disposal costs of the co-products.

Figure 3.4 Structures of adrenaline and ephedrine

Co-products and by-products
page 277

For example, the following reaction is sometimes used to obtain sulphur dioxide for sulphuric acid manufacture:

$$2ZnS(s) + 3O_2(g) \rightarrow 2ZnO(s) + 2SO_2(g)$$
$$\text{co-product} \qquad \text{main product}$$

The process would be more economical if a use could be found for zinc oxide. Another example is the industrial manufacture of sodium hydroxide by the electrolysis of brine. Chlorine is a valuable co-product. It is used to make bleach, disinfectants and a wide range of organochlorine compounds.

Structure confirmation

Once you have made a new compound, you need to find its chemical structure using analysis. The proposed structure is confirmed by **chemical synthesis**. This involves building the proposed structure using a series of known chemical reactions. The properties of the 'built' molecule are compared with those of the compound under investigation. If they match, the proposed structure is confirmed.

Preparative routes

What options are available to make compounds? Our knowledge of chemical reactions is vast. It would be impossible to list all possible routes here. Instead a selection is given in two databases at the end of this Unit:

- inorganic reactions
- organic reactions.

The use of these two databases will enable you to develop the skills you need to work with larger databases when you meet them.

Choosing the best route

You will often have a choice of **preparative routes** to make a substance. The ideal route gives the highest yield of the purest product in the shortest time using the simplest techniques and apparatus and from readily available, cheap starting materials! However, as with all things, choice is based on compromise. This means weighing up the advantages and disadvantages of each route and selecting the one which achieves the most favourable balance.

> **Chemical synthesis means building up more complex compounds from simple ones. Known chemical reactions are used to build up the desired structure.**

▶ Types of chemical reactions, page 146

▶ Database of reactions of inorganic compounds, page 153

▶ Database of reactions of organic compounds, page 156

> **Choice of preparative route depends on the following for each step being considered:**
> - **availability and costs of materials**
> - **availability and costs of apparatus**
> - **feasibility of conversion**
> - **number of steps**
> - **time and yield**
> - **safety.**

Assignment trigger

Food preservatives

Often food must be transported and stored. Various methods are used to preserve food during these periods.

What are these?
What chemicals are used in food preservation?
How are they obtained?
What regulates their use?
How is their effectiveness determined?

If a practical assignment is developed, it is essential that a risk assessment is made and checked by your teacher/lecturer.

Could lead to possible assignments relating to Unit 3.

Availability and costs of starting materials

The starting materials include the starting compound, other reactants, solvents and any other chemicals required. When planning a preparation, you need to make a check list of all starting materials, including the relative quantities needed.

	Ca, Mg and R₂O₃ precipitate ≤0.005%		
24,414-7 ★	Sodium chlorate, 99 + % [7775-09-9] NaClO₃..	5g 100g 1kg	4.10 4.40 11.50
20,443-9 ★	Sodium chloride, 99.999% [7647-14-5] NaCl FW 58.44 mp 801° d 2.165 Merck .... Index 11,8544 SI 465,D,9 Safety 2,3135D R&S 1(3),3319F RTECS# VZ4725000 Disp. N HYGROSCOPIC R: 36/37/38 S: 26-36	20g 100g	11.50 38.80
37,886-0 ★	Sodium chloride, random crystals, 99.99%, optical grade [7647-14-5] NaCl...........	10g 50g	9.60 40.60
22,351-4 ★	Sodium chloride, 99 + %, A.C.S. reagent [7647-14-5] NaCl....................................... Assay ≥99.0% Heavy metals ≤5 ppm I⁻ ≤0.002% Insolubles ≤0.005% K ≤0.005% pH (5%, 25°) 5.0-9.0 N compounds ≤0.001% ClO₃⁻ and NO₃⁻ ≤0.003% PO₄³⁻ ≤5 ppm Fe ≤2 ppm SO₄²⁻ ≤0.004% Ba ≤0.001% Br⁻ ≤0.01% Ca, Mg and R₂O₃ ppt. ≤0.005%	25g 500g 2kg 10kg	5.00 5.20 11.60 50.00
31,016-6 ★	Sodium chloride, +80 mesh, 98 + % [7647-14-5] NaCl..	1kg 5kg	6.20 21.60
31,947-3 ★	Sodium chloride volumetric standard, 0.1N solution in water [7647-14-5]...... NaCl FW 58.44 d 1.000 Fp none Merck Index 11,8544 R&S 1(3),3319F RTECS# VZ4725000 Disp. N R: 36/37/38 S: 26-36 This solution is prepared from A.C.S. reagent grade sodium chloride in ASTM reagent grade I water, and is standardized potentiometrically traceable to NIST reference material. Concentration range 0.0950-0.1050N. Exact value stated on label	500ml 6x500ml 2L 4x2L	6.40 34.80 17.50 59.80
24,415-5 ★	Sodium chlorite, tech., 80% [7758-19-2] NaClO₂ FW 90.44 Fieser 9,423 11,481 .... 13,280 Merck Index 11,8545 SI 480,D,5 Safety 2,3136A R&S 1(3),3513B RTECS# VZ4800000 Disp. J RID/ADR 5.1/14b R: 8-23/24/25-36/37/38 S: 17-26-27-36/37/39	5g 100g 1kg	5.50 6.10 18.00
30,783-1 ★	Sodium chromate, 98% [7775-11-3] Na₂CrO₄ FW 161.97 Fieser 5,605 Merck .... Index 11,8547 SI 477,A,9 Safety 2,3136B R&S 1(3),3467I RTECS# GB2955000 Disp. J RID/ADR 6.1/68c R: 8-45-46-36/37/38 S: 53-17-26-27-36/37/39	5g 100g 500g	6.50 7.50 30.00

Figure 3.5 *This extract from a supplier's catalogue shows how the cost of a chemical depends on the purity required and the quantity purchased.*

Start by checking the laboratory stock record. If an item is not there, look it up in a chemical supplier's catalogue. Remember to use more than one catalogue. The range of products, and prices, varies from one supplier to another. You should also note delivery times, costs and any special arrangements which need to be made. For example, some substances need refrigeration, others need to be stored in the dark.

Availability and costs of apparatus

The same procedure applies as for starting materials. Look in the laboratory stock record or, if necessary, in a supplier's catalogue, and make a check list.

To make a reasonable estimate of the overall costs, you should also consider how much energy will be required. After all, energy costs money. There are hidden costs as well: your time, overheads (such as electricity and water), upkeep of the laboratory and so on.

Feasibility of conversion

Many reactions which look possible on paper prove to be very difficult, and sometimes impossible, in practice. They may require reaction conditions which cannot be achieved in the laboratory (for example, extremely high pressures or temperatures). Some may take too long, require expensive reagents or specialist apparatus. You will need to consider carefully the feasibility of each conversion in the routes you are thinking of using.

Number of steps

Some compounds can be made using either a **single-step conversion** or a **multi-step conversion**. A single-step conversion usually requires only one set of apparatus and the minimum transfer of materials. If available, it is usually the route to choose.

A single step conversion involves one chemical reaction. A multi-step conversion involves more than one chemical reaction.

However, there may be advantages in choosing a multi-step conversion over a single-step. For example, on paper, the preparation of ethyl ethanoate from ethanoic acid is a single-step conversion:

$$CH_3COOH(l) + C_2H_5OH(l) \rightleftharpoons CH_3COOC_2H_5(l) + H_2O(l)$$

ethanoic acid   ethanol   ethyl ethanoate   water

▶ Establishing a position of equilibrium, page 261

It can be carried out in the laboratory by heating a mixture of the correct amounts of reactants. Concentrated sulphuric acid is added as a catalyst. After cooling, the mixture is poured into water and the ethyl ethanoate separated and purified by distillation. A typical yield is about 67%. It is not 100% because an equilibrium is set up in the reaction mixture. Not all the ethanoic acid and ethanol are converted to ethyl ethanoate and water.

A two-step conversion, however, gives a yield of nearly 100%. The –OH group in ethanoic acid is not easily replaced. However it can be converted easily to a more reactive group – an acid chloride. The following reaction occurs immediately at room temperature.

$$CH_3COOH(l) + SOCl_2(l) \rightarrow CH_3COCl(l) + SO_2(g) + HCl(g)$$

ethanoic acid   sulphur dichloride oxide   ethanoyl chloride   sulphur dioxide   hydrogen chloride

The main product, ethanoyl chloride, is easily obtained because both side-products are gaseous. The ethanoyl chloride is very reactive. Ethanol is added and the reaction is almost immediate. The side-product is gaseous and so leaves the reaction vessel.

$$CH_3COCl(l) + C_2H_5OH(l) \rightarrow CH_3COOC_2H_5(l) + HCl(g)$$

ethanoyl chloride   ethanol   ethyl ethanoate   hydrogen chloride

The ethyl ethanoate is purified by distillation.

Assignment trigger

Fertilisers
Farmers and gardeners rely on fertilisers.

What chemicals are used as fertilisers?
How can they be made in the laboratory?
How are fertilisers manufactured?
Can you determine their effectiveness?
What regulates their use?

If a practical assignment is developed, it is essential that a risk assessment is made and checked by your teacher/lecturer.

Could lead to possible assignments relating to Unit 3.

Yield and time
The chosen route should give as high a yield as possible, in the shortest time. Of course, this must be balanced against the other factors outlined above.

Safety
For each route, a risk assessment must be carried out, and the risk assessments for the different routes must be compared when making a final choice.

Preparative methods

A reaction is usually carried out by one of these methods:
- passing a gas over a solid or through a liquid
- mixing a solid with a liquid
- mixing two liquids

In all cases, the liquid may be a pure compound or a solution.

A common preparative method is to react an excess of a solid with a liquid to leave the product in solution. Excess solid can be removed by filtration and the product isolated, for example, by crystallisation.

Another important method is to react two soluble compounds in solution to give a product which is insoluble, and forms as a precipitate. This can then be isolated by filtration.

The method used must ensure that the reactants come into contact with one another. If the reaction mixture is **homogeneous** there are few problems. However, if the mixture is **heterogeneous**, stirring is usually needed to ensure maximum contact between the reactants in different phases. Since rate of reaction depends on temperature, the mixture may have to be heated (to increase the rate) or cooled (to decrease the rate).

Two other reaction conditions which sometimes need to be controlled are the presence of moisture and oxygen. Our atmosphere contains both, and reactions may require that they are excluded. The chemistry of substances in the absence of water and oxygen is often markedly different.

▶ Liquid-solid in solution, page 137

▶ Liquid-solid, page 136

> **Homogeneous reaction: the reaction mixture is a single phase (usually gaseous or liquid). Heterogeneous reaction: more than one phase is present in the reaction mixture (e.g. a mixture of a solid and liquid).**

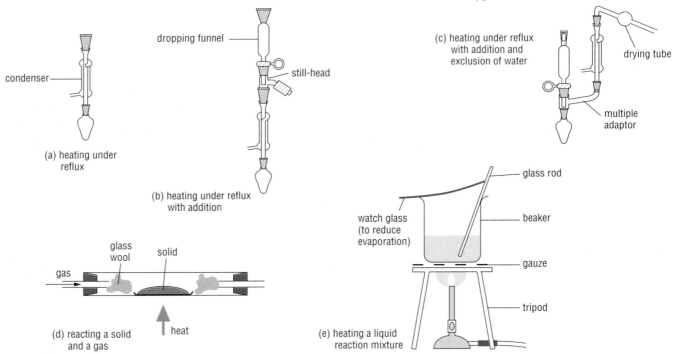

Figure 3.6 *Typical arrangements of apparatus that can be used to prepare substances.*

Choosing the right glassware

For many aqueous reactions standard laboratory glassware can be used. Beakers and conical flasks are convenient reaction vessels. Mixtures can be heated using a Bunsen burner. Heat resistant glassware should be used. This is marked 'Pyrex' or with an equivalent trade name.

However, preparations of organic compounds often use solvents which we do not want to escape into the atmosphere. They may be flammable or harmful. Quickfit glassware is particularly useful in these situations. Using

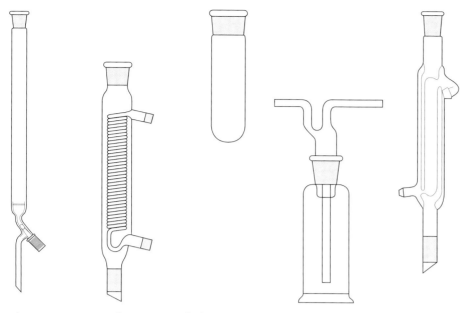

Figure 3.7 *Some of the Quickfit glassware which may be available to you in the laboratory. The joints make for easy assembling and dismantling.*

this apparatus with its ground glass joints enables apparatus to be readily assembled to carry out reactions.

Never put too much in a reaction vessel. Flasks and beakers should never be more than one-half to two-thirds full. Bear this in mind when choosing your apparatus for a particular purpose.

When using Quickfit ensure that all joints are clean before assembly. It is a good idea to lubricate the joints with a very small quantity of Vaseline or silicone grease. Teflon sleeves can also be used in joints. If chemicals are left on joints they may stick together. Should this happen, don't panic. A *gentle* tap with a spatula often enables the joint to be worked free.

Heating

It is important to heat up liquids evenly. Unless the mixture is being stirred mechanically, you should use anti-bumping granules in round bottom flasks or a glass rod in conical flasks and beakers. This ensures that liquids boil smoothly. Table 3.1 lists some of the different heating methods available.

Remember that a mixture must never be heated in a sealed apparatus (unless very special precautions are taken). Sealed apparatus may explode if heated.

Table 3.1 Heating in the laboratory

Method of heating	Comments
Bunsen burner	Only if no risk of fire
Electric heating mantle	Convenient for round bottomed Quickfit flasks
Electric hot plate	Convenient for flat bottom reaction vessels (e.g. beakers)
Water bath	If temperature < 85°C
Oil bath	If temperature > 85°C

Heating under reflux (or refluxing) describes the heating of a reaction mixture in a flask at a constant temperature. A condenser is used to ensure that the volatile components of the reaction mixture do not boil away.

Figure 3.8 *Pyrex flasks can be heated by a Bunsen burner. The flask should be placed on a gauze on top of a tripod. The glass rod prevents bumping and the funnel acts as a crude air condenser reducing the loss of water.*

Assignment trigger

Detergents

There is a vast range of cleaning products containing detergents. Different products are available for your face, hair, clothes, dirty dishes and so on.

What is the difference between a soap and a detergent?
What is a biologically active washing powder?
How are they all made?
How could you test their effectiveness?

If a practical assignment is developed, it is essential that a risk assessment is made and checked by your teacher/lecturer.

Could lead to possible assignments relating to Units 1 and 3.

Cooling

Often you need to cool down a reaction vessel after heating. Cold water can be run over the outside of the vessel using a rubber hose attached to a cold water tap. Alternatively, reactions may be cooled by placing the flask in a cold liquid. Don't put a hot flask into a cold liquid without letting it cool first: it may crack! Table 3.2 shows some of the ways of getting cold baths.

Table 3.2 Cold baths for cooling reaction mixtures

Bath	Approximate temperature °C
Ice and water	0
Ice and sodium chloride	−10
Dry ice (solid carbon dioxide) and propanone	−78

 1 What technique could you use to (a) heat a reaction in a round bottomed flask at 120°C for 2 hours and (b) cool a reaction at −5°C for 30 minutes?

Mixing

Reaction mixtures can be stirred with a glass rod. This can be tedious! An alternative is to use a magnetic stirrer. This consists of a magnet which rotates and turns a flea (a small plastic covered magnet) placed in the flask. For some reactions where the 'flea' cannot stir the reaction mixture, a mechanical stirrer is used. This is usually an electrically driven paddle. Flasks can also be shaken automatically.

Extraction methods

To obtain a substance either from a reaction mixture or from a natural source it must be extracted and then purified. Often it is possible to select a method which extracts the product you want and leaves most of the

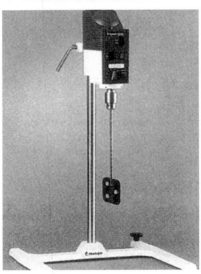

Figure 3.9 Reactions can be stirred with a magnetic stirrer or a mechanical stirrer.

impurities behind. Spending time choosing and developing such a method can yield many benefits. The fewer impurities extracted with the product, the easier the final purification stages.

The **extraction** method depends on the nature of the mixture.

Assignment trigger

Decaffeinated coffee
Coffee and tea are available as regular or decaffeinated.

What is caffeine?
What effect does it have on your body?
How are tea and coffee decaffeinated?
Can you decaffeinate tea or coffee in the laboratory?
How can you check that the products are decaffeinated?
Why are some products described as 'naturally decaffeinated'?

If a practical assignment is developed, it is essential that a risk assessment is made and checked by your teacher/lecturer.

Could lead to possible assignments relating to Units 3 and 7.

Separating mixtures of two or more solids

Solvent extraction is the most common separation method. It relies on the differing solubilities of substances in solvents.

Inorganic compounds are often soluble in water, acids or alkalis. These can be used as solvents for extraction. Organic compounds tend to be soluble in organic solvents, for example hexane and dichloromethane.

A solvent is added to the solid mixture. Heating the solvent increases the solubility of most solids. Breaking the solid into small pieces ensures the maximum surface area is available for the solvent to dissolve the solid.

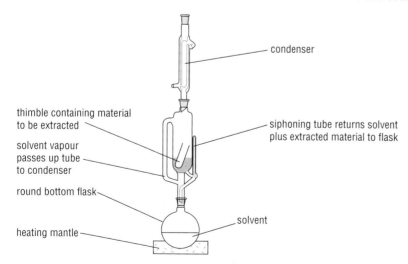

condenser

thimble containing material to be extracted

solvent vapour passes up tube to condenser

round bottom flask

heating mantle

siphoning tube returns solvent plus extracted material to flask

solvent

Figure 3.10 This apparatus, called a soxhlet, can be used to recycle hot solvent over the solid to be extracted. The solvent is heated, distils and condenses so that it drips on to the solid. The solvent periodically siphons back into the flask where the extracted solid collects in solution.

Less commonly, two solids can be separated by **sublimation**. Sublimation is when a substance turns from a solid to a gas without first becoming a liquid. Substances which sublime can be separated from others which do not by heating the mixture and collecting the subliming substance on a cold surface.

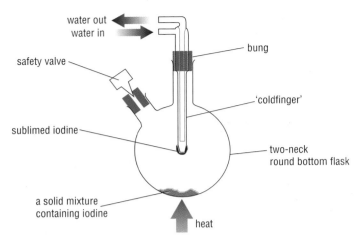

Figure 3.11 Iodine can be separated from other solids by sublimation. Cold water running through the test tube (this arrangement is called a cold finger) provides a cold surface for the iodine to crystallise on.

Insoluble solids mixed with a liquid can be separated using simple gravity filtration or filtration under reduced pressure.

Liquid-solid

Gravity filtration can be used when the solid particles are distinct and not too fine. A filter funnel and filter paper are used. Filter paper comes in a variety of grades. The grade is an indication of the pore size. The one used depends on the particle size to be filtered.

Figure 3.12 Gravity filtration. The filter paper is folded and put inside the funnel. The mixture is poured carefully into the funnel. The entire contents of the beaker are transferred using a squeezy bottle containing the solvent (usually distilled or deionised water).

The liquid which passes through a filter is called the filtrate. Material left on the filter is called the residue.

Hot solutions can be filtered as well as cold ones. It is important that the equipment is heated before use because most substances are less soluble at lower temperatures. If the solution cools too much, the solid may become insoluble, crystallise out, and clog up the filter paper.

Fine solids may make gravity filtration extremely slow. Filtration may become impossible because the solid clogs up the pores of the filter paper. A way round this is to use filtration under reduced pressure.

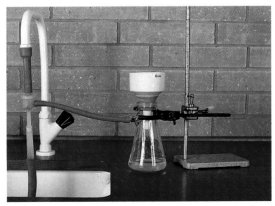

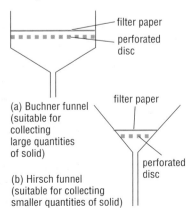

filter paper
perforated disc

(a) Buchner funnel (suitable for collecting large quantities of solid)

filter paper

perforated disc

(b) Hirsch funnel (suitable for collecting smaller quantities of solid)

Figure 3.13 The filtration funnel is connected to a water pump. A flat filter paper is placed in the funnel. It is wetted to bed it down before the mixture is poured on. The pump is turned on and the low pressure draws the liquid through. The funnels are often called Hirsch or Buchner funnels depending on their shape.

Liquid-solid in solution

A solid can be obtained from a **solution** by:
- the evaporation of the **solvent**
- making the solid insoluble in the solvent
- solvent extraction

Removing the solvent

A variety of methods are available to remove the solvent. It may be removed by heating either at normal pressure or under reduced pressure. The choice depends on the solvent. The solid is left behind in the flask. Heating under reduced pressure is used if the solvent has a high boiling point or if the solid is heat sensitive and decomposes at high temperature.

Normal distillation apparatus can be used but the most common procedure is to use a rotary evaporator. It enables evaporation to be carried out under reduced pressure in a quick and convenient way. The rotatory evaporator is used if the liquid is not required. If the liquid is needed, distillation is used.

Solvent:	a liquid used to dissolve a solid.
Solute:	a solid dissolved in a liquid.
Solution:	a liquid with one or more solutes dissolved in it.

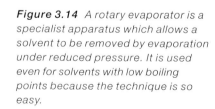
Miscible liquids, page 139

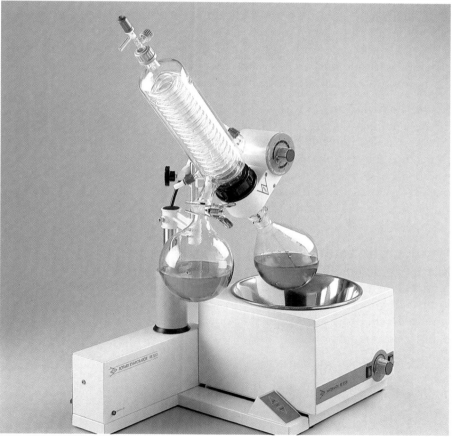

Figure 3.14 *A rotary evaporator is a specialist apparatus which allows a solvent to be removed by evaporation under reduced pressure. It is used even for solvents with low boiling points because the technique is so easy.*

Water is non-toxic and not flammable. It is safe to heat in an open laboratory, unlike most other solvents you will use. *Most organic solvents are flammable and may be hazardous to use in other ways. Always handle them with care and carry out a risk assessment before use.* The usual method for removing water and leaving the dissolved solid is by heating the solution on a hot plate or over a Bunsen burner so that the water evaporates into the atmosphere. The solution is usually contained in an evaporating basin. It is difficult to remove water using a rotary evaporator because it does not boil smoothly. Organic solvents must never be removed by heating over a Bunsen burner: use a hot water bath or an electrical heater.

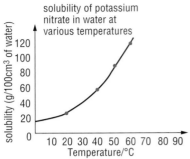

Figure 3.15 Graph of solubility of
potassium nitrate with temperature.
This graph, known as a solubility
curve, shows that the solubility of
potassium nitrate increases with
increasing temperature.

 Liquid-solid, page 136

Figure 3.16 Polarity is a measure of
how strongly a compound is attracted
to an electrostatically charged rod.
Here, a stream of highly polar water is
being bent towards a charged plastic
ruler. Non-polar liquids are deflected
much less, if at all.

Figure 3.17 A separating funnel can
be used to separate immiscible liquids.
The lower layer in the funnel is the
more dense liquid.

Making the solid insoluble in the solvent

A solid dissolved in a solvent can be made insoluble in two ways:
- concentrating the solution by evaporating some of the solvent
- changing the polarity of the solvent

In the first case the mixture is warmed to evaporate the solvent. As it evaporates the concentration of the solute rises. On cooling the solute starts to crystallise out of the solution.

The solid is obtained by filtration. The evaporation/cooling sequence is repeated to ensure that the maximum amount of solid is obtained from the solution.

The solubility of a solute is dependent on the polarity of the solvent. All solvents have different polarities. Water is a highly polar solvent. Hexane is non-polar. A rule of thumb is that non-polar solutes dissolve in non-polar solvents and polar solutes dissolve in polar solvents. For example, ionic compounds such as salts tend to be soluble in water but insoluble in non-polar solvents such as hexane.

Changing the polarity of a liquid can increase or decrease the solubility of a solute. This can be achieved by adding a second liquid which is miscible with the first but has a different polarity. For example, by adding hexane to ethanol the liquid mixture becomes less polar. Adding ethanol to dichloromethane makes the liquid more polar.

Solvent extraction

Organic compounds are generally more soluble in organic solvents, such as ethoxyethane, than water. This means that organic solids can be extracted from aqueous solutions by shaking the solutions with an organic solvent which is immiscible (i.e. does not mix) with water. The problem then becomes one of separating two immiscible liquids. The rule for solvent extraction is simple – little and often. It is better to extract with two separate 50 cm^3 portions of solvent, one after the other, than one 100 cm^3 portion.

Immiscible liquids

Mixtures of immiscible liquids can be separated by using a separating funnel. The least dense liquid forms the upper layer. Often one of the layers will be an aqueous solution. It is important to check which layer is which! To check which layer is the aqueous layer, add a few drops of distilled water and note which layer they go to.

Cleaning a reaction product

Solvent extraction can be used to extract organic compounds from reaction mixtures and to wash out co-products, unreacted starting materials and other impurities. For example, consider a product dissolved in an organic solvent which is less dense than water. The mixture can be washed with water, solutions of acids, alkalis or other aqueous reagents using the same funnel. Each time the aqueous layer will be the lower one, so it can be easily removed and discarded. The washing solution is placed in the funnel with the mixture. The funnel is stoppered and shaken and the mixture allowed to settle. When shaking, the separating funnel should be periodically inverted and the stopper held in place. Then the tap should be opened to reduce the pressure. The tap should not be pointing at anyone. The stopper is removed and the bottom layer run out. The next solution is then added and the process repeated.

Sometimes the separation of the layers takes a long time or is incomplete. A milky mixture (an emulsion) often forms. One way to solve this problem is to increase the polarity of the aqueous layer by adding a concentrated sodium chloride (brine) solution. This should separate the layers.

Miscible liquids

Two methods are available:
- simple distillation, using a condenser only
- fractional distillation using a fractionating column and a condenser

Simple distillation

In this procedure the mixture is placed in a flask with a few anti-bumping granules to ensure smooth boiling. The flask is heated using a suitable method (see Table 3.1). The temperature of the flask and its contents is slowly increased. Once the liquid starts to boil, the temperature is kept steady and recorded using the thermometer situated opposite the exit to the condenser. The vapour will condense in the condenser and collect in the flask. Once all of the liquid has distilled out of the flask the temperature will drop. The flask and contents will need to be heated more strongly now to distil the other less volatile liquid. In some cases the distillation process is aided by insulating the still-head with aluminium foil.

> **Simple distillation can be used to separate a mixture of miscible liquids if their boiling points are significantly different. It is usually used for two-component mixtures only.**

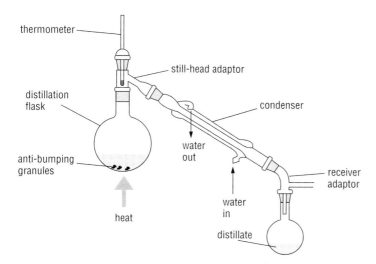

Figure 3.18 Simple distillation. The scale of apparatus depends on the quantity of liquid to be distilled. The flask (round bottom or pear-shaped) should be no more than one half to two-thirds full.

Fragrances

Perfumes and cosmetics are big business. Vast amounts of money are spent on them each year.

What types of compounds are used as fragrances in these products?
Where are they obtained?
Why are they so expensive?
Is there a relationship between the odour of a chemical and its structure?

If a practical assignment is developed, it is essential that a risk assessment is made and checked by your teacher/lecturer.

Could lead to possible assignments relating to Units 3 and 4.

Fractional distillation

The apparatus used in **fractional distillation** is the same as for simple distillation but with a fractionating column between the flask and the still-head. The column is packed with glass beads. This increases the internal surface area of the column. There are a variety of commercial fractionating columns. Each has its own design. All perform the same function.

> **Fractional distillation can be used to separate miscible liquids with similar boiling points. Mixtures containing more than two liquids are best separated by using fractional distillation.**

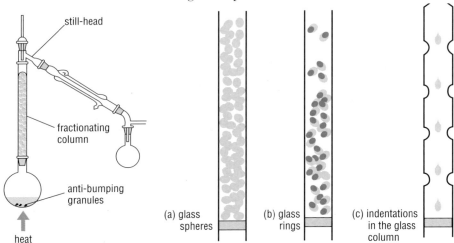

Figure 3.19 Fractional distillation involves using a fractionating column to separate the components in the mixture of miscible liquids.

The mixture is heated gently and slowly until it starts to boil. An oil bath or electrical heating mantle are the best methods. Anti-bumping granules should be used. Remember that most organic liquids are flammable, some very dangerously so. The vapour is richer in the more volatile (i.e. lower boiling point) component (or fraction) of the liquid. It passes up the fractionating column where it condenses. As it runs back towards the flask the liquid meets more hot vapour. Some of it turns to vapour, this time richer still in the more volatile component.

This process occurs many times in the column. At the top, the vapour contains only the lower boiling point component. The temperature should be noted. The vapour will pass into the condenser, condense and run into the flask. Once the **first fraction** has distilled the temperature will drop, rising again when the next fraction starts to distil over. This should be collected in a separate flask. The first drops of liquid from the **second fraction** will contain a mixture of both the first and second fractions. Hence it should be collected separately, and then discarded.

> **In fractional distillation, *fractions* of distillate are collected. In an ideal separation, the first fraction consists of the most volatile liquid, with lowest boiling point, the second fraction consists of the liquid with the second lowest boiling point and so on. The final fraction is the least volatile liquid, with the highest boiling point.**

2 What technique could you use in the following situations
(a) separation of hexane and decane; (b) purification of hexane;
(c) obtaining caffeine from tea; (d) purification of an impure sample of
methyl benzoate; (e) obtaining ammonium chloride from a mixture
with sodium chloride; (f) extracting propanoic acid from a reaction
mixture?

Purification and purity

Purification is the process of obtaining a pure sample from the crude product.
Liquids are purified by distillation. Solids are purified by recrystallisation.

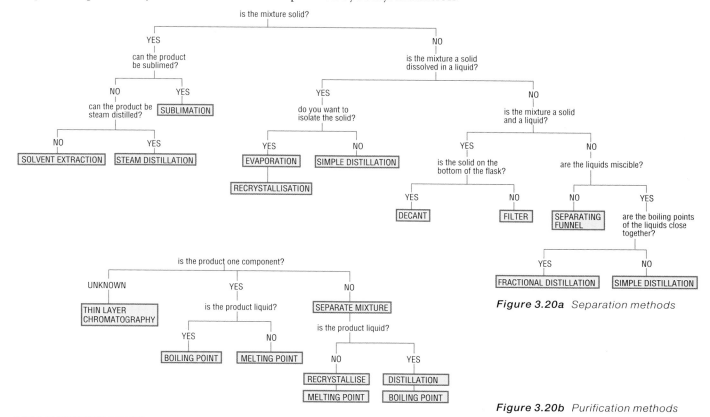

Figure 3.20a Separation methods

Figure 3.20b Purification methods

Pain relievers

Medicines to relieve pain are used all over the world. They improve the
quality of life for many.

What is an over-the-counter (OTC) pain reliever?
What active ingredients do they contain?
How are these made? How can their purity be checked?
How can you confirm that the quantities indicated on the label are
actually present? How could you identify an unknown OTC pain reliever?

*If a practical assignment is developed, it is essential that a risk assessment is
made and checked by your teacher/lecturer.*

Could lead to possible assignments relating to Unit 1.

To recrystallise a solid you need a solvent in which the solid is
- soluble when the solvent is hot
- insoluble when the solvent is cold.

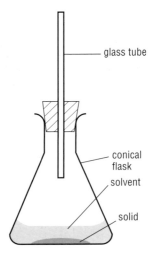

glass tube

conical flask

solvent

solid

Figure 3.21 *A length of glass tubing is used as an air condenser. Sufficient solvent is added to dissolve all the solid when hot.*

The purity of a solid is indicated by its melting point. Impure samples melt below the literature value and over a wider temperature range. The melting point is not sharp.

The literature value for the melting point or boiling point of a compound is that published in scientific papers or data books. It is the melting point or boiling point of the compound accepted by scientists.

Recrystallisation

Recrystallisation is the process of obtaining crystals of the pure substance from an impure solid or oil. It is extremely difficult to produce solids from oils but it can be done if you are patient.

The idea is that you dissolve the solid you want in the hot solvent. Impurities either don't dissolve, or stay dissolved when the solvent cools. So impurities should be either insoluble in both hot and cold solvent, or soluble in both. The solvent must be pure so that no additional impurities are added to the mixture. Laboratory solvents should be distilled before use. A pure liquid or mixture of liquids may be used.

You will usually be told which solvent to use for the recrystallisation. If not, you will need to carry out small scale tests to find a suitable solvent.

The impure substance is placed in a conical flask (see Figure 3.21). A small volume of the solvent is added and the flask is heated. A risk assessment should be carried out to choose a suitable safe solvent and a safe method of heating (see Table 3.1). More solvent is added in small quantities, and the mixture is heated between additions until the solid just dissolves. With most of the solid dissolved some particles of impurities may remain. These should be removed by filtration under reduced pressure. The funnel should be warm to prevent premature crystallisation. If crystallisation does occur in the funnel then the remedy is to wash the apparatus with hot solvent. The filtered solution is allowed to cool. As the solvent cools to room temperature the substance should crystallise out. The crystals are then collected by filtration under reduced pressure.

Sometimes crystallisation does not happen. There are a couple of possible remedies. First, there may be too much solvent, so some has to be evaporated off and the cooling process repeated. Alternatively, crystallisation is aided by scratching the side of the flask. This process has the touch of magic surrounding it. By scratching the side of a glass flask with a metal spatula or a glass rod, crystals can be made to appear. To aid the crystallisation process an ice-water cooling bath for the flask can be used. However, the slower the crystallisation process, the better the crystals.

It may be necessary to repeat the recrystallisation process more than once to obtain a pure sample of the substance. If an oil forms instead of crystals then it has to be redissolved and the process, started again.

Melting point and boiling point

Pure solids have sharp melting points and melt over ranges of 1–2 °C. The melting point can be used to determine how pure the solid is. The melting point can be measured using a melting point apparatus.

Measuring melting points

There are several different types of apparatus but they all work on the same principle. A melting point tube is made by sealing a glass capillary tube at one end. A few crushed crystals are added to the unsealed end of the tube (they can be crushed conveniently on a porcelain tile using a spatula). To get the crystals to the bottom of the tube, the sealed end is gently tapped on the top of a table. The tube is place in the apparatus and the temperature is slowly raised. The temperature at which the solid melts is then recorded.

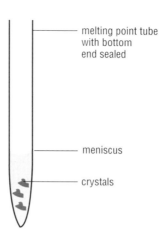

melting point tube with bottom end sealed

meniscus

crystals

Figure 3.22 *A typical melting point apparatus. The melting point is the temperature at which the first complete meniscus forms as the substance melts. The photograph shows crystals within the chamber of a melting point apparatus.*

Boiling points and purity

Pure liquids have short boiling ranges of 1–2°C. You can measure the boiling point of a liquid using the apparatus used for refluxing. A thermometer is placed in the vapour above the boiling liquid. Heat the liquid until it is refluxing steadily. Record the temperature of the vapour above the boiling liquid.

 3 How can you check the purity of (i) liquid ethyl ethanoate and (ii) solid 1-amino-4-bromobenzene?

The purity of a liquid is indicated by its boiling point. Impure samples boil below the literature value and over a wider temperature range.

Quantities, yields and scaling up

Quantity and yield

Balanced chemical equations are used to calculate quantities of reactants and theoretical yields of products. A **theoretical yield** is the quantity that would be obtained if there was complete conversion of reactants to products.

The **actual yield** is the quantity you obtain in the preparation. The efficiency of the preparation is given by the percentage yield:

$$\text{Percentage yield} = \frac{\text{actual yield of product}}{\text{theoretical yield of product}} \times 100\%$$

No reaction gives a 100% yield. Many organic reactions can give yields in the range 50–80%. Lower yields are due to competing reactions and the loss of material when transferring substances or separating products from reaction mixtures.

For preparations involving more than one reaction, the overall percentage yield is accumulative, worked out from the yield of each individual reaction. Consider a preparation with three reactions. Say the yield of the first is 50%, the second is 80% and the third is 60%. Then the overall percentage yield will be:

$(\frac{50}{100} \times \frac{80}{100} \times \frac{60}{100}) = \frac{24}{100}$ i.e. 24%

The concept of percentage yield also applies to extracting a substance from a natural source. A plant may contain a certain amount of a therapeutic compound, but only a percentage of it can be extracted.

 4 10g of calcium carbonate decomposes on heating to give 5.1g of calcium oxide. What is the yield of the reaction?

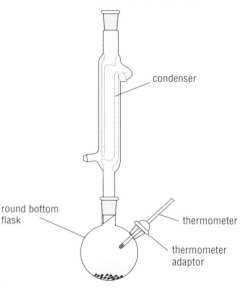

condenser

round bottom flask

thermometer

thermometer adaptor

Figure 3.23 *When measuring a boiling point remember to add anti-bumping granules to the flask and heat the liquid slowly and gently.*

▶ Chemical equations and calculations, page 70

5 A two-step route to a product has reaction yields of 76% and 55%, while a three-step route has yields of 85%, 75% and 65%. Which route should give the highest overall yield?

Scaling up

Most laboratory preparations give quantities of product measured in grams. Once perfected, a laboratory scale preparation of a new substance must be *scaled up* to production levels. This may mean a few kilograms, but also tonnes in the case of many substances.

It may be easy to transfer a small quantity of solid using a spatula, but how could this transfer be carried out when tonnes of solid are being used? This is the sort of question you need to think about when considering scaling up to production scale.

Key considerations when scaling up a laboratory preparation to production quantities are:

- the apparatus
- the transfer of material
- heating
- use or disposal of co-products
- formation of side products
- disposal of effluent.

Assignment trigger

Weedkillers

Weedkillers are readily available from garden centres and DIY stores.

What are the active ingredients?
How are they obtained?
What instructions and warnings accompany them?
What regulates their use?
How is their effectiveness determined?

If a practical assignment is developed, it is essential that a risk assessment is made and checked by your teacher/lecturer.

Could lead to possible assignments relating to Units 3 and 4.

Apparatus

In the laboratory it is easy to weigh solids, measure volumes of liquids using measuring cylinders, separate mixtures by filtration, stir reaction mixtures and so on. This is because of the small quantities involved. But how easy will it be to stir kilograms of solid in the bottom of a flask? How can 1000 dm^3 of a hot solution be filtered? Must a mixture be separated or could it be used for the next reaction step as it is?

For any preparative route you should consider all apparatus used and identify where possible problems could occur if the reaction is scaled up.

Transfer of materials

Pouring a liquid from one vessel to another or using a spatula to transfer a solid are straightforward laboratory operations on a small scale. However, transfer on a large scale is often not easy, particularly if solids are involved. Production methods are designed to minimise such transfers.

Heating

There are two problems with heating reaction mixtures on a large scale. It is often difficult to heat mixtures uniformly and it is always expensive. It is also costly to maintain reactions at low temperatures, as is sometimes required.

Can an alternative reagent be found which does not require heating or cooling? Can the temperature change be controlled by adding the reactants more slowly or in a different order? After considering the options it may be that heating or cooling is still necessary. The problem then becomes one for the chemical engineer – to design a chemical plant to overcome these problems.

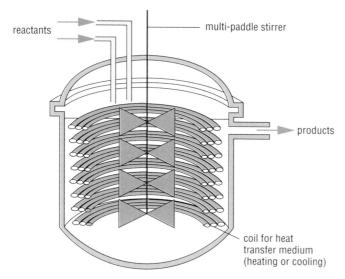

Figure 3.25 *This stirred flow reactor, shown here in cross-section, is used for many large scale reactions. It is designed to ensure efficient mixing and even heating or cooling.*

Products and effluent

As well as the main product, most reactions give co-products. What will happen to the co-products? Do they have a potential use? Often unreacted substances remain. Is it economical to recover and recycle them (use them again)? Substances which do not have any further use must be safely disposed of. These are the *effluent*.

Sometimes, especially with organic reactions, side products also form. These arise from other reactions which can occur within the reaction mixture. Reaction conditions are controlled to minimise such reactions.

▶ Database of reactions of inorganic compounds, page 153

▶ Database of reactions of organic compounds, page 156

Types of chemical reactions

There are millions of possible chemical reactions. It is impossible to memorise them all so chemists group them by type, using common characteristics. This enables chemists to use reaction type when selecting reactions to use in the synthesis of a compound.

Assignment trigger

Colour

Dyes and pigments add colour to the world.

What products contain dyes and pigments?
What chemicals are used for colouring?
How are they made?
Are they extracted from naturally-occurring materials
or made in the laboratory?
Can you make them in the laboratory?
What makes some dyes more suitable for certain applications than others?

If a practical assignment is developed, it is essential that a risk assessment is made and checked by your teacher/lecturer.

Could lead to possible assignments relating to Units 3 and 4.

Acid-base reactions

An acid and a base react to give a salt and water only.

An **acid** is a substance which dissolves in water to give a solution of hydrated hydrogen ions, $H^+(aq)$, also called oxonium ions. For example,

$$HCl(g) + aq \rightarrow H^+(aq) + Cl^-(aq)$$

hydrogen   oxonium   chloride
chloride   ions   ions

A base is a substance which reacts with an acid to give a salt and water only. For example,

$$ZnO(s) + 2HCl(aq) \rightarrow ZnCl_2(aq) + H_2O(l)$$

zinc   hydrochloric   zinc   water
oxide   acid   chloride

$$NaOH(aq) + HNO_3(aq) \rightarrow NaNO_3(aq) + H_2O(l)$$

sodium   nitric   sodium   water
hydroxide   acid   nitrate

Bases which are soluble in water are called **alkalis**. They dissolve in water to give hydrated hydroxide ions, $OH^-(aq)$. For example,

$$NaOH(s) + aq \rightarrow Na^+(aq) + OH^-(aq)$$

sodium   sodium   hydroxide
hydroxide   ions   ions

Some acids and alkalis dissociate completely into ions when put into water. They are called strong acids or strong alkalis. Others do not. Instead an equilibrium mixture of ions and undissociated molecules forms. These are called weak acids or weak alkalis. For example,

$$CH_3COOH(l) + aq \rightleftharpoons CH_3COO^-(aq) + H^+(aq)$$
ethanoic acid   ethanoate ions   oxonium ions

$$NH_3(g) + aq \rightarrow NH_3(aq)$$
ammonia   aqueous ammonia

$$NH_3(aq) + H_2O(l) \rightleftharpoons NH_4^+(aq) + OH^-(aq)$$
ammonia   water   ammonium ions   hydroxide ions

Whether strong or weak, acids and alkalis still react to give a salt and water only. For example:

$$CH_3COOH(aq) + NaOH(aq) \rightarrow CH_3COONa(aq) + H_2O(l)$$
ethanoic acid   sodium   sodium ethanoate   water
               hydroxide

A more sophisticated definition is that an acid is a proton donor and a base is a proton acceptor. It is useful to use the terms *Lowry-Brønsted acids and bases* to differentiate between this definition and the simple one.

Redox reactions

In a **redox** reaction, oxidation and reduction reactions occur simultaneously. The term redox comes from *reduction-oxidation*.

    There are a number of definitions of redox in use. We will consider some of them now.

> **In a redox reaction, oxidation and reduction reactions occur simultaneously.**

Gain or loss of oxygen

A simple definition of oxidation is gain of oxygen. Reduction is loss of oxygen.

    When a substance reacts with oxygen, that substance is said to be oxidised since it has 'gained' oxygen. Burning natural gas (methane) is a good example:

$$CH_4(g) + 2O_2(g) \rightarrow CO_2(g) + 2H_2O(l)$$
methane   oxygen   carbon   water
                    dioxide

Here, both carbon and hydrogen in methane have 'gained' oxygen.

    Similarly, the rusting of iron is a redox reaction. The iron is oxidised:

$$4Fe(s) + 3O_2(g) \rightarrow 2Fe_2O_3(s)$$
iron   oxygen   iron(III) oxide

In the following reaction, copper(II) oxide has been reduced because it has lost oxygen. The hydrogen has gained oxygen so it has been oxidised.

$$CuO(s) + H_2(g) \rightarrow Cu(s) + H_2O(l)$$
copper(II)   hydrogen   copper water
oxide

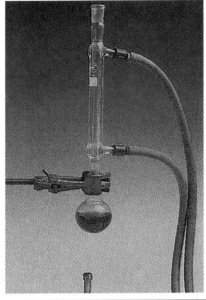

Figure 3.26 *Ethanol is converted to ethanoic acid if refluxed with potassium dichromate(VI) in dilute sulphuric acid.*

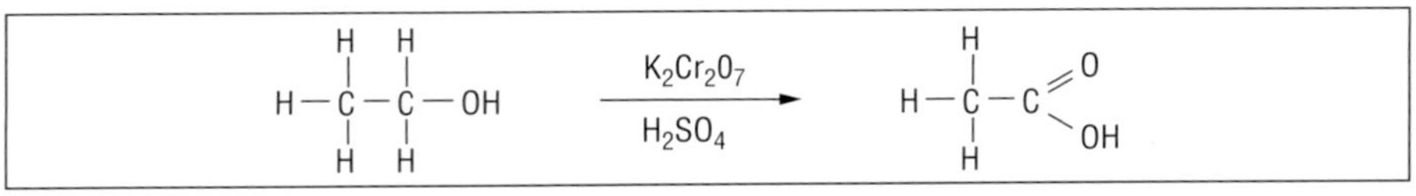

Figure 3.27
When ethanol is converted into ethanoic acid it can be said to have gained oxygen. Therefore it has been oxidised. Chromium is reduced from dichromate(VI) to chromium(III).

$$H-\underset{\underset{H}{|}}{\overset{\overset{H}{|}}{C}}-\underset{\underset{H}{|}}{\overset{\overset{H}{|}}{C}}-OH \quad \xrightarrow[\text{H}_2\text{SO}_4]{\text{K}_2\text{Cr}_2\text{O}_7} \quad H-\underset{\underset{H}{|}}{\overset{\overset{H}{|}}{C}}-C\overset{\displaystyle O}{\underset{\displaystyle OH}{<}}$$

Redox reactions may be defined as those which involve:

- gain (oxidation) or loss (reduction) of oxygen
- loss (oxidation) or gain (reduction) of hydrogen
- loss (oxidation) or gain (reduction) of electrons

Electron transfer

Redox reactions may be defined as those which involve the transfer of electrons. **A substance which loses electrons is oxidised. One which gains electrons is reduced.** This definition takes on board the simpler 'loss of oxygen' definition described above.

It is helpful to think of electron transfer reactions as consisting of two half-reactions. For example, consider the reaction:

$$Zn(s) + Cu^{2+}(aq) \rightarrow Zn^{2+}(aq) + Cu(s)$$
zinc   copper(II) ions   zinc(II) ions   copper

Electrons are transferred from zinc to copper(II) ions. We can represent this with two half-equations:

Oxidation half-equation: $Zn(s) \rightarrow Zn^{2+}(aq) + 2e^-$

Reduction half-equation: $Cu^{2+}(aq) + 2e^- \rightarrow Cu(s)$

Adding these gives the full equation for the reaction, with the electrons (e^-) cancelling out.

Another example to illustrate this is:

$$2Fe^{2+}(aq) + Cl_2(g) \rightarrow 2Fe^{3+}(aq) + 2Cl^-(aq)$$
iron(II) ions   chlorine   iron(III) ions   chloride ions

Oxidation half-equation: $2Fe^{2+}(aq) \rightarrow 2Fe^{3+}(aq) + 2e^-$

Reduction half-equation: $Cl_2(g) + 2e^- \rightarrow 2Cl^-(aq)$

Redox reactions involving electron transfer can be represented by half-equations. One shows the oxidation (loss of electrons). The other shows the reduction (gain of electrons).

Hydrolysis and dehydration

Hydrolysis reactions involve breaking covalent bonds in compounds by reaction with water. Often an acid or alkali is used as a catalyst. Hydrolysis reactions often used in the preparation of compounds include:

- the hydrolysis of covalent inorganic chlorides to give oxides or hydroxides, for example

$$TiCl_4(l) \ + \ 2H_2O(l) \ \rightarrow \ TiO_2(s) \ + \ 4HCl(g)$$
titanium   water   titanium   hydrogen
tetrachloride   oxide   chloride

$$AlCl_3(s) \quad + \quad 3H_2O(l) \ \rightarrow \ Al(OH)_3(s) \ + \ 3HCl(g)$$
aluminium   water   aluminium   hydrogen
chloride   hydroxide   chloride

- halogenoalkanes to give alcohols, for example

$$CH_3CH_2CH_2I \ + \ OH^- \ \rightarrow \ CH_3CH_2CH_2OH \ + \ I^-$$
1-iodopropane   hydroxide ions   propan-1-ol   iodide ions

- esters, acid chlorides and amides to give carboxylic acids, for example

$$CH_3COOCH_3 \ + \ H_2O \ \rightarrow \ CH_3COOH \ + \ CH_3OH$$
methyl ethanoate   water   ethanoic acid   methanol

$$CH_3COCl \quad + \quad H_2O \ \rightarrow \ CH_3COOH \ + \ HCl$$
ethanoyl chloride   water   ethanoic acid   hydrogen chloride

$$CH_3CONH_2 \ + \ H_2O \ \rightarrow \ CH_3COOH \ + \ NH_3$$
ethanamide   water   ethanoic acid   ammonia

Dehydration means loss of water. Commonly in organic chemistry it describes reactions in which the elements of water are removed from a larger molecule. For example,

$$CH_3CH_2OH \ \rightarrow \ CH_2{=}CH_2 \ + \ H_2O$$
ethanol   ethene   water

$$2CH_3COOH \ \rightarrow \ (CH_3CO)_2O \ + \ H_2O$$
ethanoic acid   ethanoic anhydride   water

Hydrolysis reactions involve breaking covalent bonds in compounds by reaction with water. The reacting species are either water molecules or, more often, hydroxide ions.

$$CH_3CONH_2 \rightarrow CH_3CN + H_2O$$
ethanamide ethanenitrile water

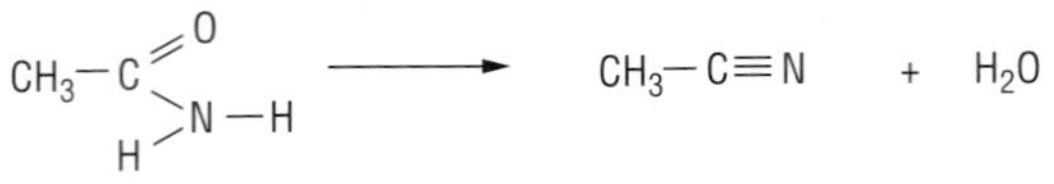

$$CH_3-C{\stackrel{\displaystyle O}{\underset{\displaystyle N-H}{}}} \longrightarrow CH_3-C\equiv N + H_2O$$

Dehydration also describes the loss of water from hydrated salts. For example:

$$CuSO_4.5H_2O(s) \rightarrow CuSO_4(s) + 5H_2O(l)$$
copper(II) anhydrous water
sulphate-5-water copper(II) sulphate

Dehydration reactions involve the loss of water from a compound.

Substitution, addition and elimination

Substitution

In a **substitution** reaction, one atom or group of atoms in a molecule is replaced (substituted) by another atom or group of atoms.

Substitution reactions are often used to prepare compounds. They include:

- substitution of a halogen atom in halogenoalkanes, for example

$$CH_3CH_2Br + CN^- \rightarrow CH_3CH_2CN + Br^-$$
bromoethane cyanide propanenitrile bromide ions
ions

- hydrolysis reactions (described above)
- ligand substitution in co-ordination compounds.

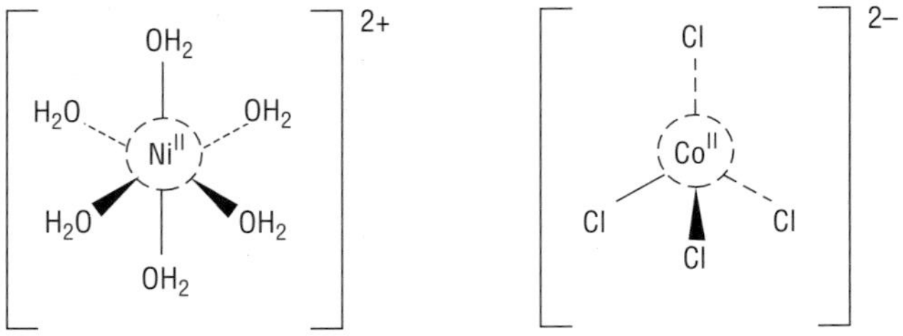

hexaaquanickel (II) ion   tetrachlorocobaltate (II) ion

Figure 3.28 A co-ordination compound consists of a central metal ion surrounded by other ions or molecules (called ligands) which are bonded to it. Often this cluster carries an overall charge and is called a complex ion.

Examples of ligand substitution;

$$[Ni(H_2O)_6]^{2+}(aq) + 6NH_3(aq) \rightarrow [Ni(NH_3)_6]^{2+}(aq) + 6H_2O(l)$$
(water ligands substituted by ammonia ligands)

$$[Co(H_2O)_6]^{2+}(aq) + 4Cl^-(aq) \rightarrow [CoCl_4]^{2-}(aq) + 6H_2O(l)$$
(water ligands substituted by chloride ligands)

Addition

In **addition** reactions, a small molecule combines with (adds to) a molecule containing a double or triple bond. They include

- addition of hydrogen

$$CH_2{=}CH_2 \quad + \quad H_2 \quad \rightarrow \quad CH_3CH_3$$

ethene   hydrogen   ethane

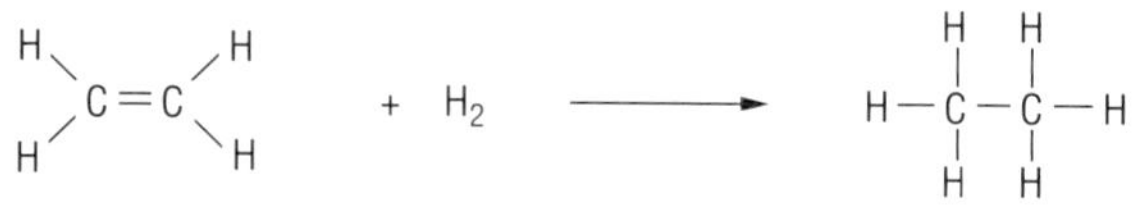

$$(CH_3)_2C{=}O + \quad H_2 \quad \rightarrow \quad (CH_3)_2CHOH$$

propanone   hydrogen   propan-2-ol

Addition of hydrogen is also called *reduction*.

- addition of HX, where X = Cl, Br, I, CN, OH

$$CH_3CH{=}CH_2 + HX \rightarrow CH_3CHXCH_3$$
$$CH_3CHO + HX \longrightarrow CH_3CH(OH)X$$

Addition of water (in which case X = OH) is also called *hydration*.
   Polymerisation of alkenes is also an example of *addition*.

Elimination

In **elimination** reactions, a small molecule is removed (eliminated) from a large molecule leaving a double or triple bond. They include

- elimination of hydrogen (also called dehydrogenation)

$$CH_3CH_2CH_3 \rightarrow CH_3CH{=}CH_2 \quad + \quad H_2$$

propane   propene   hydrogen

- elimination of water (also called *dehydration*)

$$CH_3CH_2CH_2OH \quad \rightarrow \quad CH_3CH{=}CH_2 + H_2O$$

propan-1-ol   propene   water

$$CH_3CH_2CONH_2 \rightarrow CH_3CH_2CN + H_2O$$

propanamide   propanenitrile   water

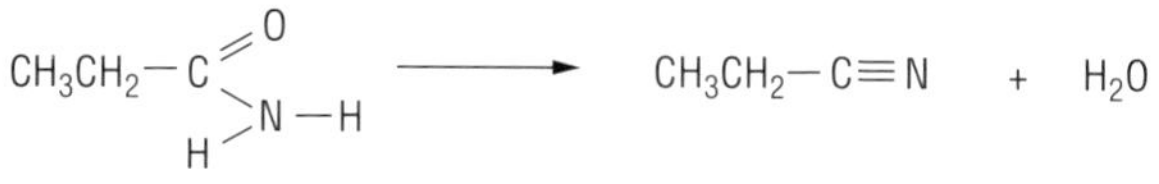

Condensation reactions

In condensation reactions two or more molecules react together with the elimination of a smaller molecule such as water. Often these reactions are addition reactions followed by an elimination reaction. Examples useful in the preparation of compounds include:

A molecule undergoes
- *substitution* when an atom or group of atoms are replaced in it
- *addition* when a small molecule is added to it
- *elimination* when a small molecule is removed from it.

- esterification, where a carboxylic acid and an alcohol combine to form an ester with the elimination of water, for example

$$CH_3COOH + CH_3OH \rightleftharpoons CH_3COOCH_3 + H_2O$$

ethanoic acid   methanol   methyl ethanoate   water

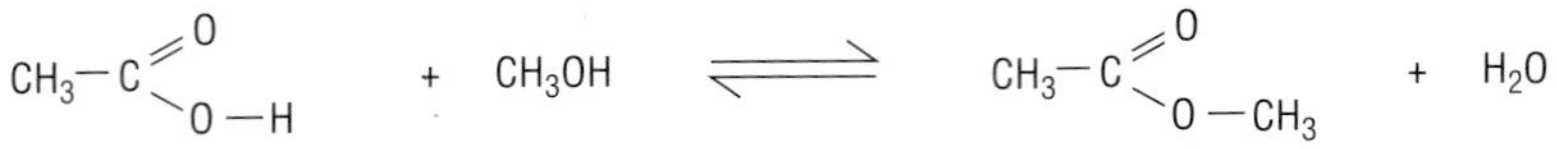

Esters can also be formed by the reaction of acid chlorides or acid anhydrides with alcohols, for example

$$CH_3COCl + CH_3CH_2OH \rightarrow CH_3COOCH_2CH_3 + HCl$$

ethanoyl chloride   ethanol   ethyl ethanoate   hydrogen chloride

$$(CH_3CO)_2O + CH_3OH \rightarrow CH_3COOCH_3 + CH_3COOH$$

ethanoic anhydride   methanol   methyl ethanoate   ethanoic acid

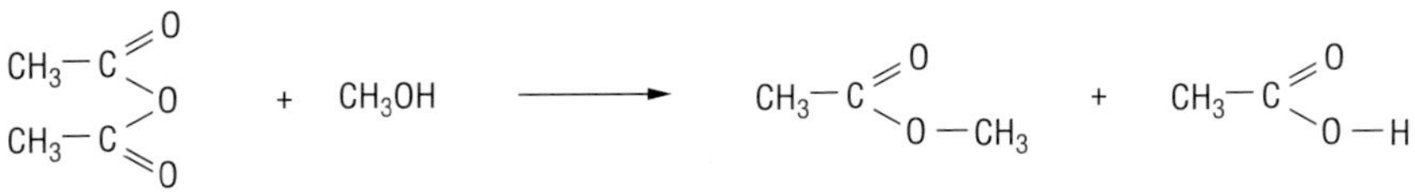

- amide formation, where a carboxylic acid and an amine combine to form an amide with the elimination of water, for example

$$CH_3COOH + CH_3NH_2 \rightarrow CH_3CONHCH_3 + H_2O$$

ethanoic acid   aminomethane   N-methyl ethanamide   water

Amides can also be formed by the reaction of acid chlorides or acid anhydrides with amines, for example:

$$CH_3CH_2COCl + CH_3CH_2NH_2 \rightarrow CH_3CH_2CONHCH_2CH_3 + HCl$$

propanoyl chloride   aminoethane   N-ethyl propanamide   hydrogen chloride

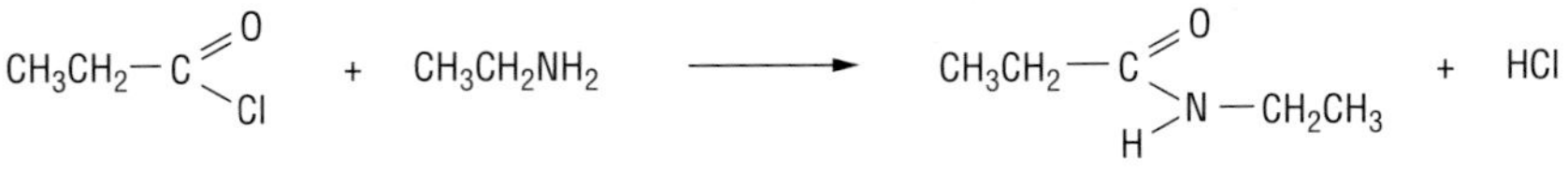

Q 6 Classify the following reactions:
(a) $CuO(s) + Mg(s) \rightarrow Cu(s) + MgO(s)$
(b) $CH_3C \equiv CH + 2H_2 \rightarrow CH_3CH_2CH_3$
(c) $CH_3COONH_4 \rightarrow CH_3CONH_2 + H_2O$
(d) $2CuSO_4(aq) + 4KI(aq) \rightarrow 2CuI(s) + 2K_2SO_4(aq) + I_2(s)$
(e) $BrCH_2CH_2Br(l) + Mg(s) \rightarrow MgBr_2(s) + CH_2 = CH_2(g)$

Database of reactions of inorganic compounds

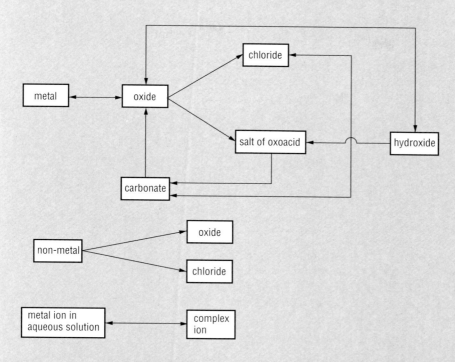

Figure 3.29 *Some routes for the preparation of inorganic compounds. You need to check to see if a particular reaction actually works in practice.*

▶ Nomenclature: naming compounds, page 15

OXIDES

Most oxides can be formed by direct combination of the heated element with oxygen. These are redox reactions.

$4M(s) + O_2(g) \rightarrow 2M_2O(s)$ M = Na, K (sometimes complex oxides e.g. Na_2O_2, K_2O_2 and KO_2 are formed in a plentiful supply of oxygen)

$2M(s) + O_2(g) \rightarrow 2MO(s)$ M = Mg, Ca, Co, Ni, Cu, Zn

$4M(s) + 3O_2(g) \rightarrow 2M_2O_3(s)$ M = Al, Fe

$S(s) + O_2(g) \rightarrow SO_2(g)$

$4P(s) + 3O_2(g) \rightarrow 2P_2O_3(s)$

$4P(s) + 5O_2(g) \rightarrow 2P_2O_5(s)$

$Si(s) + O_2(g) \rightarrow SiO_2(s)$

Metal oxides can also be formed by the thermal decomposition of metal hydroxides (e.g. $M(OH)_2$), metal nitrates (e.g. $M(NO_3)_2$) and metal carbonates (e.g. MCO_3).

$M(OH)_2(s) \rightarrow MO(s) + H_2O(g)$ M = Mg, Ca, Cu, Sn

$2M(OH)_3(s) \rightarrow M_2O_3(s) + 3H_2O(g)$ M = Al, Fe

$2M(NO_3)_2(s) \rightarrow 2MO(s) + 4NO_2(g) + O_2(g)$ M = Mg, Ca, Co, Ni, Cu, Zn, Sn

$MCO_3(s) \rightarrow MO(s) + CO_2(g)$ M = Mg, Ca, Fe, Co, Ni, Cu, Zn, Sn

HYDROXIDES

Some metal hydroxides can be prepared by the reaction of metals with water.

$2M(s) + 2H_2O(l) \rightarrow 2MOH(aq) + H_2(g)$ M = Na, K

$M(s) + 2H_2O(l) \rightarrow M(OH)_2(aq) + H_2(g)$ M = Mg, Ca

Other metal hydroxides can be prepared by the reaction of the metal ion with hydroxide ions.

$M^{2+}(aq) + 2OH^-(aq) \rightarrow M(OH)_2(s)$ M = Mg, Ca, Fe, Co, Ni, Cu, Zn, Sn
$M^{3+}(aq) + 3OH^-(aq) \rightarrow M(OH)_3(s)$ M = Al, Fe

Halides

The halides of most elements can be formed by the direct combination of the element with halogens. These are redox reactions. The element is oxidised and the halogen reduced. With chlorine, the chloride usually forms with the element in its highest oxidation number.

$2M(s) + Cl_2(g) \rightarrow 2MCl(s)$ M = Na, K
$M(s) + Cl_2(g) \rightarrow MCl_2(s)$ M = Mg, Ca, Co, Ni, Cu, Zn
$2M(s) + 3Cl_2(g) \rightarrow M_2Cl_6(s)$ M = Al, Fe
$M(s) + 2Cl_2(g) \rightarrow MCl_4(l)$ M = Sn, Ti

$2S(s) + Cl_2(g) \rightarrow S_2Cl_2(l)$
$2P(s) + 3Cl_2(g) \rightarrow 2PCl_3(l)$
$2P(s) + 5Cl_2(g) \rightarrow 2PCl_5(s)$
$Si(s) + 2Cl_2(g) \rightarrow SiCl_4(s)$

An alternative route is to pass hydrogen chloride gas over the heated element. The chloride usually forms with the element with a lower oxidation number.

$2M(s) + 2HCl(g) \rightarrow 2MCl(s) + H_2(g)$ M = Na, K
$M(s) + 2HCl(g) \rightarrow MCl_2(s) + H_2(g)$ M = Mg, Ca, Fe, Co, Ni, Cu, Zn, Sn
$2Al(s) + 6HCl(g) \rightarrow Al_2Cl_6(s) + 3H_2(g)$

A third method for making chlorides is to use hydrochloric acid in an acid-base reaction. The base can be the metal oxide or metal hydroxide. Metals or metal carbonate can also be used. To use this method the chloride must be soluble in water.

$M_2O(s) + 2HCl(aq) \rightarrow 2MCl(aq) + H_2O(l)$ M= Na, K
$MO(s) + 2HCl(aq) \rightarrow MCl_2(aq) + H_2O(l)$ M = Mg, Ca, Fe, Co, Ni, Cu, Zn, Sn
$M_2O_3(s) + 6HCl(aq) \rightarrow 2MCl_3(aq) + 3H_2O(l)$ M = Al, Fe

$MOH(aq) + HCl(aq) \rightarrow MCl(aq) + H_2O(l)$ M = Na, K
$M(OH)_2(s) + 2HCl(aq) \rightarrow MCl_2(aq) + 2H_2O(l)$ M = Mg, Ca, Fe, Co, Ni, Cu, Zn
$Fe(OH)_3(s) + 3HCl(aq) \rightarrow FeCl_3(aq) + 3H_2O(l)$

$M_2CO_3(s) + 2HCl(aq) \rightarrow 2MCl(aq) + CO_2(g) + H_2O(l)$ M = Na, K
$MCO_3(s) + 2HCl(aq) \rightarrow MCl_2(aq) + CO_2(g) + H_2O(l)$ M = Mg, Ca, Fe, Co, Ni, Cu, Zn, Sn

Chlorides can also be made by the redox reaction between metals and hydrochloric acid. The reaction is slow in the case of nickel and cobalt.

$M(s) + 2HCl(aq) \rightarrow MCl_2(aq) + H_2(g)$ M = Mg, Ca, Fe, Co, Ni, Zn, Sn

Many elements have more than one chloride. For example iron forms iron(II) chloride, $FeCl_2$ and iron(III) chloride, $FeCl_3$. These can be interconverted and are examples of redox reactions.

$2FeCl_2(aq) + Cl_2(g) \rightarrow 2FeCl_3(aq)$

$2FeCl_3(aq) + SO_2(aq) + 2H_2O(l) \rightarrow 2FeCl_2(aq) + H_2SO_4(aq) + 2HCl(aq)$

SULPHATES AND HYDROGENSULPHATES

Metal sulphates (e.g. MSO_4) can be prepared by the reaction of the metal, metal oxide, metal hydroxide or metal carbonate with dilute sulphuric acid providing the sulphate is soluble in water.

$M(s) + H_2SO_4(aq) \rightarrow M_2SO_4(aq) + H_2(g)$ M = Mg, Ca, Fe, Co, Ni, Zn, Sn

$MO(s) + H_2SO_4(aq) \rightarrow MSO_4(aq) + H_2O(l)$ M = Mg, Ca, Fe, Co, Ni, Cu, Zn, Sn

$M_2O_3(s) + 6H_2SO_4(aq) \rightarrow 2M_2(SO_4)_3(aq) + 3H_2O(l)$ M = Al, Fe

$SnO_2(s) + 2H_2SO_4(aq) \rightarrow Sn(SO_4)_2(aq) + 2H_2O(l)$

If the alkali is in excess, you get the sulphate

$2MOH(aq) + H_2SO_4(aq) \rightarrow M_2SO_4(aq) + 2H_2O(l)$ M = Na, K

while if the acid is in excess you get the hydrogensulphate (e.g. $MHSO_4$)

$MOH(aq) + H_2SO_4(aq) \rightarrow MHSO_4(aq) + H_2O(l)$ M = Na, K

$M(OH)_2(s) + H_2SO_4(aq) \rightarrow MSO_4(aq) + 2H_2O(l)$ M = Mg, Fe, Co, Ni, Cu, Zn

$2Fe(OH)_3(s) + 3H_2SO_4(aq) \rightarrow Fe_2(SO_4)_3(aq) + 3H_2O(l)$

$M_2CO_3(s) + H_2SO_4(aq) \rightarrow M_2SO_4(aq) + CO_2(g) + H_2O(l)$ M = Na, K

$MCO_3(s) + H_2SO_4(aq) \rightarrow MSO_4(aq) + CO_2(g) + H_2O(l)$ M = Mg, Fe, Co, Ni, Cu, Zn

Insoluble sulphates can be prepared by reaction of the metal ions with sulphate ions.

$Ba^{2+}(aq) + SO_4^{2-}(aq) \rightarrow BaSO_4(s)$

NITRATES

Metal nitrates (e.g. MNO_3) can be prepared by the reaction of the metal, metal oxide, metal hydroxide or metal carbonate with dilute nitric acid, $HNO_3(aq)$.

$M(s) + 2HNO_3(aq) \rightarrow M(NO_3)_2(aq) + H_2(g)$ M = Mg, Ca, Fe, Co, Ni, Zn

$3Cu(s) + 8HNO_3(aq) \rightarrow 3Cu(NO_3)_2(aq) + 2NO(g) + 4H_2O(l)$

$M_2O(s) + 2HNO_3(aq) \rightarrow 2MNO_3(aq) + H_2O(l)$ M = Na, K

$MO(s) + 2HNO_3(aq) \rightarrow M(NO_3)_2(aq) + H_2O(l)$ M = Mg, Ca, Co, Ni, Cu, Zn, Sn

$M_2O_3(s) + 6HNO_3(aq) \rightarrow 2M(NO_3)_3(aq) + 3H_2O(l)$ M = Al, Fe

$MOH(aq) + HNO_3(aq) \rightarrow MNO_3(aq) + H_2O(l)$ M = Na, K

$M(OH)_2(s) + 2HNO_3(aq) \rightarrow M(NO_3)_2(aq) + 2H_2O(l)$ M = Mg, Ca, Co, Ni, Cu, Zn

$M(OH)_3(s) + 3HNO_3(aq) \rightarrow M(NO_3)_3(aq) + 3H_2O(l)$ M = Al, Fe

$M_2CO_3(s) + 2HNO_3(aq) \rightarrow 2MNO_3(aq) + CO_2(g) + H_2O(l)$ M = Na, K

$MCO_3(s) + 2HNO_3(aq) \rightarrow M(NO_3)_2(aq) + CO_2(g) + H_2O(l)$ M = Mg, Ca, Co, Ni, Cu, Zn

CARBONATES

Apart from carbonates of metals in Group I of the Periodic Table, all carbonates are insoluble (to varying extents) in water. This means that most carbonates can be prepared by the reaction of the metal ion with carbonate ions.

$M^{2+}(aq) + CO_3^{2-}(aq) \rightarrow MCO_3(s)$ M = Ca, Cu

Group I carbonates can be prepared from the reaction of the metal hydroxide and carbon dioxide.

$MOH(aq) + CO_2(g) \rightarrow MHCO_3(aq)$

$MHCO_3(aq) + MOH (aq) \rightarrow M_2CO_3(aq) + H_2O(l)$ M = Na, K

COMPLEX IONS

A complex ion is one that contains a central metal ion linked to other atoms, ions and molecules (such as NH_3 and H_2O), which are called ligands. Complex ions are mainly formed by transition metals. The complex ions may be prepared by substitution reactions. An aqueous solution of the required ligand is added to an aqueous solution of the metal ion. Water ligands around the hydrated metal ion are replaced by new ligands. For example:

$[Ni(H_2O)_6]^{2+}(aq) + 6NH_3(aq) \rightarrow [Ni(NH_3)_6]^{2+}(aq) + 6H_2O(l)$
hexaaquanickel(II)   ammonia   hexaaminenickel(II)   water

$[Ni(H_2O)_6]^{2+}(aq) + 4CN^-(aq) \rightarrow [Ni(CN)_4]^{2-}(aq) + 6H_2O(l)$
hexaaquanickel(II)   cyanide ions   tetracyanonickelate(II)   water

Database of reactions of organic compounds

In the route maps, R and R[1] are alkyl groups. Although ease of reaction depends on the exact nature of these groups, the reaction conditions given below are generally applicable.

You will need to look in more specialist books if you want more detail or specific reaction conditions.

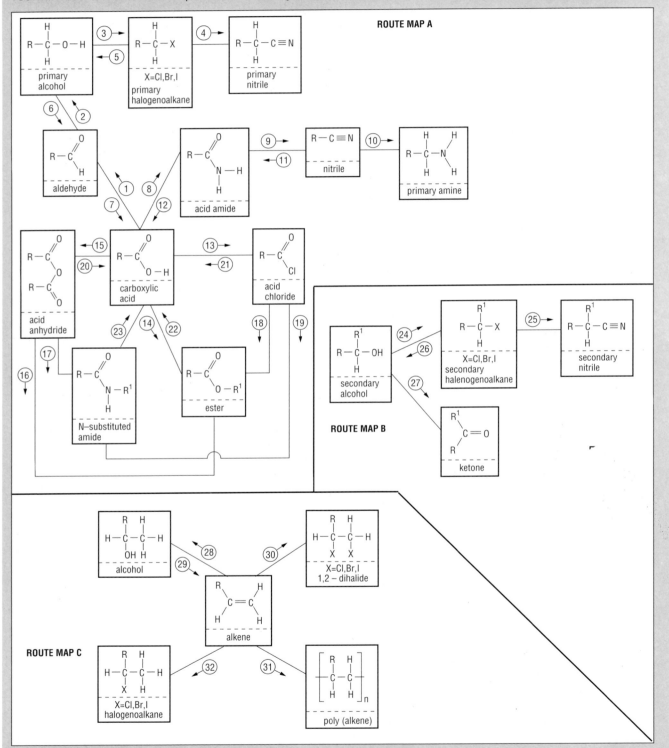

Figure 3.30 *Some routes for the preparation of organic compounds. Conditions for the conversions and types of reaction are found in the database.*

ROUTE MAP A

1 & 2	Carboxylic acid to aldehyde (reaction 1): **reduction**
	Aldehyde to primary alcohol (reaction 2): **reduction**
	Conditions (for reactions 1 and 2): reflux with lithium aluminium hydride, $LiAlH_4$, in ethoxyethane (reaction does not stop at RCHO)
3	Primary alcohol to primary halogenoalkane: **substitution**
	Conditions: phosphorus pentachloride, PCl_5 or sulphur dichloride oxide, $SOCl_2$, at room temperature
4	Primary halogenoalkane to primary nitrile: **substitution**
	Conditions: reflux with potassium cyanide, KCN, in water/ethanol mixture
5	Primary halogenoalkane to primary alcohol: **hydrolysis (substitution)**
	Conditions: reflux with dilute NaOH(aq)
6	Primary alcohol to aldehyde: **oxidation**
	Conditions: heat with potassium dichromate(VI), $K_2Cr_2O_7$, in dilute H_2SO_4 and distil off RCHO as it forms (this process is essential to produce the aldehyde since further oxidation takes place through to the carboxylic acid,
7	Aldehyde to carboxylic acid: **oxidation**
	Conditions: reflux with potassium dichromate(VI), $K_2Cr_2O_7$, in dilute H_2SO_4
8	Carboxylic acid to amide: **substitution**
	Conditions: heat the solid ammonium salt of the carboxylic acid
9	Acid amide to nitrile: **dehydration**
	Conditions: heat with phosphorus pentoxide, P_2O_5
10	Nitrile to primary amine: **reduction**
	Conditions: reflux with sodium in ethanol, or lithium aluminium hydride, $LiAlH_4$, in ethoxyethane
11	Nitrile to acid amide: **hydrolysis**
	Dissolve in concentrated H_2SO_4 and pour into cold water
12	Acid amide to carboxylic acid: **hydrolysis**
	Conditions: reflux with dilute NaOH or dilute H_2SO_4
13	Carboxylic acid to acid chloride: **substitution**
	Conditions: phosphorus pentachloride, PCl_5, or sulphur dichloride oxide, $SOCl_2$, at room temperature
14	Carboxylic acid to ester: **substitution** (esterification)
	Conditions: reflux with R^1OH in presence of a little concentrated H_2SO_4
15	Carboxylic acid to acid anhydride: **dehydration**
	Conditions: heat strongly with phosphorus pentoxide P_2O_5
16	Acid anhydride to ester
	Conditions: warm with R^1OH (reflux if necessary)
17	Acid anhydride to N-substituted amide
	Conditions: warm with R^1NH_2 (reflux if necessary)
18	Acid chloride to ester
	Conditions: R^1OH at room temperature (warm if necessary)
19	Acid chloride to N-substituted amide
	Conditions: R^1NH_2 at room temperature (warm if necessary)
20	Acid anhydride to carboxylic acid: **hydrolysis**
	Conditions: water (warm if necessary)
21	Acid chloride to carboxylic acid: **hydrolysis**
	Conditions: cold water
22	Ester to carboxylic acid: **hydrolysis**
	Conditions: reflux with dilute NaOH or dilute H_2SO_4
23	N-substituted amide to carboxylic acid: **hydrolysis**
	Conditions: reflux with dilute NaOH or dilute H_2SO_4

ROUTE MAP B

24   Secondary alcohol to secondary halogenoalkane: **substitution**
      Conditions: phosphorus pentachloride, PCl_5 or sulphur dichloride oxide, $SOCl_2$, at room
      temperature
25   Secondary halogenoalkane to secondary nitrile: **substitution**
      Conditions: reflux with potassium cyanide, KCN, in water/ethanol mixture
26   Secondary halogenoalkane to secondary alcohol: **hydrolysis** (substitution)
      Conditions: reflux with dilute NaOH
27   Secondary alcohol to ketone: **oxidation**
      Conditions: reflux with potassium dichromate(VI), $K_2Cr_2O_7$, in dilute H_2SO_4

ROUTE MAP C

28   Alkene to alcohol: **hydration** (addition)
      Conditions: concentrated H_2SO_4, followed by water at room temperature
29   Alcohol to alkene: **dehydration** (elimination)
      Conditions: reflux with phosphoric(V) acid, H_3PO_4
30   Alkene to 1,2-dihalide: **addition**
      Conditions: halogen at room temperature
31   Alkene to poly(alkene): **polymerisation** (addition)
      Conditions: Ziegler-Natta catalyst (conditions vary)
32   Alkene to halogenoalkane: **addition**
      Conditions: hydrogen halide at room temperature

Case study

RECYCLING OLD TYRES AND PLASTICS

Oil, gas, minerals and ores are rich sources of chemicals. We rely on these to make countless substances and materials which improve the quality of our lives. However, resources from the Earth's crust are finite. So how can we best manage them? One way is to re-use materials. You are probably familiar with recycling centres for glass, paper, aluminium cans and so on. Plastics and rubber, both of which we use in vast quantities, are difficult to recycle. Many projects have looked at ways of tackling this recycling problem. Here are brief reports on two processes that may help crack the problem.

There's oil in them there plastics

Andy Coghlan

BP CHEMICALS is building a pilot plant that will convert most of the plastic items we throw away into a rich oil from which chemicals companies can synthesise virgin plastics.

BP has shown already that the technology can work at the company's research laboratories at Sunbury-on-Thames, Surrey. Now BP is joining forces with four other major European chemical and oil companies to build a pilot plant at its Grangemouth refinery, on the Firth of Forth, Scotland.

BP's process converts plastic waste into an oil which is very similar to naphtha, the fraction of crude oil from which most plastics are derived. John Brophy, the research general manager at BP Chemicals, explains that typically, chemical companies can 'crack' up to 45 per cent of the hydrocarbons in naphtha into ethylene and propylene, the molecules which are the building blocks of the plastics industry.

'We anticipate getting 80 per cent yields of oil from our process,' says Brophy, 'and this will crack to give the same amounts of ethylene and propylene as you would get from naphtha.' Some 10 to 15 per cent of the remainder will be burnt as a gas to provide the energy to drive the process. 'It's self-sufficient in energy,' he explains.

The key to the process is a vessel containing sand called a 'fluidised bed reactor' in which the plastic waste is cracked at 400 °C to 600 °C into hydrocarbon gases that are condensed to form the oil.

But first, plastic items have to be extracted from household waste, cleaned up and chopped into flakes about 2 centimetres across. They are fed into the reactor where the long polymer chains break down into shorter hydrocarbon chains.

Polyethylene and polypropylene, the commonest plastics found in household waste, break down into paraffins. Polystyrene breaks up into styrene and aromatic molecules. Polyvinyl chloride splits into hydrocarbons and hydrogen chloride, which can be separated off.

Brophy says that hot gases are fed in at the bottom of the reactor and these cause the sand to 'fluidise' like a hot boiling liquid. When the chunks of polymer are fed in, they crack thermally.

'You have very good heat transfer from the sand to the polymer,' adds Brophy. 'It's a very manageable way of dealing with sticky and difficult materials.'

OLD TYRES DON'T DIE, THEY JUST DISSOLVE AWAY

A JAPANESE research group claims to have found a way of banishing the environmental headache of discarded tyres - decomposing them into recyclable components. The need worldwide is enormous: in the US alone, more than 230 million tonnes of used tyres pile up every year. About 80 per cent end up in landfills, while most of the rest are either dumped or burnt.

The researchers use a combination of "supercritical" water, which is at such a high temperature and pressure that its liquid and gas states merge, and sodium hydroxide. The organic components of the tyres can then be re-used in other products.

The technique was developed over the past few years by a research team led by Toshinari Tennoh of the Nishikawa Rubber Company in Hiroshima. The tyres are cut into pieces a few centimetres across and then heated to 400 °C at a pressure of more than 40 atmospheres in a one-molar (about 4 per cent by weight) solution of sodium hydroxide. Under these conditions, water can dissolve organic compounds. After 15 minutes the rubber in the tyres decomposes into an oily mixture of long-chain hydrocarbons. This mixture is separated from the steel and textiles within the tyres, which are then recovered for recycling.

Nishikawa's process can also separate and recover the sulphur added to most tyres in the vulcanisation process that hardens them. The sulphur forms cross-links between the rubber polymer chains, making them more rigid.

As the rubber decomposes during the recycling process, these sulphur crosslinks break and the sulphur is converted to hydrogen sulphide. This gas is then passed over zinc oxide pellets, forming zinc sulphide. No organic sulphur compounds have been detected in the hydrocarbons recovered from the process for recycling.

The advantage of this process is that it goes further than any other in devulcanising the rubber and decomposing it into smaller organic molecules, so more products can be made from them. Other processes are less efficient at removing the sulphur used in vulcanisation.

Rick Gould

Questions

1 What substances can be recovered by the two processes and what chemicals may be obtained from these substances?

2 List the key features of each process. Explain why it is more feasible to carry out the plastics process using conventional laboratory apparatus than it is to carry out the rubber recycling.

A practical idea: You could try to construct a laboratory apparatus to investigate factors which affect the effectiveness and efficiency of the conversion of plastic waste into an oil. Remember to make a risk assessment, and to get it checked by your teacher or lecturer.

3 Amongst the organic compounds which may be obtained from each process are alkenes. Explain, with the aid of equations, how alkanes, halogenoalkanes, alcohols, aldehydes, ketones and carboxylic acids can be made from the alkenes, ethene and propene. Give the name for each type of reaction involved.

Some specific questions

Plastics and oil:

4 Explain the term 'fluidised bed reactor' and try to find some other examples of the use of this kind of reactor.

5 How is naphtha usually obtained?

6 How is naphtha 'cracked' into ethene and propene?

Rubber tyres:

7 Zinc sulphide can be converted back into zinc oxide by heating it strongly in air. It reacts with the oxygen in the air to form zinc oxide and sulphur dioxide.

(a) Write an equation for this reaction.
(b) What uses might be found for the sulphur dioxide that is formed as a co-products?

Case study

GRIGNARD REAGENTS: SCALING UP LABORATORY REACTIONS

The large-scale reactions used in industry are often very different from the methods developed in the laboratory. Scaling up reactions usually involves making the product with simpler reagents, less extreme conditions of temperature or without using inert atmospheres. The yield, rate, costs and safety of the process are important considerations.

The preparation of a Grignard reagent illustrates some of the differences between a laboratory preparation and large-scale manufacture.

$$RX + Mg \longrightarrow R\,Mg\,X$$

where R = alkyl group (e.g. CH_3, C_2H_5)

X = Cl, Br, I

$$R\,Mg\,X + \begin{matrix} R' \\ | \\ C = O \\ | \\ R'' \end{matrix}$$

Step 1 ↓

$$R'' - \overset{R'}{\underset{R}{\overset{|}{\underset{|}{C}}}} - O\,Mg\,X$$

Step 2 ↓ H_2O (dilute acid)

$$R'' - \overset{R'}{\underset{R}{\overset{|}{\underset{|}{C}}}} - OH \;+\; Mg(OH)\,X$$

Illustration 1 Grignard reagents are used extensively in industry. They can be used to convert aldehydes and ketones to alcohols.

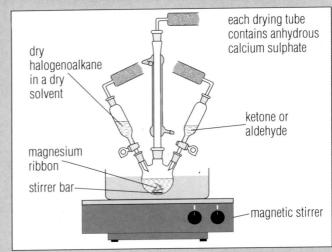

Illustration 2 Laboratory apparatus for making a Grignard reagent and reacting it subsequently with an aldehyde or ketone. Notice the precautions taken to exclude moist air.

Once the Grignard reagent has been formed the aldehyde or ketone can be added. Cooling may be necessary to control the reaction. When complete the reaction is quenched by pouring into cold dilute hydrochloric acid and the product is extracted from the reaction mixture, typically with more ethoxyethane.

Table 1 Comparison of laboratory and large scale Grignard reactions

	Laboratory	Industrial
Solvent	ethoxyethane	tetrahydrofuran
Halogenoalkane	iodoalkane	chloro- or bromoalkane
Catalyst	iodine	secret
Quenching	acid such as dilute hydrochloric acid	acid such as dilute hydrochloric acid

Laboratory scale

On a laboratory scale, a Grignard reagent is made by adding magnesium turnings to an halogenoalkane dissolved in a dry solvent typically ethoxyethane. Grignard reagents react with water. Therefore:
- the solvent and the reagents are dried
- the apparatus is dried
- the reaction is carried out under an inert atmosphere of nitrogen.

The reaction can be started by warming. However, this type of reaction is notoriously difficult to start and so a few crystals of iodine are added as a catalyst. Once started, the exothermic reaction refluxes without further heating. Cooling may be needed to control the reaction.

Industrial scale

Zeneca use Grignard reactions on a large scale. In scaling up the reaction different processes and reagents have been developed. On an industrial scale you cannot use ethoxyethane. Ethoxyethane is flammable and very volatile, making it difficult to recycle. As with all ethers, it tends to form peroxides which may explode. The answer is to find another solvent. Trial and error led to tetrahydrofuran as the preferred solvent.

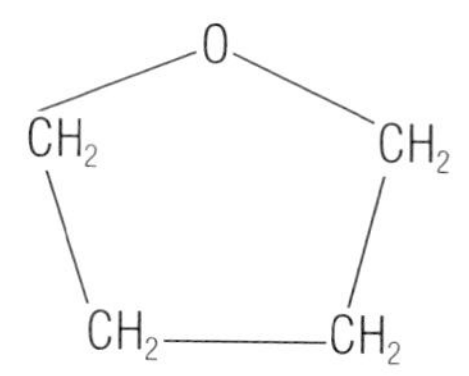

Illustration 3 *Tetrahydrofuran (THF)*

Tetrahydrofuran is an ether and it has to be purified to remove any peroxides, but its other characteristics are ideal. It has a higher boiling point than ethoxyethane.

Just like in the laboratory situation, the reaction is difficult to start. Once started, energy is released and on a large scale it becomes extremely important to control this release. Because the volumes used in the industrial process are larger, the surface area-to-volume ratio of the reaction mixture is smaller than in the laboratory. This means that the reaction mixture has relatively less surface area from which it can lose heat. Therefore cooling arrangements are very important. In this case the condenser in the industrial plant must be designed to cope with the demands that are put upon it and a smooth release of energy helps.

It is important that the solvent does not escape into the atmosphere. The solvent is recovered from the reaction mixtures, purified then re-used. This process makes sound economic sense and protects the environment.

Illustration 4 *The reaction vessel where the main chemical reactions take place.*

Often, because the scaled up route is different from the laboratory one, the efficiencies of the reactions are different. You can predict the effect of changing the temperature, concentration and other conditions, but the effect of using alternative reagents is only found by trial and error. In the case of the Grignard reagent the biggest economy that can be made is to avoid using iodomethane.

Iodomethane is expensive while bromomethane is available from a variety of sources. Chloromethane could be used but it is more difficult to initiate the formation of Grignard reagents from chloroalkanes.

Safety is an important issue. On a larger scale, laboratory operations take on a new perspective. The use of iodine to start the reaction is not favoured because it has been known to cause fires. Other techniques such as scratching the flask or mild heating are possibilities. The technique used by Zeneca is a secret but it allows them to initiate a reaction of 4500 dm^3 in the reactor in one go and safely!

Environmental conditions are also important. To quench the reaction, the mixture has to be pumped into the acidified solution and the magnesium and other solid products separated. The organic layer containing the product is isolated and the aqueous layer treated before discharge. The National Rivers Authority has strict guidelines on what can and cannot be discharged into rivers. Most chemical companies pre-treat all effluent before discharge, so much so that in some cases the water is purer than tap water! Any residues are treated and most tend to be buried in special sites if they cannot be reused.

Questions

1 How do the laboratory and industrial scale preparations differ?

2 What types of reaction are involved (steps 1 and 2) in the preparation of an alcohol from a Grignard reagent and an aldehyde or a ketone?

3 In the laboratory preparation described, explain how the required product could be extracted from the reaction mixture.

4 Carry out a risk assessment for the laboratory preparation described.

5 Why do you think that it is more difficult to make a Grignard reagent starting with chloromethane than with iodomethane?

6 You are asked to make 7.4 g of butan-2-ol in the laboratory. Describe how you would set about this task, giving details of reagents and their quantities and reaction conditions and the safety measures you would take. Where more than one reagent might have been used, give the options you considered and explain your choice.

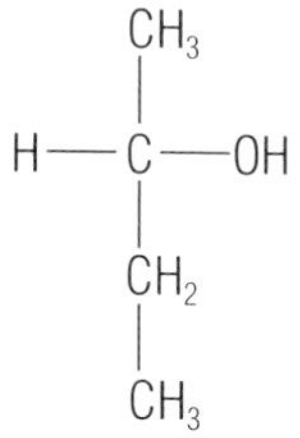

Illustration 5 *Butan-2-ol*

7 What other uses are made of Grignard reagents?

Case study

1,4-AMINOBROMOBENZENE: CHOOSING PREPARATIVE ROUTES

The characteristics of a good preparative route are that it

- has the minimum number of reactions
- uses readily available starting materials
- gives easily purified products
- produces a good yield
- has a low cost.

When more than one route is possible it is not always the true that the minimum number of steps will be the best. Consider the preparation of 1,4-aminobromobenzene (also known commonly as 4-bromophenylamine), an important compound in the manufacture of dyestuffs. It can be prepared from either bromobenzene or aminobenzene. Both of these starting materials are readily available but involve different routes.

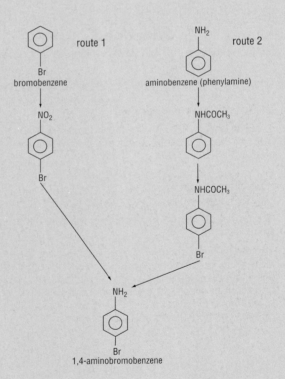

Illustration 1 Caption: Two routes for the preparation of 1,4-aminobromobenzene

ROUTE 1

Two-step route
Starting compound: bromobenzene
Overall yield = 27%

Step 1: Nitration. Bromobenzene and a mixture of concentrated nitric and sulphuric acids are swirled together for 15 minutes and the temperature controlled so that it does not rise above 60°C. Controlling the temperature minimises the amount of side products formed. The mixture is then heated on a water bath for 1 hour. Crystals of 1,4-bromonitrobenzene are produced on cooling and pouring the reaction mixture into ice. Recrystallisation from ethanol/water gives a yield of 58% of product.

Step 2: Reduction. 1,4-bromonitrobenzene is reduced by heating for 1 hour with a tin/concentrated hydrochloric acid mixture. The product is isolated by steam distillation and recrystallised from petroleum ether. The yield is 47%.

ROUTE 2

Three-step route
Starting compound: aminobenzene
Overall yield = 52%

Step 1: Ethanoylation. Aminobenzene is refluxed with ethanoic anhydride for 30 minutes. Crystals form on cooling and recrystallisation from water/ethanol gives a 68% yield.

Step 2: Bromination. Bromine is added to the ethanoylated starting material. Recrystallisation of the product from an ethanol/water mixture gives a 83% yield of product.

Step 3: Hydrolysis. The product from the bromination reaction is refluxed with dilute hydrochloric acid. After neutralisation the crude solid is recrystallised from petroleum ether to give a 93% yield.

Cost

The two-step route (starting with bromobenzene) is five times more expensive than the three-step route (which starts with aminobenzene). Although the two-step route looks shorter on paper, it gives a low yield of 27%. In contrast, the three-step route involves three reactions each of high yield.

For any synthesis it is important not to prejudge which route will be best solely on the basis of the number of steps.

Questions

1 Classify the reactions involved in each route, using this list: acid-base, redox, hydrolysis, dehydration, substitution, elimination, addition, condensation.

2 Carry out a risk assessment for each of the routes described.

3 Use a chemical supplier's catalogue to compare the cost of making 10 g of 1,4-aminobromobenzene by each of the two routes.

4 1,4-aminobromobenzene is used to make dyes. The process involves *diazotisation*. What does this involve? Give the structures and colours of some diazo dyes.

4 Obtain products from organisms

Humans have obtained products from organisms for tens of thousands of years. The living environment provides us with many material, including food, fuels, fibres and medicines. Without our use of other species we could not survive. In this unit we shall concentrate on products obtained from plants and from micro-organisms. To obtain products from plants and micro-organisms, scientists require skills and knowledge in a number of fields including plant breeding and genetic engineering. This allows the commercial performance of the organisms to be improved. Scientists also need to be aware of the economic, environmental, social and ethical implications of using organisms for commercial production.

Figure 4.1 In obtaining products from plants and micro-organisms scientists need to know about plant breeding and genetic engineering. Scientists also need to consider the economic, environmental, social and ethical implications of such work. These identical two-year-old date palms were produced by tissue culture.

The Elements

Element 4.1 Evaluate organisms as sources of useful products

In order to evaluate organisms as sources of useful products you need to:
- describe how materials are produced in plants and micro-organisms
- identify useful products of organisms
- explain how a suitable organism is selected and identify the conditions required for the growth of an organism
- grow the organism under specified conditions, observing safe practice.

Figure 4.2 *For organisms to be valuable sources of useful products, the products themselves must be needed and the organisms must be grown in captivity, or abundant and accessible in the wild. Barley, yeast and hops are the organisms from which these products are made.*

Element 4.2 Investigate the genetic manipulation of organisms to increase production

In order to investigate the way in which organisms can be genetically manipulated, so as to increase their production, you need to:

- describe the principles involved in breeding and selection
- demonstrate the pattern of inheritance in an organism
- describe the role of DNA in the replication of organisms
- describe mechanisms available for the transfer of genes between cells
- describe factors involved in the use of genetic manipulation in commercial production.

▶ What do plant breeders do?, page 184

▶ Patterns of inheritance, page 188

▶ What does DNA do?, page 194

▶ Practicalities of genetic engineering, page 198

Figure 4.3 *Scientists can genetically manipulate organisms, so as to improve their production, by moving genes from one organism to another, or by selectively breeding the organisms. One of the earliest commercial applications of genetic engineering was the production of human insulin used in the treatment of diabetes.*

▶ Why regulate commercial production?, page 201

▶ What regulations exist?, page 202

Element 4.3 Investigate constraints on commercial production from organisms

Finally, it is important to understand the constraints that exist on the commercial use of organisms. To do this you need to :

- explain the need for regulatory controls and the environmental impact of commercial production
- describe the economic, social and ethical considerations involved in commercial production from organisms
- describe the effects of safety regulations on commercial production from organisms.

How do plants and micro-organisms produce materials?

In order to understand the development of products from organisms, you first need to understand how the organisms produce the raw materials.

Production by plants

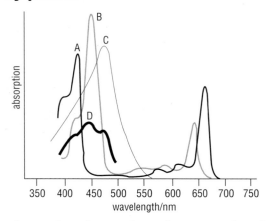

Figure 4.4 Absorption spectra of the main photosynthetic pigments: *A* chlorophyll a; *B* chlorophyll b; *C* xanthophyll; *D* carotene. The most abundant of these pigments is chlorophyll a, a blue-green compound. The pigments found in most plants absorb both blue and red light in the visible spectrum of light, but do not absorb much green light.

Plant leaves get their colour from coloured compounds called *pigments* (see Figure 4.4). Because these pigments mostly reflect green light, rather than absorbing it, plant leaves are usually green.

Q 1 What colour would leaves be if most of the wavelengths in the visible spectrum were absorbed except for those between 600 nm and 650 nm?

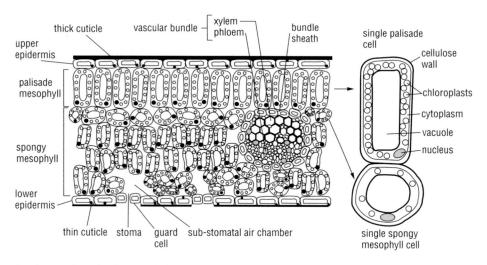

Figure 4.5 Diagrammatic transverse section of a leaf.

Light is absorbed mainly by cells in the *palisade mesophyll* and *spongy mesophyll* of leaves (see Figure 4.5). The various pigments are located in small bi-convex structures called **chloroplasts**. Measuring some 2 μm × 5 μm, these structures are found in the cytoplasm of palisade cells and spongy mesophyll cells. The pigments in the chloroplasts are held on internal membranes (see Figure 4.6). These membranes are arranged so as to spread the pigments out, exposing them as much as possible to the light.

Figure 4.6 Transmission electron micrograph of a chloroplast. Internal membranes are visible and photo-synthetic pigments are held on these. A large central starch grain can also be seen.

The chloroplasts trap the energy from sunlight and use it to join carbon dioxide and water in a series of chemical reactions which can be summarised as follows:

$$nCO_2 \ + \ nH_2O \ \rightarrow \ (CH_2O)_n \ + \ nO_2$$
$$\text{carbon dioxide + water} \ \rightarrow \text{carbohydrate + oxygen}$$

This process is known as **photosynthesis**. You can see that it results in the formation of carbon compounds containing hydrogen atoms and oxygen atoms in the ratio two to one. Such compounds are called **carbohydrates**. Small, soluble carbohydrates are known as **sugars**.

Photosynthesis involves many stages. The first carbohydrate formed is a small sugar with three carbon atoms. From this 3-carbon sugar, a tremendous range of plant compounds can be produced.

- Two 3-carbon sugars joined together give 6-carbon sugars, known as *monosaccharides* (single sugars), such as glucose (see Figure 4.7).
- Two 6-carbon sugars joined together give 12-carbon sugars, known as *disaccharides* (double sugars), such as sucrose. The substance we refer to as sugar in everyday life is sucrose and has the formula $C_{12}H_{22}O_{11}$.

> **Plants produce materials as a result of photosynthesis, a series of chemical reactions which take place in chloroplasts. In these reactions energy from sunlight is used to synthesise carbohydrates from carbon dioxide and water.**

i)   α glucose

ii)   β glucose

Figure 4.7(a) *The two forms of glucose: (i) α glucose; (ii) β glucose.*

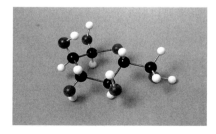

4.7(b) A space-filling model of glucose.

167

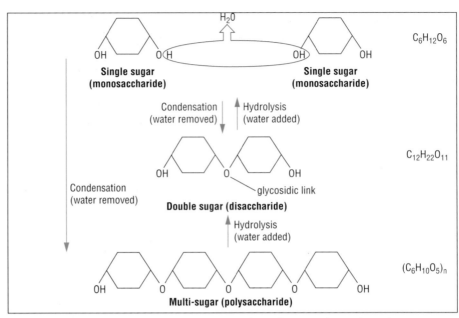

$C_6H_{12}O_6$

Single sugar (monosaccharide)　　　　**Single sugar (monosaccharide)**

Condensation (water removed)　Hydrolysis (water added)

$C_{12}H_{22}O_{11}$

glycosidic link

Condensation (water removed)

Double sugar (disaccharide)

Hydrolysis (water added)

$(C_6H_{10}O_5)_n$

Multi-sugar (polysaccharide)

Figure 4.8 *Removal of water (condensation) from monosaccharides results in the formation of disaccharides and polysaccharides. Addition of water (hydrolysis) reverses these reactions.*

- The addition of successive monosaccharides to a disaccharide gives a *polysaccharide* (see Figure 4.8). **Starch**, a storage compound found, for example, in potato tubers, is an important polysaccharide (see Figure 4.9). So too is **cellulose**, a major component of cell walls (see Figure 4.10).

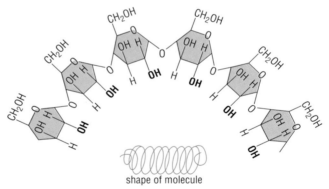

shape of molecule

Figure 4.9 *The structure of starch, a chain of α-glucoses linked by glycosidic bonds*

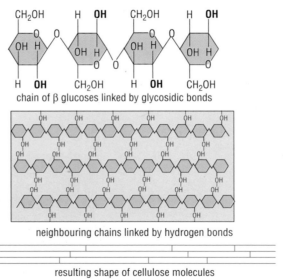

chain of β glucoses linked by glycosidic bonds

neighbouring chains linked by hydrogen bonds

resulting shape of cellulose molecules

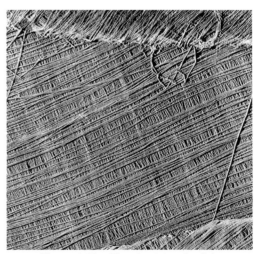

Figure 4.10a *The structure of cellulose*

- Amino acids, which have the formula $RCHNH_2COOH$, are made from a series of reactions which begin with the addition of nitrate, NO_3^-, to sugars. Many amino acids, when joined together, give rise to *polypeptides*. **Proteins** in organisms are formed from polypeptides.
- A great variety of chemical reactions lead to the synthesis of **lipids** – biomolecules that are insoluble in water but dissolve in organic solvents such as ethanol. Fats and oils are lipids. Lipids, like carbohydrates, contain only carbon, hydrogen and oxygen. However, they contain much less oxygen than a carbohydrate of the same mass.

Q 2 Look carefully at Figures 4.9 and 4.10a. Why are starch and cellulose so different in their properties even though they are both polymers of glucose?

Production by micro-organisms

Most micro-organisms are unicellular (one-celled) organisms. There is a tremendous diversity of micro-organisms. One group, which includes bacteria, lack a nucleus and are known as *prokaryotes* (see Figure 4.11). Some micro-organisms, including yeasts, other fungi and algae, have a more complicated internal structures and possess a nucleus (see Figure 4.12). Organisms that possess a nucleus are known as *eukaryotes*.

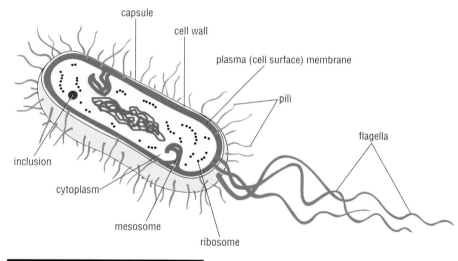

capsule
cell wall
plasma (cell surface) membrane
pili
flagella
inclusion
cytoplasm
mesosome
ribosome

Photosynthesis results in the synthesis of a sugar with three carbon atoms. Plants use this small compound, sometimes in combination with other chemicals, to make sugars, starch, cellulose, proteins and lipids.

Useful products from plants and micro-organisms, page 170

Figure 4.11 The structure of a typical prokaryote. Not all prokaryotes possess pili, flagella or a capsule.

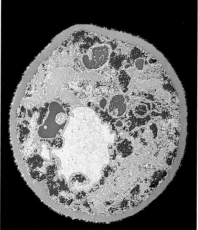

Figure 4.12 False colour transmission electron micrograph of a yeast cell. The large pink area at the lower left is the nucleus. The green shapes are mitochondria (sites of aerobic respiration). The blue structure just to the upper left of the nucleus is a vacuole.

From an industrial point of view, one useful thing about most micro-organisms is that they increase in numbers quickly. Many bacteria have a generation time of only 20 minutes: they double in numbers every 20 minutes. In addition, micro-organisms are often relatively easy to keep in storage until required. These two properties mean that, provided they are given the right conditions for their growth and reproduction, micro-organisms can often be used in industry to make useful products rapidly as and when needed.

▶ Finding the right conditions, page 177

Q 3 From a single bacterium with a generation time of 20 minutes, how many bacteria could be produced after (a) one hour; (b) four hours; (c) twenty-four hours?

The fundamental processes by which micro-organisms produce useful materials are as follows:
- **Biosynthesis** of chemicals that are useful to the cell. These chemicals include proteins, carbohydrates, lipids and the nucleic acids DNA and RNA.
- Growth of the cell.
- Cell division giving rise to two daughter cells, each of which in turn starts to make useful chemicals (i.e. biosynthesis again).

Q 4 Which of these processes happen in plants too?

> **The production of useful materials by micro-organisms relies on biosynthesis, cell growth and cell division.**

Useful products from plants and micro-organisms

The processes by which plants and micro-organisms produce materials are very similar. However, there are many products which only micro-organisms produce, and certain products which only plants produce. We shall now look at the range of products produced by plants and micro-organisms that are useful to humans.

Useful products from plants
The range of useful products from plants is huge.

Oils
A natural *oil* is a lipid that is liquid at room temperature. Most oils are a product of the reaction of *glycerol* (propane-1,2,3-triol) with three *fatty acids*. The structure of glycerol is shown in Figure 4.13a and that of a common fatty acid, stearic acid, in Figure 4.13b. An example of an oil is shown in figure 4.14. Oils are examples of *esters* – compounds made by a reaction between an alcohol and a carboxylic acid.

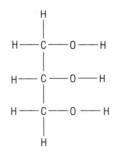

Figure 4.13(a) *The structure of glycerol.*

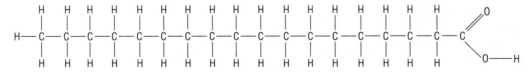

Figure 4.13(b) *The structure of stearic acid, a common fatty acid.*

▶ Naming hydrocarbons, page 19

Two of the fatty acids that joined with glycerol to make the oil in Figure 4.14 contain only single C—C bonds, but one of the fatty acids contains one C=C double bond. This fatty acid is therefore said to be *unsaturated*, because it could contain two more hydrogen atoms, were the bond a single C—C bond. As it contains only one C=C bond, it is said to be *monounsaturated*. Fatty acids containing two or more C=C bonds are said to be *polyunsaturated*.

Plant fatty acids are generally unsaturated, whereas animal fatty acids usually contain no C=C bonds and so are said to be saturated. Lipids containing saturated fatty acids have higher melting points than lipids with unsaturated fatty acids. This is why animal fats, such as lard and butter, are typically solid at room temperature, whereas plant oils, such as olive oil and sunflower oil, are usually liquid (see Figure 4.15).

Among the great range of plant oils that are used by humans are:
- Edible oils such as olive oil and oil from rape seed (see Figure 4.16)
- Cosmetic oils used to make soaps, shampoos, bath oils and cosmetics (see Figure 4.17)
- Lubricant oils used in engineering. Some of the very best quality lubricating oils come from plants. Castrol M™, for instance, is 95% castor oil.

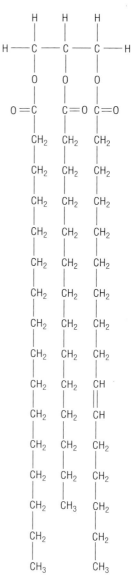

Figure 4.14 The structure of a representative oil.

Figure 4.15 Plant oils are usually liquid at room temperature. This is convenient for cooking, and essential when making a salad dressing.

Figure 4.16 A field of rape in flower. The major sources of oils used to make margarine include palm, soya, sunflower, rape, coconut and peanut. With the exception of palm oil, which is obtained from the fleshy fruit layer surrounding the palm kernel, all these oils come from crushed seeds.

Figure 4.17 Commercial lavender field. Oils extracted from lavender have been used in baths since Roman times. Many people travel to lavender farms just for the view.

Q 5 Why do you think many plants naturally have high concentrations of oils in their seeds?

Assignment trigger: Choosy eaters page 203

Foods

In addition to edible oils, plants produce other foods such as starch, sugar and proteins. Although most humans are *omnivores*, eating both plant and animal products, plants can provide us with all the nutrients we need – as every *vegetarian* knows. Vegetarians may have to take some care to ensure they get all the amino acids that are essential for growth, as most plants contain a narrower range of amino acids than many animals. However, many vegetarians are healthier than people who eat meat. Vegetarians are less likely to get heart attacks, be obese or suffer from certain cancers (e.g. bowel cancer).

Some 12 000 of the estimated 250 000 plant species in existence have been used by people as food, but only around 150 have been cultivated to any extent. The most important plant families for food, and the foods they provide us with, are listed in Table 4.1.

Table 4.1 The most important plant families for food

Family	Main foods
Grass family (*Poaceae*)	Wheat, rice, maize
Pea family (*Fabaceae*)	Peas, beans, pulse grains
Rose family (*Rosaceae*)	Apples, pears, plums, cherries, almonds
Cabbage family (*Brassicaceae*)	Cabbage, cauliflower, broccoli
Palm family (*Arecaceae*)	Coconuts, dates, sago
Spurge family (*Euphorbiaceae*)	Cassava
Nightshade family (*Solanaceae*)	Potatoes, red peppers and tomatoes

Medicinal products

The importance of plants for medicine can hardly be overstated. A quarter of all prescriptions contain ingredients derived from plants. The commercial value of these products is some £25 billion a year.

Plants are widely used for medicinal purposes in many cultures. Even in the west, the range of medicines we derive from plants is impressive (see Table 4.2). These drugs are derived from fewer than a hundred plant species. It has been estimated, however, that of the 250 000 species of plants some 50 000 have been used as medicines by local people. Only some 10% of these, though, have been investigated by pharmaceutical companies in the west. One problem is that it typically takes 10 years and costs £75 million to develop a new drug.

Table 4.2 Medicines used in the west and derived from plants

Heart drugs	Laxatives (to treat constipation)
Pain relievers (analgesics)	Diuretics (to increase the production of urine)
Anti-cancer drugs	Oral contraceptives
Anti-inflammatory drugs	Antibiotics (though most of these come from fungi)

Natural pain killers

The opium poppy, *Papaver somniferum*, contains some 25 *alkaloids* – basic, nitrogen-containing organic compounds. One of these is the painkiller morphine (see Figure 4.18). Morphine is obtained from the seed capsules of the opium poppy (see Figure 4.19).

Morphine takes its name from Morpheus, the Greek god of dreams. This is not because it is a *sedative*, causing people to fall asleep, but simply because its pain-relieving properties allow the patient to fall asleep when naturally tired. Morphine is still widely used to relieve severe pain. It is difficult to make synthetically, and opium poppies are its only source of commercial supply.

Heroin is made by modifying morphine and was discovered in 1874. It has a few medical uses, but is, of course, much better known for its effects when taken illegally. The 1994 street price is around £100 a gram and a year's supply costs some £10 000. At least a third of all crime in Britain is drug-related.

 6 Given that the price of heroin is approximately £100 a gram, while a year's supply costs some £10 000, what is the typical amount used daily by someone who regularly uses heroin?

Other plant products

Other plant products include:
- **paper**, which today is mostly made from conifer or *Eucalyptus* trees
- **clothing fibres,** such as cotton, from the cotton plant (*Gossypium*), and linen, made from flax (*Linum usitatissimum*)
- **wood** used in the construction of houses, furniture and elsewhere
- **dyes** such as indigo, which is blue
- **rubber** from the rubber tree *Hevea brasiliensis*
- natural **insecticides** such as the pyrethrins
- **alcohol**, made from sugar cane, which can be used as a fuel or a solvent.

Assignment trigger

Genetic engineering and plants

Many food plants can be genetically engineered to make them more resistant to pests and diseases.

What are the advantages of using these techniques to control pests and diseases?
What are the potential dangers to the ecosystem?
What safeguards are applied to the use of genetically altered plants?

If a practical assignment is developed, it is essential that a risk assessment is made and checked by your teacher/lecturer.

Could lead to possible assignments relating to Unit 4.

Useful products from micro-organisms

The range of useful products from micro-organisms is already enormous, and is growing year by year.

Antibiotics

An *antibiotic* is an organic compound, characteristically produced by a soil micro-organism, which inhibits the growth of bacteria. The first antibiotic

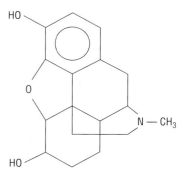

Figure 4.18 *The structure of the painkiller morphine. In the nineteenth century morphine was widely prescribed in medicines such as laudanum. Because it is highly addictive, many people became dependent on it, including the poets Samuel Taylor Coleridge and Elizabeth Browning.*

Figure 4.19 *Collecting raw opium from the seed capsules of the opium poppy. Morphine and the other alkaloids found in the opium poppy, including codeine, are present in the latex that oozes from the immature seed capsules when cut.*

Useful products from plants include oils, foods, medicines, paper, cotton, linen, wood, dyes, rubber and insecticides.

isolated and used for human benefit was *penicillin* (see Figure 4.20). Penicillin is made by a mould fungus to enable the fungus to destroy bacteria which compete with it. It is still one of the most widely prescribed drugs in the world, though some people are allergic to it.

Not all antibiotics are made by fungi. For instance *streptomycin* and *chloromycetin* are made by bacteria.

Figure 4.20 *Pharmacist pouring penicillin tablets from a triangle into a drug bottle. The triangle is used to count the tablets. Penicillin was isolated from the fungus* Penicillium notatum. *It works by disrupting the manufacture of cell walls by certain bacteria.*

Hormones

In recent years, certain micro-organisms have been genetically engineered to make various mammalian hormones such as *growth hormone* and *human insulin*. Human growth hormone can be used to treat *pituitary dwarfism*. In this condition, a person's pituitary gland fails to produce enough growth hormone, so they are very small (see Figure 4.21).

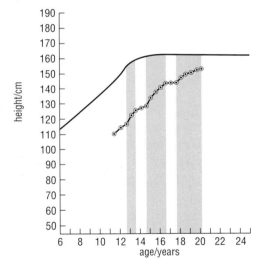

Figure 4.21 *Human growth curves. The upper continuous curve shows the growth curve typical of females in the UK. The lower curve with dots on it shows the growth curve of a particular female who had a very low natural production of human growth hormone. Notice the results of giving her human growth hormone during the three shaded periods.*

Before the advent of genetic engineering, the only way to treat pituitary dwarfism was by obtaining human growth hormone from the pituitary glands of corpses. As each pituitary gland only contains an extremely small amount of growth hormone, a very large number of corpses were needed to obtain enough human growth hormone to treat a single case of pituitary dwarfism. This made the product extremely expensive. It also increased the chance that the product was contaminated by pathogens such as viruses.

Enzymes

Enzymes obtained from micro-organisms are called microbial enzymes. Microbial enzymes have been used for many years – the first biological washing powder was made in 1913! However, it is only recently that the large-scale production of microbial enzymes has really taken off. Examples of the uses of microbial enzymes are given in Table 4.3.

Table 4.3 Examples of enzymes produced by micro-organisms

Enzyme	Uses (selected examples)	Organism	Enzyme	Uses (selected examples)	Organism
α-amylases	Break down stains on clothes; paper manufacture; formation of glucose syrups	*Aspergillus oryzae; Bacillus subtilis*	Lipases	Accelerate ripening in cheeses	*Pseudomonas; Candida*
			Pectinase	Clarify fruit juices by degrading pectins	*Aspergillus awamori*
Catalase	Preservative in soft drinks; oxygen for foam rubber manufacture	*Aspergillus niger*	Proteases	Break down protein stains on clothes; degrade gluten in strong flour for biscuit making; make leather pliable	*Bacillus subtilis*
Cellulases	Animal feed from straw	*Trichoderma*			
Glucose oxidase	Preservative in soft drinks; detect glucose in diabetics' blood	*Aspergillus niger; Gluconobacter*	Streptokinase	Treat blood clots and bruises	*Streptomyces*

Vitamins

Micro-organisms can provide an inexpensive source of **vitamins**. For example, vitamin B_{12} is produced by certain bacteria, while the vitamin riboflavin can be produced during fermentation by some fungi.

Dairy products

Certain bacteria have been used for thousands of years to obtain dairy products from milk:

- yoghurt is made by the action of two bacteria, *Streptococcus thermophilus* and *Lactobacillus bulgaricus* on milk
- different cheeses are made by the actions of different bacteria or fungi on milk. Roquefort cheese, for example, is made by the action of the fungus *Penicillium roqueforti* on ewes' (sheep's) milk (see Figure 4.22).

Figure 4.22 *Roquefort cheeses maturing in limestone cliffs in France. Air currents at a constant temperature of 8 °C and 95% relative humidity naturally circulate, providing the best conditions for the slow growth of the fungus.*

Assignment trigger

Milk foods

Many different foods are made from milk.

What are they?
How are they made?
Can you investigate factors affecting their production?
Why do they make a valuable contribution to a balanced diet?

If a practical assignment is developed, it is essential that a risk assessment is made and checked by your teacher/lecturer.

Could lead to possible assignments relating to Units 4 and 7.

Alcohol

Beers, wines and other alcoholic drinks have been made by people for thousands of years.

Single-cell protein

Since the 1960s scientists have hoped to help solve the food shortage in some parts of the world by the production of protein synthesised by micro-organisms. To be honest, this hasn't proved a great success. There are a number of reasons for this:

- Most people aren't very keen on the idea of eating protein made by bacteria, fungi or algae – they prefer traditional plant and animal protein.
- Development costs have generally proved far greater than predicted. As a result, industrialists have become wary, fearing heavy economic losses.
- Some early single-cell food led to health problems. Foods from micro-organisms tend, unless specially treated, to be high in nucleic acids and this can cause kidney damage.
- Food shortages tend to be the result of problems in distribution. Starvation and malnutrition require political as well as scientific and technological solutions. Most food shortages occur in parts of the world where the technology for single-cell protein is not available.

Despite the difficulties experienced in developing single-cell proteins, some human foods do now contain them (see Figure 4.23).

 7 Why are foods made by single-celled organisms generally high in nucleic acids?

Figure 4.23 *Food made from single-cell protein.*

> Useful products from micro-organisms include antibiotics, mammalian hormones, industrial enzymes, vitamins, dairy products, alcohol and single-cell protein.

Finding the right organism

Before a plant or micro-organism is grown so as to obtain a desired product, careful thought is needed about exactly which **species** should be used. Unless such selection is carried out, a great deal of time and money can be wasted. Whether the species in question is a plant or a micro-organism, the overall question is 'What is the likely economic yield if this species is grown?' In other words, 'Will it be profitable, and so commercially viable?'

In the case of plants, the sorts of questions that need to be answered to see if a species is worth growing are:

- Which plant species can grow in the environment available (growing medium, rainfall, temperature, etc.)?

- What pests are likely to attack the crop?
- How much will insecticides, fungicides, herbicides and fertilisers cost?
- What is the likely yield of the crop?
- Does the plant require people with specialised skills to grow or harvest the crop? If so, are such people locally available?
- Are grants available, for example from the European Union, to encourage growth of this species (e.g. Figure 4.24)?
- Does a market exist for the crop?

In the case of micro-organisms, the sorts of questions that need to be answered to see if a species is worth culturing are:

- How easily can the micro-organism be grown?
- What specialised facilities are needed (e.g. Figure 4.25)?

Figure 4.24 A field of flax, Linum usitatissimum. *The planting of this species has increased greatly in the UK in recent years. This is because farmers who grow this crop get grants from the European Union. Linseed oil and flax (used to make linen) are both obtained from this plant.*

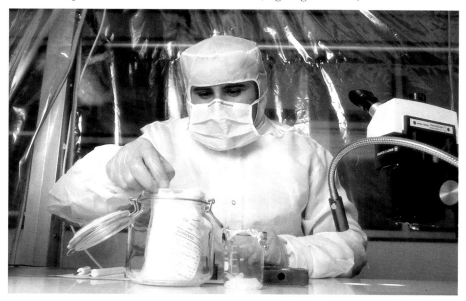

- Are there relevant safety considerations to be borne in mind?
- How efficiently can the desired product be extracted from the culture in which the micro-organism is growing?
- Is there a market for the product?

Figure 4.25 The "clean room" at Bio-medical Omicron Scientific in Rehovot, Israel. Ultra-clean environments are needed for some modern biotechnological procedures.

Commercial success requires that the right species is chosen to be grown and harvested. Factors to borne in mind include ease of growth, likely yield, safety considerations and the size of the market.

Finding the right conditions

Once a commercial operator has identified the right plant or micro-organism to be grown and harvested, the next vital issue is to get the right conditions for growth. We shall consider first plants and then micro-organisms.

The right conditions for plant growth

Plant growth requires the following environmental conditions to be at the right levels:

- light
- temperature
- carbon dioxide concentration
- nutrient availability
- soil structure and pH
- moisture
- space.

We shall look briefly at each in turn.

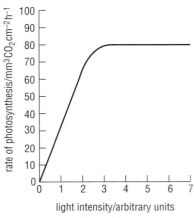

Figure 4.26 *The effect of light intensity on the rate of photosynthesis. The precise shape of this graph varies from plant to plant.*

 Production by plants, page 166

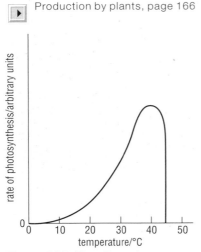

Figure 4.27 *The effect of temperature on the rate of photosynthesis.*

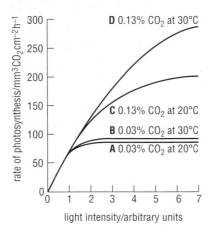

Figure 4.28 *The joint effects of light intensity, carbon dioxide concentration and temperature on the rate of photosynthesis.*

Light level

Plants use light of particular wavelengths for photosynthesis in preference to others. Light *intensity* – i.e. how bright the light is – is also important (see Figure 4.26). Notice that the graph in Figure 4.26 shows only the rate of *photosynthesis*; it does not show the rate of *respiration*. Even when it is dark, so that there is no photosynthesis, a plant still respires, producing carbon dioxide. The light intensity at which the loss of carbon dioxide by respiration exactly equals the uptake of carbon dioxide by photosynthesis is called the compensation point. Its value differs from species to species.

8 Would you expect the compensation point of a herb growing in a wood to be at a lower or a higher light intensity than a plant of the same species growing in the open? Explain your answer.

9 Suggest what internal features of a plant might lead to it having a compensation point at a lower light intensity.

Temperature

A plant contains a thousand or more different enzymes. It is not surprising, therefore, that temperature has much the same effect on photosynthesis, and hence plant growth, as it does on the activity of an enzyme (see Figure 4.27). Few plants can grow at temperatures below 0 °C. Above this temperature, increasing temperatures are associated with an increase in the rate of photosynthesis; that is, until the temperature reaches a critical temperature somewhere between about 35 °C and 55 °C. At this point enzymes become irreversibly damaged, i.e. denatured, and the plant dies.

10 Why are submerged aquatic plants generally unable to survive temperatures in excess of 40 °C, even though such temperatures can generally be tolerated by most land plants?

Carbon dioxide concentration

Plants need carbon dioxide in order to photosynthesise, and hence grow. The atmosphere normally contains about 0.035% carbon dioxide, but most plant species grow best at levels three or four times this level. This means that at high temperatures and light intensities, carbon dioxide is generally the *limiting factor* for plant growth (see Figure 4.28). Some greenhouse plants are grown at artificially raised carbon dioxide levels so as to maximise yield (see Figure 4.29).

Figure 4.29 *A tank of carbon dioxide supplying greenhouses at an agricultural research station*

Nutrient availability

Plants need a number of inorganic ions for their growth. Those needed in relatively large amounts are the cations calcium (Ca^{2+}), magnesium (Mg^{2+}) and potassium (K^+), and the anions nitrate (NO_3^-), phosphate (PO_4^{3-}) and sulphate (SO_4^{2-}). Those needed in smaller amounts are known as *micronutrients* or *trace elements* and include cobalt (Co^{2+}), copper (Cu^{2+}), iron (Fe^{2+} or Fe^{3+}), manganese (Mn^{2+}), molybdenum (generally found as MoO_4^{2-}), zinc (Zn^{2+}) and chloride (Cl^-).

11 How could you attempt to investigate whether a particular nutrient, say copper, is required by plants?

Soil structure and pH

As every gardener knows, soil structure and pH have a great effect on plant growth. A *clay* soil, for instance, is composed largely of very small particles (see Table 4.4). Clay soils can hold large volumes of water and release this water only slowly to plants. As a result, clay soils rarely dry out completely, though when they do they are extremely hard. However, they may become waterlogged (see Figure 4.30). *Sandy* soils, on the other hand, hold little water and drain rapidly.

Table 4.4 Soil particle sizes

Soil type	Particle diameter
Clay	<2 μm
Silt	2 μm – 20 μm
Fine sand	20 μm – 200 μm
Coarse sand	200 μm – 2 mm
Gravel	2 mm – 20 mm

Figure 4.30 Soils with a high clay content all too easily become water-logged. This shows on a waterlogged sugar beet crop.

12 Why do sandy soils hold less water and drain more rapidly than clay soils?

However, soils are made up of much more than the inorganic particles that make up the clay, silt or sand that they contain. Soils also include:
- water
- air (generally saturated in water vapour and high in carbon dioxide)
- organic matter (fungi and bacteria decompose dead organic matter into *humus*)
- dissolved minerals (i.e. cations and anions)
- soil organisms (including bacteria, plant roots, soil invertebrates and moles).

Soil pH normally lies within the range 3.0 to 8.0. Bogs often have soils with a pH of around 4.5. Under these acidic conditions, nitrogen and phosphorus become less accessible to plants. This is the reason why a number of plants found in bogs are carnivorous (see Figure 4.31).

13 From where do carnivorous plants obtain their nitrogen and phosphorus?

Different plant species are adapted to different soil types. A plant that

Figure 4.31 A sundew of the genus Drosera *growing in a British bog. The sundew supplements its intake of nitrogen and phosphorus by catching and digesting insects on sticky hairs on its specially adapted leaves.*

grows well in a waterlogged, acidic bog may be completely unable to grow in a well-drained, slightly alkaline grassland.

Plants do not have to grow in soil. *Most* of the tomatoes, cucumbers and sweet peppers grown in the UK are grown without soil, by providing them with a solution of nutrients in water. Growing plants without soil is known as *hydroponics*. One form of hydroponics uses the *nutrient film technique* (see Figure 4.32). An advantage of this approach is that it is possible to control very precisely the supply of nutrients to the plants, ensuring maximum growth rates.

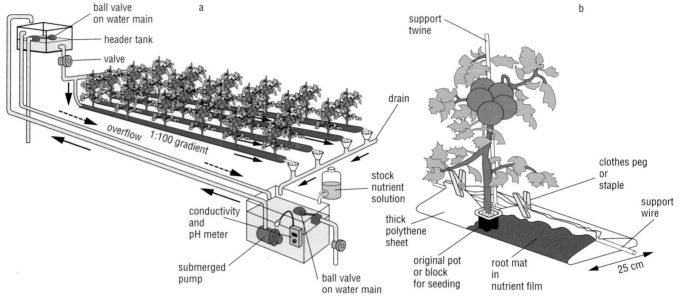

Figure 4.32 Nutrient film technique. (a) The nutrient solution is pumped up to a header tank and then passes down polythene sheets under the force of gravity. (b) Close-up of part of A.

> For their growth, plants need appropriate levels of light intensity, temperature, carbon dioxide, nutrients and water. They also need space and the right medium in which to grow.

Moisture level

All plants need water, but some can survive on very little – indeed many are killed by waterlogging. Others require total submersion.

Space

Every plant needs space to grow, but some can tolerate high densities (number of individual plants per unit area), while others require more area per plant.

 14 What might you expect to be the consequences of overcrowding for the mass and height of a young plant?

Assignment trigger

Greenhouses

Many food plants are grown commercially in greenhouses.

What plants are grown in this way?
What are the advantages of growing plants in greenhouses?
What are the disadvantages of greenhouses?
Why is glass often used in preference to plastic?

If a practical assignment is developed, it is essential that a risk assessment is made and checked by your teacher/lecturer.

Could lead to possible assignments relating to Units 2 and 4.

The right conditions for the growth of micro-organisms

Successful growth of most micro-organisms requires the following environmental conditions to be at the right levels:

- temperature
- availability of energy and nutrients
- pH of medium
- oxygen concentration.

We shall look at each of these briefly in turn.

Temperature

Most micro-organisms grow best at temperatures of around 35 °C. Such species are known as *mesophiles* (medium-temperature-loving organisms). However, some micro-organisms grow best at temperatures as high as 60 °C. These are known as *thermophiles* (heat-loving organisms). Finally there are the *psychrophiles* (cold-loving organisms). These grow best at low temperatures, typically 5 °C – 15 °C. Standard responses to temperature by these three classes of micro-organism are shown in Figure 4.33.

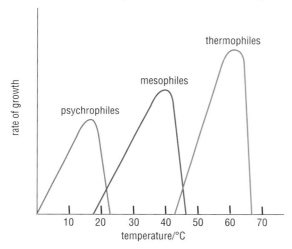

Figure 4.33 *The effect of temperature on the rate of growth of three different classes of micro-organisms.*

In nature, thermophiles are found growing in hot springs and other natural habitats where it is very hot. This means they may not be killed by routine methods of heat sterilisation. Psychrophiles can be a problem in refrigerators, as they will grow, albeit slowly, at common refrigerator temperatures (4 °C).

Availability of energy and nutrients

Micro-organisms can be divided into three main categories, according to the way in which they obtain the energy they need:

- Algae and blue-green bacteria are *photosynthetic*, requiring light, carbon dioxide and water, just as green plants do.
- Some micro-organisms are *chemosynthetic*. Like photosynthetic organisms, they synthesise organic materials from inorganic compounds, but instead of using energy from light, they obtain their energy by oxidising inorganic compounds such as iron(II) salts (Fe^{2+}), hydrogen sulphide (H_2S) and hydrogen (H_2).
- Many micro-organisms are *heterotrophic*. They require an organic source of carbon, just as animals do.

Q 15 To what do you think (a) H_2, (b) H_2S, (c) Fe^{2+} are oxidised respectively by chemosynthetic organisms?

Micro-organisms generally require much the same elements as plants do (see Table 4.5). Some micro-organisms can obtain their nitrogen directly from the atmosphere as gaseous nitrogen, $N_2(g)$ and then convert it into a soluble form as ammonium ions, NH_4^+ (see Figure 4.34).

Table 4.5 Elements typically required by micro-organisms

Calcium (Ca)	Manganese (Mn)
Carbon (C)	Molybdenum (Mo)
Chlorine (Cl)	Nitrogen (N)
Cobalt (Co)	Oxygen (O)
Copper (Cu)	Phosphorus (P)
Hydrogen (H)	Potassium (K)
Iron (Fe)	Sulphur (S)
Magnesium (Mg)	Zinc (Zn)

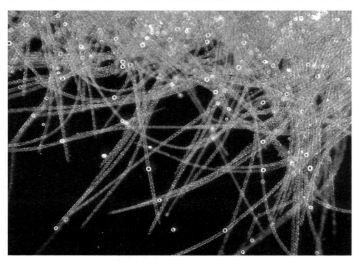

Figure 4.34 Anabaena *is a blue-green bacterium that can obtain its nitrogen directly from the air. It is filamentous, and nitrogen fixation takes place in the occasional thick-walled cells that can be seen on this light micrograph. Magnification x 200.*

pH of medium

Most fungi and yeasts grow best in slightly acidic conditions, at a pH of between 5.0 and 6.0. Most bacteria grow best at a more neutral pH of between 6.5 and 7.5. A few bacteria, though, are *acidophiles* (acid-loving) and grow best at very low pHs. For example, *Thiobacillus ferrooxidans* can grow at a pH of 1. The reason for this is that it is chemosynthetic and derives its energy from the oxidation of iron pyrites (FeS_2) as follows:

$$FeS_2(s) + 2H^+(aq) + 2O_2(g) \rightarrow Fe^{3+}(aq) + H_2SO_4(aq) + S(s)$$

The bacterium has to be able to survive low pHs, otherwise it would be killed by its own production of sulphuric acid (H_2SO_4).

Thiobacillus ferrooxidans plays a crucial role in the extraction of copper from low-grade copper ore in a process called leaching. Millions of tonnes of copper are extracted in this way each year (see Figure 4.35). The mining industry has now begun to use bacteria to recover selenium, vanadium, manganese, molybdenum and uranium from low-grade ores, and to clean up soil and ground water polluted by unextracted metal ions in waste water.

Figure 4.35 *Copper smelting. Where the ore is of a low grade, bacteria may be used to extract copper from it.*

Oxygen concentration

Micro-organisms vary greatly as to their requirements for molecular oxygen, O_2, (see Figure 4.36):

- *obligate aerobes* require oxygen concentrations of close to 20%
- *facultative aerobes* use oxygen if it is available, but can grow in its absence
- *obligate anaerobes* cannot use oxygen and are poisoned by it
- *aerotolerant anaerobes* cannot use oxygen but are not poisoned by it
- *microaerophiles* require oxygen but at concentrations significantly lower than 20%.

> **Micro-organisms vary greatly in their requirements for temperature, pH, oxygen and nutrients.**

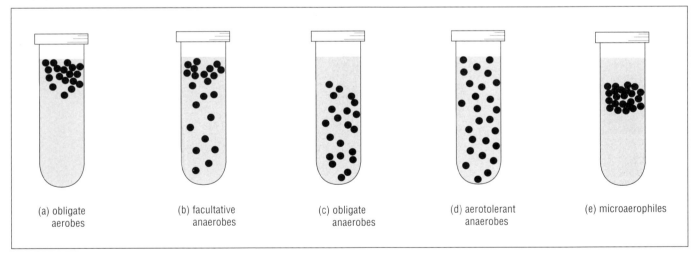

| (a) obligate aerobes | (b) facultative anaerobes | (c) obligate anaerobes | (d) aerotolerant anaerobes | (e) microaerophiles |

Investigating the growth of organisms

In order to grow plants or micro-organisms successfully yourself, you need to answer the following questions before you start:

1 Which organism do I wish to grow (e.g. yeast, potato)?
2 What apparatus is required (e.g. Petri dishes, fermenter, seed trays, plant pots)?
3 What growth medium is needed (e.g. agar, broth, sterilised soil)?
4 Can I provide the necessary environmental conditions (e.g. correct

Figure 4.36 *The effect of oxygen on the growth of five different classes of micro-organisms. Oxygen concentration is highest at the top of the tube, where the solution is in contact with air.*

▶ Useful products from plants and micro-organisms, page 170

▶ Finding the right organism, page 176

▶ Finding the right conditions, page 177

All agriculture requires the following four processes:
- **sowing of seeds**
- **caring for the plants (e.g. weeding and irrigation)**
- **harvesting the crop**
- **keeping some of the seed for the next generation.**

Figure 4.37 *Emmer wheat* (Triticum turgidum), *one of the earliest plants to be cultivated.*

Figure 4.38 *Farmers have always collected seed from their crops. Nowadays grain is often stored in huge grain stores in which the environment is carefully regulated. Most of the seed is used for food, but some is kept back for the next generation of the crop.*

temperature, pH, water supply)?

5 Can I look after the organism from initial establishment through to final harvesting (e.g. problems of week-ends, holidays)?

6 How can I measure growth (e.g. increase in population size of yeast, increase in leaf area of plants)?

7 What useful products can be obtained from the organism (e.g. yoghurt, sunflower seeds)?

8 What is the risk assessment (e.g. sterilised working environment, controlled access to micro-organisms and dangerous plants)?

What do plant breeders do?

Plant breeding has a long history. The domestication of plants (and animals) seems to have happened independently some 12 000 to 10 000 years ago in the Middle East, the Orient and the Americas. By 7500 BCE (Before the Common Era), emmer wheat (see Figure 4.37) and barley were being cultivated in Canaan, potatoes and beans in Peru, rice in Indochina and pumpkins in middle America.

By 6000 BCE einkorn wheat was being cultivated in Syria, macaroni wheat in Anatolia, sugar cane in New Guinea, yams, bananas and coconuts in Indonesia, flax in south-western Asia and maize and peppers in the Tehuacan valley of Mexico.

For more than ten thousand years, therefore, farmers have bred, sown, cared for and harvested plants. They have then kept some of the seed back for the next generation of the crop (see Figure 4.38).

Often, farmers *selected* the seed to give better crops. Some of the selection would have been unconscious and some deliberate. For instance, farmers consciously choose to sow next year's crop from the best of this year's seed at the same time as unconsciously choosing seed that remains in the head of the plant rather than blowing away in the wind.

Traditional plant breeding

Plant breeding aims to improve the *quality* and/or *yield* of a crop. A plant breeder hopes to achieve these ends by breeding for such characteristics as:

- better pest and disease resistance
- less carbohydrate in the stem and more in the grain or other end product (see Figure 4.39)
- decreased sensitivity to drought or poor soil conditions
- increased response to fertilisers.

Figure 4.39 *A modern dwarf variety of wheat grown alongside a much taller, older variety.*

The crop concerned may be one such as wheat, maize or rice in which relatively few people produce large numbers of plants. Such crops are called *agricultural crops*. Alternatively, the crops may be ones such as chrysanthemums or tomatoes in which more people are involved and the crop is consequently more expensive. These crops are called *horticultural crops*, though the borderline between agriculture and horticulture is unclear, particularly in the large-scale production of vegetables.

The type of breeding programme used in *traditional plant breeding* depends on whether the plant is naturally *outbred* or *inbred*:

- An outbred plant is one in which *cross-fertilisation* occurs: each egg cell is fertilised by pollen from a different plant.
- An inbred plant is one in which *self-fertilisation* is the norm: each egg cell is usually fertilised by pollen from the same plant.

Some plants are capable both of cross-fertilisation and self-fertilisation.

Whether a plant is outbred or inbred, the fundamental principles of any breeding programme are basically as follows:

1. Select individuals with potentially useful characteristics (e.g. slightly higher yield than normal)
2. Cross these individuals *either* with one another *or* with other individuals with another potentially useful characteristic (e.g. signs of disease resistance)
3. Select offspring with best characteristics
4. Repeat the process for a number of generations.

These fundamental principles of *artificial selection* (i.e. selection by humans) can be carried out for traditional plant breeding in the following main ways:

- **Pedigree breeding.** Here plants from two different varieties, or *cultivars*, are crossed. Each cultivar has a characteristic that is of value

Patterns of inheritance, page 188

(e.g. one is high yielding, the other disease resistant). The aim is to produce a new variety with both characteristics. Typically it takes about a dozen generations of breeding to end up with a variety that gives consistent results (i.e. breeds true) and combines both desired characteristics (see Figure 4.40). The plants will be planted out in field trials (see Figure 4.41). If these prove successful, the plant may officially be registered as a new cultivar.

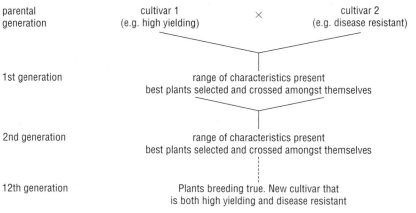

| parental generation | cultivar 1 (e.g. high yielding) | × | cultivar 2 (e.g. disease resistant) |

1st generation — range of characteristics present / best plants selected and crossed amongst themselves

2nd generation — range of characteristics present / best plants selected and crossed amongst themselves

12th generation — Plants breeding true. New cultivar that is both high yielding and disease resistant

Figure 4.40 *Pedigree breeding in crops*

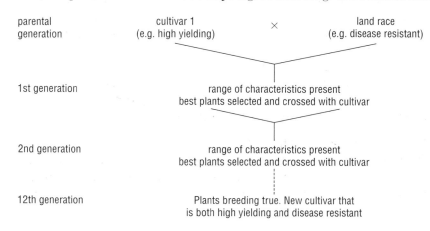

Figure 4.41 *Field trials, in which new crop varieties are planted out for testing in the field.*

- **Backcross breeding.** This technique is used to introduce a favourable characteristic from a wild variety, known as a *land race*, into a cultivar that lacks this favourable characteristic but is otherwise suitable. For example, land races often show resistance to particular diseases. At first, the practice is the same as in pedigree breeding: the cultivar and

| parental generation | cultivar 1 (e.g. high yielding) | × | land race (e.g. disease resistant) |

1st generation — range of characteristics present / best plants selected and crossed with cultivar

2nd generation — range of characteristics present / best plants selected and crossed with cultivar

12th generation — Plants breeding true. New cultivar that is both high yielding and disease resistant

Figure 4.42 *Backcross breeding in crops*

the land race are crossed and the best plants are selected. However, these plants are then backcrossed to the cultivar, rather than being bred amongst themselves. Eventually a new cultivar may result (see Figure 4.42).

- Production of **F₁ hybrids.** Here two cultivars are separately inbred over some eight to twelve generations. Two inbred lines result. Then the two inbred lines are crossed, giving rise to so-called F₁ hybrids (see Figure 4.43). Crops grown from F₁ hybrid seed display so-called hybrid vigour and show little variation so they produce highly consistent crops. Examples of commercially important F₁ hybrids include Brussels sprouts, cauliflowers and cabbages (see Figure 4.44).

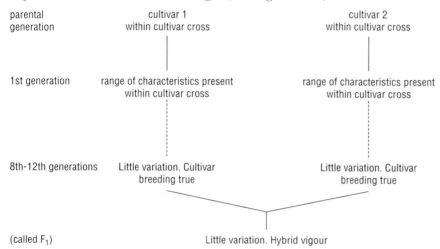

parental generation	cultivar 1 within cultivar cross	cultivar 2 within cultivar cross
1st generation	range of characteristics present within cultivar cross	range of characteristics present within cultivar cross
8th–12th generations	Little variation. Cultivar breeding true	Little variation. Cultivar breeding true
(called F₁)	Little variation. Hybrid vigour	

Traditional plant breeding uses pedigree breeding, backcross breeding and the production of **F₁** hybrids to improve crop yield and quality.

Figure 4.43 The production of F₁ hybrids in crops.

16 Why is backcross breeding more appropriate than pedigree breeding when one of the parents is a wild variety?

17 Read the section 'How can Mendel's results be explained?' on page 189 and then suggest why F₁ hybrids are so vigorous.

Modern techniques of plant breeding

Since the 1970s the traditional approaches to plant breeding have been added to by new techniques. Perhaps the best known is genetic engineering. We shall consider this in detail later. First we shall look at the use of tissue culture in plant breeding.

Tissue culture in plant breeding

The fundamental aim of tissue culture in plant breeding is to generate large numbers of identical plants from a single individual. As can be imagined, this can speed up the production of new varieties, as a single plant can give rise to a whole new line. Some of the exotic plants sold by garden centres, such as orchids and carnivorous plants, are propagated (i.e. multiplied up) by this means.

The technique relies on the fact that a single plant cell can often give rise to an entire new plant. This useful property shown by plants is known as *totipotency*. A typical procedure is as follows:

1 A young leaf is selected from the parent plant.
2 The leaf is sterilised on its surface, washed and dipped in a solution of mannitol to plasmolyse the cells slightly, i.e. to cause the cell surface membranes to pull away from the cell walls.
3 The lower epidermis is removed.

Figure 4.44 Hybrid seeds that will give rise to an F₁ cabbage

▶ Practicalities of genetic engineering, page 198

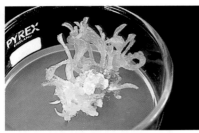

Figure 4.45 *A callus of tobacco* (Nicotiana tabacum) *growing in a Petri dish on nutrient agar. This callus is beginning to give rise to shoots and leaves.*

Figure 4.46 *Regenerated plantlets produced by tissue culture. Three different species are shown.*

Modern approaches to plant breeding can significantly shorten the time required to produce a new variety. One important technique is micro-propagation.

Figure 4.47 *The garden pea* (Pisum sativum) *used by Mendel in his classic breeding experiments.*

4 The whole leaf is then subjected to enzyme hydrolysis of the mesophyll cell walls. This involves using *cellulase* and other enzymes to break down the cell walls.
5 Separate naked plant cells (i.e. plant cells lacking cell walls) are produced – these are called *protoplasts*.
6 The protoplasts are washed and placed in an osmotically balanced *nutrient medium*.
7 The cells begin to rebuild their cell walls and form small clumps of cells called *calluses* (see Figure 4.45).
8 The plant growth regulators *cytokinin* and *indoleacetic acid* are added in the correct concentrations, to bring about the production of roots and shoots, giving rise to *regenerated plantlets* (see Figure 4.46).

9 The regenerated plantlets are grown up, producing a *clone* of genetically identical plants.

Q 18 Why does this approach lead to a clone of genetically identical plants?

This approach is sometimes referred to as plant **micro-propagation** as it involves the multiplying up of plants (propagation) using small (micro-) bits of plants.

Patterns of inheritance

The way in which organisms inherit characteristics from their parents is the subject of *genetics*. The science of genetics really began with the activities of a Central European monk, Gregor Mendel. From 1856 Mendel carried out a huge number of breeding experiments in the garden of his monastery. His chosen organism was the garden pea (see Figure 4.47).

At first Mendel studied the inheritance of just one pair of contrasting characteristics. In one of his early experiments he took a pure-breeding tall pea plant and crossed it with a pure-breeding short pea plant. He did this by taking pollen grains from one plant and dusting them onto the stigma of another plant, having first removed the anthers of the second plant, so as to avoid self pollination.

Mendel found that the offspring of the cross, referred to as the F_1 generation, were all tall. When, though, he crossed the F_1 generation amongst themselves he found a ratio of 787 tall to 277 short, i.e. 2.84 tall to 1 short (see Figure 4.48). Other characteristics gave similar ratios (see Table 4.6).

Table 4.6 The results of some of Mendel's experiments in which the F₁ generation was crossed amongst itself to give an F₂ generation

Character investigated	Parental cross	F₂
Cotyledon colour	Yellow × green	6022 yellow, 2001 green
Seed texture	Wrinkled × smooth	5474 smooth, 1850 wrinkled
Petal colour	Purple × white	705 purple, 244 white

19 What are the ratios among the F₂ generation in Table 4.6?

Nowadays we refer to these sorts of crosses, in which each cross involves just one pair of contrasting characteristics, as **monohybrid crosses.** Note that in each case there is **discontinuous variation**, in other words, Mendel did not find plants with heights half-way between short and tall. Of course, not all variation is discontinuous. Human height, for example, shows **continuous variation**. We are not either tall or short; rather there is a continuous distribution of height among adults.

How can Mendel's results be explained?

Mendel realised that his results could be explained if he assumed that each pea plant has a *pair* of factors which determine height. A pure-breeding tall pea plant has two identical factors, each of which is responsible for tall height. A pure-breeding short plant has two identical factors, each of which is responsible for short height.

Nowadays we don't use the word 'factor'. Instead we say that height in pea plants is controlled by the *gene* for height. Each of the cells in a pea plant contains two copies of the gene for height, one from each parent. A gene is a length of genetic material which is responsible for the synthesis of a polypeptide chain (a number of amino acids linked together). Different genes are responsible for the production of different polypeptides. The various polypeptides made determine the appearance of the organism.

Alternative forms of a gene are called *alleles*. For example, the gene for height in pea plants can be the allele for tallness or the allele for shortness. An interpretation of Mendel's monohybrid cross involving tall and short pea plants is given in Figure 4.49. You can see that the F₁ plants have an allele for tallness, *T*, and an allele for shortness, *t*. Despite this, the F₁ plants are all tall. For this reason the allele for tallness is said to be *dominant* and the allele for shortness *recessive*. The F₁ plants are said to be *heterozygous*, as they contain two different alleles. The pure-breeding parents, however, are *homozygous* (the same two alleles in one individual).

We call the appearance of an organism its *phenotype* and the combination of alleles that it has its *genotype*. So the phenotype of the F₁ plants in Figure 4.49 is *tall*, whilst their genotype is *Tt*.

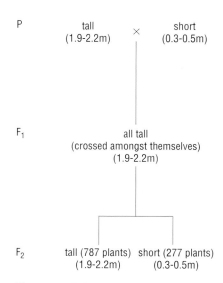

Figure 4.48 The results of Mendel's breeding experiment with tall and short pea plants. 'P' stands for the parental generation, 'F₁' the first generation of descendants, and 'F₂' the second generation.

> **Mendel worked on pea plants which show discontinuous variation in a number of characteristics. Some variation is continuous.**

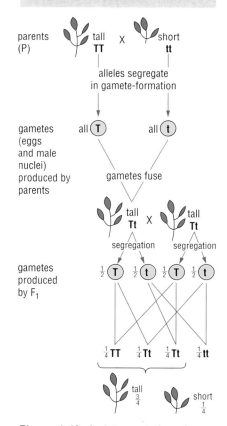

Figure 4.49 An interpretation of Mendel's monohybrid cross involving tall and short pea plants.

189

Q 20 In the F_2 generation, what percentage of the tall plants are heterozygous? What percentage of the short plants are heterozygous?

Alleles are not always simply dominant or recessive. For example, a cross between pure-breeding red and pure-breeding white snapdragons leads to all the F_1 plants being pink. The alleles for red flowers and white flowers are said to be co-dominant. If these F_1 plants are then crossed among themselves, approximately a quarter of the offspring are red, half are pink and a quarter are white. An interpretation of this is given in Figure 4.50.

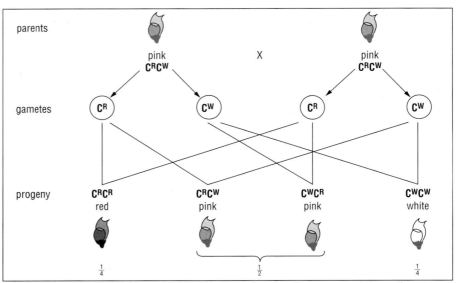

Figure 4.50 An interpretation of the results of crossing pink snapdragons amongst themselves. C^R is the allele for red flower colour; C^W for white. The alleles are co-dominant.

Mendel knew nothing about the details of cell division. Nowadays, though, we can see that Mendel's findings are a natural consequence of **meiosis**. Meiosis is the type of cell division that gives rise to **gametes**, that is, sex cells – eggs and sperms or male nuclei from pollen. Gametes contain only one set of chromosomes and are said to be *haploid*. The individuals that produce gametes, though, have two sets of chromosomes. There are said to be *diploid*.

Meiosis can be contrasted with *mitosis*. Mitosis is the type of cell division that leads to the production of two identical daughter cells, each with exactly the same genotype as the parent cells. Mitosis is responsible for growth and for the replacement of old or damaged cells. The fundamental difference between meiosis and mitosis is illustrated in Figure 4.51.

Q 21 What is the diploid number of chromosomes in humans, given that a human sperm contains 23 chromosomes?

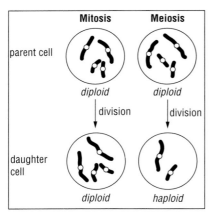

Figure 4.51 A comparison of mitosis and meiosis. Notice how mitosis preserves chromosome number, while meiosis halves it.

Meiosis is the type of cell division responsible for the production of gametes. It leads to a halving of the chromosome number.

Dihybrid inheritance and linkage

Mendel didn't only look at the inheritance of single pairs of characteristics. He also studied the inheritance of two pairs of characteristics, known as a *dihybrid cross*. For example, he crossed pure-breeding tall pea plants that had purple flowers with pure-breeding short pea plants that had white flowers. All the F_1 plants were tall and had purple flowers. These F_1 plants were then crossed amongst themselves. The results of this cross are given in Figure 4.52.

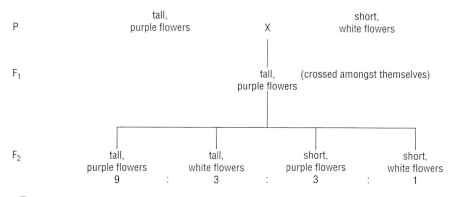

Figure 4.52 The results of one of Mendel's dihybrid crosses.

Ⓠ **22** What ratio of phenotypes would you expect if the F₁ plants had been crossed with pure-breeding short pea plants that possessed white flowers?

An interpretation of this finding is given in Figure 4.53. Note that in this interpretation the alleles for height and flower colour behave independently. They are said to *segregate with independent assortment*.

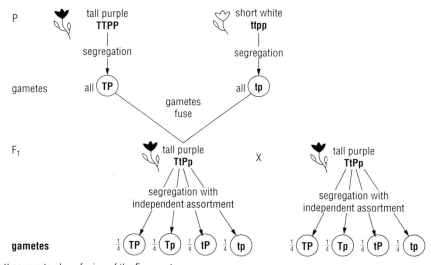

Figure 4.53 Interpretation of Mendel's cross between pure-breeding tall pea plants with purple flowers and pure-breeding short pea plants with white flowers. T is the allele for tallness, t for shortness, P for purple flowers and p for white.

However, alleles do not always segregate with independent assortment. Consider the breeding experiment illustrated in Figure 4.54. This shows a cross between a maize plant which has kernels that are dark and smooth and a second maize plant which has kernels that are pale and shrunken (see Figure 4.55). All the F$_1$ plants have kernels that are dark and smooth – each kernel being the result of a single fertilisation. This suggests that dark is dominant to pale and smooth is dominant to shrunken. The F$_1$ plants are then crossed with the pale, shrunken type, which we presume must be doube recessive. This procedure is known as a *test cross*. If the alleles for kernel colour and texture are on different chromosomes, we would expect four phenotypes to be produced in approximately equal numbers.

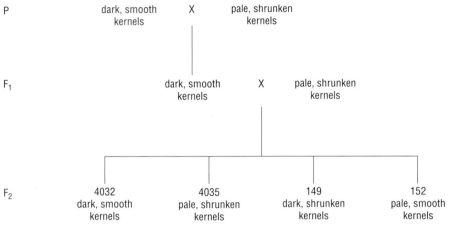

Figure 4.54 *The results of a cross involving maize.*

Figure 4.55 *The results of cross-breeding in maize plants, showing kernels which differ in colour and shape.*

Q 23 Which four phenotypes would we expect to see? Choose appropriate symbols and list their genotypes. Explain why we would expect to see them in approximately equal numbers.

If though, the alleles for kernel colour and texture are on the same chromosome, we might expect to see just the two parental phenotypes, again in approximately equal numbers.

Q 24 Produce a genetic diagram to explain this prediction.

In fact, though, as Figure 4.54 shows, neither of our two predictions is fulfilled. What seems to be happening is that the two genes are *mostly* but not *entirely* inherited together. The reason is that they are on the same chromosome, but during an early stage of meiosis, portions of chromosomes sometimes exchange places with one another in a process called *crossing over*. The two genes are said to show *linkage*. However, the linkage is not 100%, as some crossing over takes place. This process is illustrated in Figure 4.56. An interpretation of the maize breeding experiment is given in Figure 4.57.

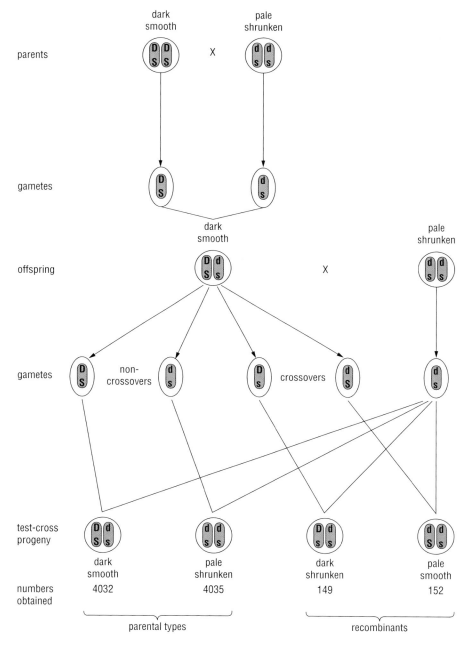

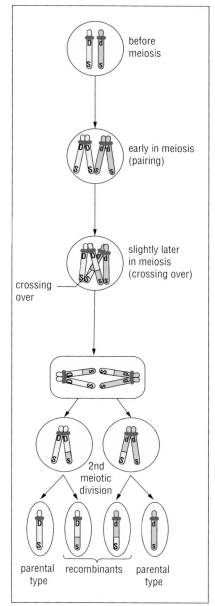

Figure 4.56 *Crossing over in meiosis can undo the effects of linkage. D is the allele for dark-coloured kernels, d for light-coloured kernels, S for smooth kernels and s for shrunken kernels.*

Figure 4.57 *An interpretation of the maize cross illustrated in Figure 4.54. D is the allele for dark-coloured kernels, d for light-coloured kernels, S for smooth kernels and s for shrunken kernels.*

Q 25 Would you expect the percentage of recombinants in Figure 4.57 to be smaller or greater if the distance separating the two genes on the chromosome was halved?

These principles of inheritance are much the same for any eukaryotic organism. Suitable organisms that can be used for practical work include fruit flies (*Drosophila*), pea plants (*Pisum sativum*), rapid-cycling brassicas (*Brassica rapa*) and certain strains of yeast (*Saccharomyces*).

Genes that occur on the same chromosome are said to be linked and are usually inherited together. Crossing over during meiosis can greatly reduce the effect of linkage.

What does DNA do?

Nowadays almost everyone has heard about **DNA (deoxyribonucleic acid).** Yet it was only some 50 years ago, in 1944, that DNA was proved by the American Oswald Avery to be the genetic material. Nowadays we know that DNA has two main functions:

- It copies itself from generation to generation, a process called **replication.**
- It controls cell metabolism by regulating the **synthesis of proteins** in a cell.

Both functions are direct consequences of its structure.

The structure and replication of DNA

A molecule of DNA consists of two long chains made by linking together smaller molecules called **nucleotides.** Together these two chains constitute a **double helix**. Each chain is the length of a chromosome, so that each of our diploid cells, for example, contains 46 molecules of DNA, 23 inherited from our mother, 23 from our father.

A DNA double helix has two backbones, each with a highly repetitive structure that consists simply of alternating **phosphate groups** and **deoxyribose sugars**. However, each sugar is attached to one of four different organic bases (see Figure 4.58) and it is these bases which give DNA its variability.

> DNA replicates itself from generation to generation and controls the synthesis of proteins in a cell.

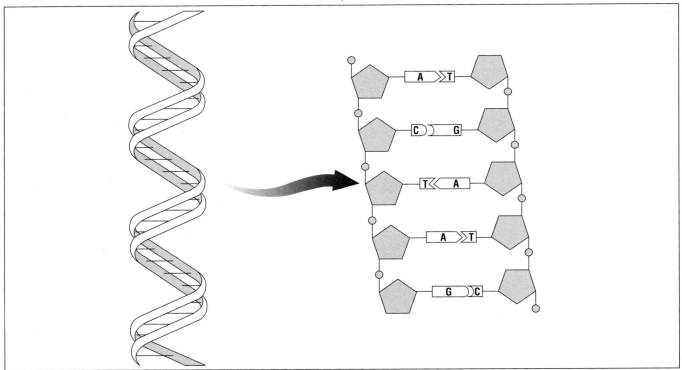

Figure 4.58 The outline structure of DNA. The shaded pentagons represent the sugar deoxyribose; the shaded circles phosphate groups.

The structures of the four bases are shown in Figure 4.59. This figure also shows that **adenine** (A) and **thymine** (T) form hydrogen bonds with each other, as do **guanine** (G) and **cytosine** (C) with one another. It is this precise bonding between the pairs of bases that allows DNA to replicate. The two *complementary strands* of the DNA helix separate. Then free nucleotides, consisting of a phosphate group, a deoxyribose sugar and one of the four bases, simply move into place (see Figure 4.60).

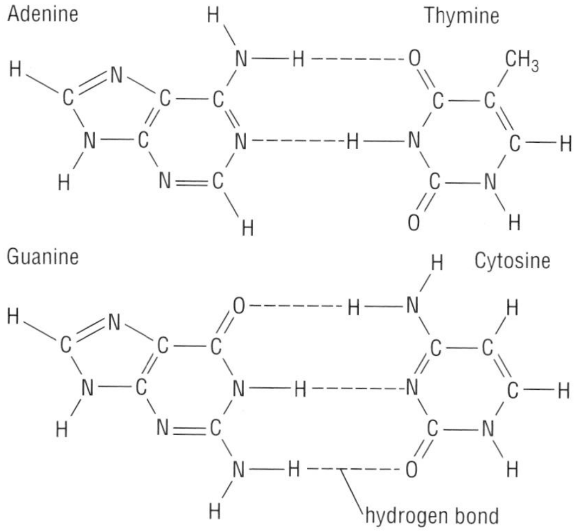

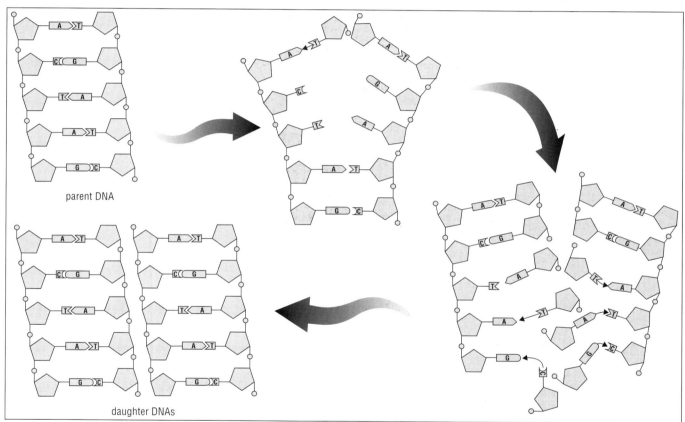

Figure 4.59 *The structural formulae of the four organic bases in DNA. Notice how hydrogen bonds form between base pairs.*

Figure 4.60 *Replication of DNA.*

Q 26 Suppose that one strand of a DNA double helix has the following order of bases: CGGACATTACCG. What would be the order of bases on the complementary strand?

DNA and protein synthesis

DNA controls the synthesis of proteins via an intermediary called **messenger RNA**. Messenger RNA, like DNA, is a nucleic acid, consisting of a backbone of alternating phosphate groups and sugars to which bases are attached. However it differs from DNA in the following respects:

- it is single-stranded rather than double-stranded
- it contains *ribose* as its sugar instead of deoxyribose
- it contains *uracil* (U) as one of its four bases instead of thymine

> **DNA is a double helix. Each strand consists of a backbone of alternating phosphate groups and deoxyribose sugars. Each sugar also has one of four bases attached: adenine, thymine, cytosine, guanine. Hydrogen bonds between adenine and thymine and between cytosine and guanine allow DNA replication to proceed quickly and easily.**

• It is much shorter than DNA as it is only the length of a single gene, typically less than 1500 nucleotides.

The formation of messenger RNA by DNA is illustrated in Figure 4.61. You can see that the two strands of the DNA double helix part. Then one of the strands, the transcribing DNA strand, acts as a template for the synthesis of messenger RNA. This is known as *transcription*. Once formed the messenger RNA leaves the nucleus via a pore in the nuclear envelope.

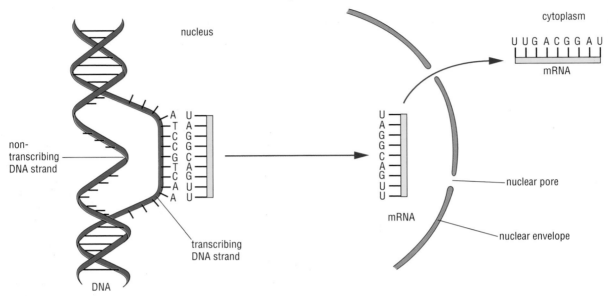

Figure 4.61 The synthesis of messenger RNA by DNA in a eukaryote, and its movement from the nucleus to the cytoplasm. Notice that only one of the two DNA strands, the transcribing strand, is being copied.

Once in the cytoplasm the messenger RNA attaches itself to a ribosome (see Figure 4.62). Here amino acids are drawn into position by a second type of RNA known as **transfer RNA**. Transfer RNAs bind to amino acids at one end and then to specific sequences of bases on messenger RNA at the other end. The net result is that a polypeptide chain is synthesised.

1 messenger RNA becomes attached to ribosome

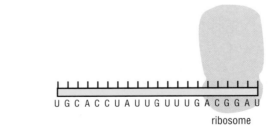

Protein synthesis results from the synthesis of messenger RNA on the transcribing strand of the DNA double helix. This messenger RNA leaves the nucleus and results in the synthesis of a polypeptide chain on a ribosome via the action of transfer RNAs.

2 amino acids drawn into position by transfer RNA molecules

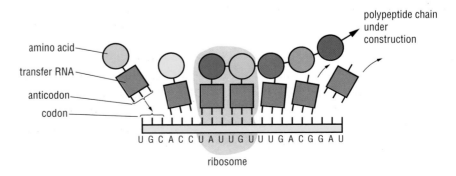

Figure 4.62 The synthesis of a polypeptide chain on a ribosome as a result of the interaction of messenger RNA and transfer RNAs.

Each transfer RNA is specific to a particular amino acid, and this allows the information contained in the messenger RNA to be translated into amino acids. The information is contained in triplets of bases – each triplet on a messenger RNA being known as a *codon*. The three complementary bases on the transfer RNA are called the *anticodon*. The complete genetic dictionary, as it is known, is given in Figure 4.63. All organisms are written with this four-letter code.

second base

first base		U	C	A	G		third base
U		UUU ⎫ Phe UUC ⎭ UUA ⎫ Leu UUG ⎭	UCU ⎫ UCC ⎪ Ser UCA ⎬ UCG ⎭	UAU ⎫ Tyr UAC ⎭ UAA stop UAG stop	UGU ⎫ Cys UGC ⎭ UGA stop UGG Trp		U C A G
C		CUU ⎫ CUC ⎪ Leu CUA ⎬ CUG ⎭	CCU ⎫ CCC ⎪ Pro CCA ⎬ CCG ⎭	CAU ⎫ His CAC ⎭ CAA ⎫ Gln CAG ⎭	CGU ⎫ CGC ⎪ Arg CGA ⎬ CGG ⎭		U C A G
A		AUU ⎫ AUC ⎬ Ile AUA ⎭ AUG Met	ACU ⎫ ACC ⎪ Thr ACA ⎬ ACG ⎭	AAU ⎫ Asn AAC ⎭ AAA ⎫ Lys AAG ⎭	AGU ⎫ Ser AGC ⎭ AGA ⎫ Arg AGG ⎭		U C A G
G		GUU ⎫ GUC ⎪ Val GUA ⎬ GUG ⎭	GCU ⎫ GCC ⎪ Ala GCA ⎬ GCG ⎭	GAU ⎫ Asp GAC ⎭ GAA ⎫ Glu GAG ⎭	GGU ⎫ GGC ⎪ Gly GGA ⎬ GGG ⎭		U C A G

Ala = alanine
Arg = arginine
Asn = asparagine
Asp = aspartic acid
Cys = cysteine
Gln = glutamine
Glu = glutamic acid
Gly = glycine
His = histidine
Ile = isoleucine
Leu = leucine
Lys = lysine
Met = methionine
Phe = phenylalanine
Pro = proline
Ser = serine
Thr = threonine
Try = tryptophan
Tyr = tyrosine
Val = valine

Q 26 What sequence of amino acids would the following sequence of DNA bases result in: AGCTGGCCTACT?

Figure 4.63 The genetic dictionary showing how triplets of messenger RNA bases, called codons, code for amino acids.

The significance of mutations

A *mutation* is a change in the structure of a cell's DNA that may result in a changed phenotype. From Figure 4.63 you can see that in certain cases the substitution of one base for another will lead to a different amino acid being incorporated into the growing polypeptide chain. This is why mutations can be so important. In the short-term mutations are generally harmful. For example, mutations are responsible for such genetic diseases as sickle cell anaemia (see Figure 4.64) and cystic fibrosis (see Figure 4.65). In the long-term, however, mutations are essential for evolution. If there hadn't been any mutations in the last thousand million years there would still only be single-celled prokaryotes.

Figure 4.64 *Scanning electron micrograph of red blood cells from someone with sickle cell anaemia. The left hand red blood cell is sickled; its immediate neighbour is normal. Ignore the central, spiny red blood cell which owes its appearance to the preparation technique. The red blood cell just above it is beginning to sickle, and the one above it is normal. The normal red blood cells are approximately 7 μm in diameter. Sickle cell anaemia is an inherited disorder caused by a recessive allele. It occurs mainly in black people.*

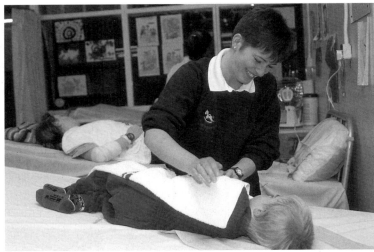

Figure 4.65 *Three year-old boy with cystic fibrosis receiving physiotherapy to help clear his lungs of excess mucus. Cystic fibrosis is an inherited disorder caused by a recessive allele. It occurs mainly in white people.*

 27 Give an example of a base substitution that will not affect the organism's phenotype.

 28 Would you expect the insertion of a single extra base into each strand of a DNA molecule to have a smaller or greater effect than a single base substitution in each strand? Explain your answer.

Practicalities of genetic engineering

Since the late 1980s the commercial breeding of micro-organisms, plants and animals has been revolutionised by **genetic engineering**. In genetic engineering, genes are moved from one organism to another. As virtually all organisms have double-stranded DNA as their genetic material and share the same genetic dictionary (see Figure 4.63), genes can be moved not only within a species but also between species.

It is the movement of genes between species that is so significant. Traditional breeding relied almost entirely on breeding within a species – the only exception to this rule being the occasional hybridisation of closely related plant species (see Figure 4.66). However, genetic engineering allows scientists to move genes, almost at will, from humans to bacteria, from animals to plants, and so on.

The fundamental principles of genetic engineering, also known as *recombinant DNA technology*, are illustrated in Figure 4.67. This shows how a human gene can be moved from a human cell to a bacterium. The human DNA is normally inserted not into the main bacterial chromosome, but into one of the small pieces of DNA that bacteria typically possess, known as *plasmids*.

Bacteria are prokaryotes. The details of prokaryotic genetics need not concern us. It is sufficient for our purposes to know that prokaryotes have various means of exchanging DNA amongst themselves:

- In *conjugation* two bacteria come into contact. One bacterium acts as a donor, the other as a recipient (see Figure 4.68).
- In *transformation* the bacterium simply pick up bits of DNA lying around in its environment.
- In *transduction* bits of bacterial DNA are carried from one bacterium to another by viruses.

> Genetic engineering makes use of the fundamental similarities in the genetics of very different organisms to allow the transfer of genes between almost any two species.

Figure 4.66 *A commercially-bred* Odontoglossum *orchid resulting from a cross between two different orchid species.*

In addition to being able to insert foreign genetic material into their own DNA, bacteria can also protect themselves against viruses that try to insert viral DNA into them. It is because of this that bacteria have the enzymes needed for the genetic engineer. The removal of foreign, e.g. human, DNA and its insertion into bacterial DNA is shown in more detail in Figure 4.69. Two types of enzymes are particularly important:

- **Restriction endonucleases** which cut DNA at particular sites
- *DNA ligases* which join together bits of DNA.

One of the most difficult aspects of genetic engineering involves correctly identifying and locating the gene the genetic engineer wants to move from one organism to another. Suppose you want to find where the gene for human insulin is, so that you can subsequently remove it and insert it into a bacterium. One technique (greatly simplified here) goes as follows:

1 Determine the order of amino acids in human insulin.
2 Use the genetic dictionary (Figure 4. 63) to work out a possible order of bases for the messenger RNA that codes for this protein.
3 Synthesise, in the laboratory, a short sequence of RNA with some of this order of bases.
4 Use this short RNA sequence as a *probe* by radioactively labelling it and then placing it with a cell culture of human chromosomes.
5 See to which human chromosome the probe binds.
6 You now know to which of the 23 pairs of human chromosomes the gene belongs. Further steps involve isolating the gene itself and transferring it to a suitable organism.

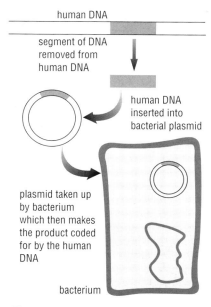

Figure 4.67 *The fundamental principles of genetic engineering illustrated by the transfer of a piece of human DNA to the plasmid of a bacterium.*

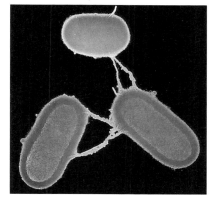

Figure 4.68 *Conjugation in the bacterium* Escherichia coli *as revealed on a transmission electron micrograph. One donor and two recipient bacteria are shown.*

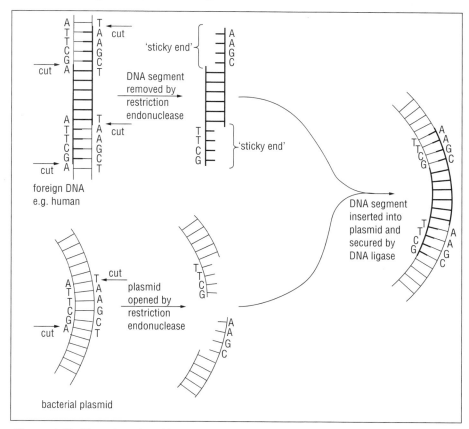

Figure 4.69 *The roles played by restriction endonucleases and DNA ligases in gene splicing.*

Q 29 Why can you only work out a possible order of bases for the messenger RNA that codes for the protein in question?

Q 30 Why is the probe radioactively labelled?

So far we have simply considered moving DNA from one organism into a bacterium. The advantage of this procedure is that bacteria reproduce very quickly. As a result, a large population rapidly builds up. Each bacterium treats the foreign DNA as if it were its own, and so synthesises the polypeptide that the foreign DNA codes for.

Sometimes, though, genetic engineers want to insert foreign DNA not into a bacterium, but into an animal or a plant. They might wish, for example, to produce a particular polypeptide from a human gene. They might insert the human gene into a ewe, so that the sheep produces the desired polypeptide in her milk (see Figure 4.70). Or they might want to transfer a gene for disease resistance from one plant crop species to another.

Figure 4.70 *The most valuable milk in the world is produced by a sheep called Tracey. Tracey is a product of genetic engineering. Each litre of her milk contains some 35 g of the human protein α_1-antitrypsin. Some people have a genetic inability to produce α_1-antitrypsin, as a result of which they suffer from the lung disorder emphysema. The protein in Tracey's milk can help that condition. The photograph shows Tracey and two of her offspring, both of whom also secrete α_1-antitrypsin in their milk.*

Enzymes called restriction endonucleases can be used to cut particular genes from DNA. This DNA can be transferred into a new host in various ways.

One way of doing this is to use viruses to carry the genetic material between the species. A more direct approach has proved surprisingly effective with crop plants. The gene in question is literally shot into the crop plant on tiny tungsten pellets fired by a small gun. Remarkably, a significant proportion of the damaged cells take up the gene and insert it into their own DNA.

Assignment trigger

Genetic engineering and medicines

Many medicinal products such as hormones and antibiotics are made commercially from genetically altered organisms.

What organisms are used?
How is the gene obtained and transferred?
How are the organisms modified?
How are they grown?
Why is it done at all?

If a practical assignment is developed, it is essential that a risk assessment is made and checked by your teacher/lecturer.

Could lead to possible assignments relating to Unit 4.

Why regulate commercial production?

Practically all human activities are regulated. Simply living in society requires this. Imagine a world in which there were no traffic regulations, no laws to require people to pay back money they owe, indeed no laws of any kind. A society in which there are no laws is in a state of anarchy.

So human activities need to be regulated, and this includes commercial production from organisms. There are two fundamental classes of reasons why human activities are regulated:

- **Extrinsic ethical reasons.** These relate to the *consequences* of actions. For instance, laws exist to regulate the food industry. This is partly so that we don't suffer unfortunate consequences, such as food poisoning, and partly so that unfortunate consequences for any *animals* involved, such as suffering, are controlled.
- **Intrinsic ethical reasons.** These relate to whether an action is right or wrong *in itself*, regardless of the consequences. For example, many people believe that torture is wrong, whatever the consequences. Vegetarians mostly believe that it is intrinsically wrong to kill animals for food.

Intrinsic ethical reasons are very important to most of us as individuals. However, commercial production is mainly regulated for extrinsic ethical reasons.

How should commercial production from organisms be regulated?

Many questions need to be answered in deciding how to regulate commercial production from organisms:

- How much benefit will the application of the technology bring? For example, will breeding a new rice variety reduce the cost of our food or reduce the risk for some people of malnutrition?
- What are the safety implications? For instance, might the movement of genes between organisms in genetic engineering lead to disease-causing micro-organisms that are more resistant to antibiotics?
- Are there welfare implications for animals? For example, genetic engineering has been used to breed mice that are a hundred times more likely to develop cancers, so-called *oncomice*. There is no doubt that such mice are useful – they can be used to test how effective anti-cancer drugs are. But is it right deliberately to produce animals that suffer?
- What effects might the practice have on the environment? Most crops are grown as single varieties over a large area of land – so-called **monocultures**. Such monocultures are easier for a farmer to sow and

What regulations exist?, page 202

Human actions can be defended or attacked either on extrinsic or on intrinsic grounds. Extrinsic grounds involve looking at the consequences of an action; intrinsic grounds question whether the action is right in itself, regardless of the consequences.

The implications of any new technology need careful consideration before its use becomes widespread. Implications to consider include the safety of biological products, the possible spread of genetically engineered organisms and the welfare of animals.

Figure 4.71 A large farm in the Cotswolds, Gloucestershire growing a single variety of one species – aquila wheat. The natural habitat here is mixed deciduous oakwood, with over a hundred species of plants, over a hundred species of fungi and about a thousand species of animals.

Commercial production generally has a significant impact on the natural flora and fauna as a result of the establishment of monocultures and the use of fertilisers and pesticides.

Regulations to control the use of organisms for commercial production may exist to protect the environment (e.g. for aesthetic reasons and to allow landscapes to be used as amenities) or to protect humans (e.g. to limit the occurrence of pesticides and hormones in the human food chain).

Why regulate commercial production?, page 201

Economic issues that arise from the use of organisms for commercial production include market restrictions and consumer preferences, for example for organic and low-intensity production.

harvest. However, they attract pests and diseases and generally lead to a loss of genetic diversity among the crop species and a loss of biodiversity of wildlife on farms (see Figure 4.71). In addition, most modern crop varieties require high levels of fertiliser and pesticide application, leading to damage to the local environment. A more recent worry is that genetically-engineered plants, micro-organisms and even animals might escape into the wild with unforeseen results.

What regulations exist?

The range of **regulations** that exist to control commercial production from organisms is huge and we can only outline some of them here. Some of the regulations that relate to safety are considered in more detail in Unit 0. Regulations exist at a number of different levels:

- individual choice
- national legislation
- international legislation.

Individual choice

Individual choice, or **consumer preference**, is sometimes forgotten when the regulation of commercial production from organisms is considered, but it is a most powerful force. Consumer preferences can be for religious, cultural, ethical, aesthetic or health reasons. Examples of consumer preference include:

- Muslims and Jews refusing to eat pigs (religious)
- vegetarians refusing to eat animal sources of foods (ethical)
- people choosing to buy organic foods (ethical)
- people choosing meat that looks red (cultural/aesthetic)
- people choosing not to eat genetically-engineered foods (cultural/ethical) (see Figure 4.72).

Assignment trigger

Thin pigs

Pigs can be fatty but fatty foods are now considered by some to be unhealthy.

How have pig breeders responded to this change in demand?
Do the farmers' requirements differ from those of the consumer?

If a practical assignment is developed, it is essential that a risk assessment is made and checked by your teacher/lecturer.

Could lead to possible assignments relating to Units 2 and 7.

Figure 4.72 *All these tomatoes are the same age. However, one group has been genetically-engineered to last for longer before going rotten.*

 31 Suggest ways in which consumer preference may affect how farm animals are kept.

 32 How do you think a supermarket might alter the composition of the gases within the packaging that surrounds meat so as to make the meat redder?

Assignment trigger

Choosy eaters
Different people eat different things.

What factors affect their choice of diet?
Why do some people have more choice than others?
How are people's choices affected by regulation, culture or advertising?

If a practical assignment is developed, it is essential that a risk assessment is made and checked by your teacher/lecturer.

Could lead to possible assignments relating to Unit 4.

National legislation

Some of the earliest legislation in the UK dates back over a century and relates to animal welfare. More recent legislation falls into various categories:

- legislation to protect consumers (e.g. to regulate pesticide, antibiotic and hormone levels in foods)
- legislation to protect the animals from which food is obtained (e.g. minimum standards for the keeping of poultry, veal calves and pigs with their young)
- legislation to protect wildlife (e.g. the establishment of **National Nature Reserves, Sites of Special Scientific Interest** and **Environmentally Sensitive Areas**)
- legislation relating specifically to genetic engineering (e.g. minimum safety standards to prevent the escape of genetically-engineered organisms into the wild).

> **Environmental legislation, including the establishment of Sites of Special Scientific Interest, National Nature Reserves and Environmentally Sensitive Areas, influence the use and location of commercial production based on organisms.**

International legislation

There are various levels of international legislation in this field:

- The European Union has, through the *Common Agricultural Policy*, various regulations that relate to export restrictions and *quotas* (i.e. maximum production levels). For example, quotas are set annually for the production of milk and wine and for fish catches.
- *Patents*, though issued within a country, are recognised internationally. Patents allow the developer of a new product or process to enjoy the exclusive rights to the commercial exploitation of that process or product for a fixed period, usually 20 or 25 years (see Figure 4.73).

> **Food production is regulated by individuals, by nations and internationally.**

Figure 4.73 Research into an anti-cancer drug called taxol. Taxol is found in the bark of the Pacific yew (Taxus brevifolia) *and been found to restrict various cancers. The tree is very rare and research is underway to find a way of synthesising taxol in the laboratory. If successful, the method will be patented, enabling the company to make a profit from its work.*

Case study

Alcohol production

Humans have produced alcoholic drinks for thousands of years. By 6000 BCE a type of beer was being made with yeast in Egypt. By 1000 BCE the Sumerians brewed at least 19 brands of beer – a whole book on the subject survives.

Most alcoholic drinks are made by allowing yeasts belonging to the species *Saccharomyces cerevisiae* or *S. carlsbergensis* to metabolise glucose to ethanol, CH_3CH_2OH:

- Wine is made from various species of grapes in the genus *Vitis*
- Ale is produced by the action of yeasts on glucose produced from grains such as barley
- Beer is produced in much the same way as ale, but hops (*Humulus lupus*) are added for flavour.

Although brewing is nowadays a major industry which produces a number of by-products in addition to the beer itself (Illustration 1), the basic science of brewing has changed little over the centuries. The raw materials are barley, water, sugar, hops and yeast.

Brewing begins with the soaking of cleaned barley grains in water. The grains are then moved to aerated chambers where the temperature and moisture are controlled to ensure uniform and maximum germination. During germination, amylases and other enzymes set to work, breaking down the storage compounds, such as starch, in the barley. This process is then helped by milling (breaking up) the grain and then mashing it (mixing it with warm water).

Hops give beer its distinctive flavour. They also inhibit the growth of certain bacteria and help to give beer its 'head'. The final alcohol content of the beer is determined by the amount of sugar that is added, as the yeast (also added) breaks the sugar down to alcohol. However, too much alcohol kills the yeast, so a point comes when it is not worth adding any more sugar as the beer cannot become more alcoholic.

A very different reason for producing alcohol is so that it can be used as a fuel. Brazil has pioneered the way in this field. A small modification allows cars to run on a mixture of petrol and alcohol. The main advantage is that less petrol is used so conserving fossil fuels. A second advantage is that alcohol can be produced from waste products from plants, such as sugar cane, once the sugar has been extracted.

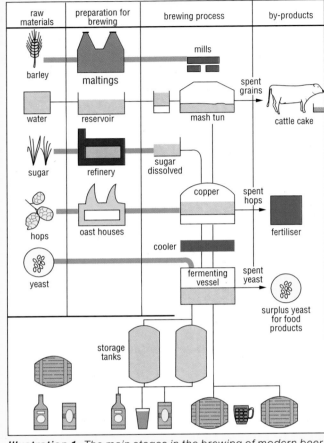

Illustration 1 The main stages in the brewing of modern beer.

Questions

1. Draw up a table, summarising the functions of each of the raw materials in beer.

2. What difficulties do you think makers of home-brewed beer may experience, and why?

3. What do you notice about the name of one of the yeasts used to make alcohol?

4. Does alcohol production rely on aerobic or anaerobic respiration by the yeast?

5. What would happen if too much oxygen got into beer while the yeast was breaking down sugar to alcohol?

6. Summarise the arguments in favour of using alcohol as a fuel for cars.

7. Can you suggest why alcohol has not caught on as a car fuel in the UK?

Case study

Wheat breeding

In recent years tissue culture, genetic engineering and other modern techniques of plant breeding have begun significantly to affect wheat breeding. Research is now under way to find wheat varieties that do not require so much fertiliser, and that can grow in areas with low, irregular rainfall.

However, most of the most important changes to wheat were carried out thousands of years ago (Illustration 1).

The evolution of wheat demonstrates the phenomenon of polyploidy in which the number of chromosome sets in an organism increases. Modern wheat has a total of 42 chromosomes in six chromosome sets and is said to be hexaploid. Research on these chromosomes suggests that modern wheat is a descendant of three ancestral species, each species having only 14 chromosomes in two chromosome sets, as shown in Illustration 1.

One possibility is that farmers deliberately crossed these species to give new, larger and more vigorous hybrid species. Another possibility is that these hybrids happened naturally, though rarely. Early farmers may then have sought out these hybrids and bred from them.

Turning to more recent times, research is under way to use a genetically engineered bacterium to make alcohol from straw. Farmers in Britain produce some ten million tonnes of straw each year – left over when cereals such as wheat and barley are harvested. However, only about four million tonnes of this is used for bedding and animal feed. The rest of the straw is wasted.

Now, though, a genetically engineered bacterium called *Bacillus stearothermophilus* has been found which can turn much of this straw into ethanol. As the bacteria consume the straw, they produce enough heat energy to keep the reactants at about 70 °C. At this temperature the ethanol produced vaporises, allowing it to be drawn out of the reactor vessel continuously with a mild vacuum and then condensed.

Illustration 1 *Possible evolutionary history of wheat over the last 10 000 years. The letters A, B and D each refer to a different set of seven chromosomes.*

Questions

1 Do you think new plant varieties should be patented, or should anyone be able to grow them without paying a fee to a patent-holder?

2 Can you suggest why polyploid plants are often larger and more vigorous that the plants from which they are descended?

3 Today's wheat plants are less than half the height of wheat plants from only thirty years ago. Why do you think plant breeders have bred these 'dwarf' varieties?

4 Give at least two commercial advantages of *Bacillus stearothermophilus* being able to survive temperatures of 70 °C.

5 Suggest possible uses of alcohol made from straw.

6 List alternative uses of straw.

7 Can you think of any advantages of using genetically engineered bacteria such as *Bacillus stearothermophilus*?

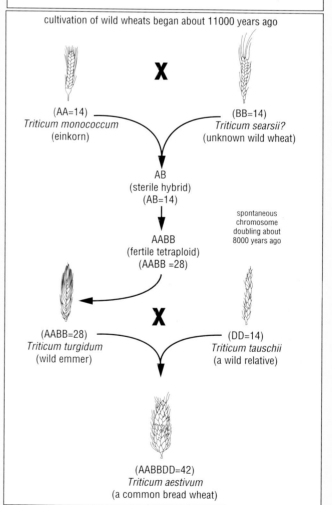

cultivation of wild wheats began about 11000 years ago

X

(AA=14)
Triticum monococcum
(einkorn)

(BB=14)
Triticum searsii?
(unknown wild wheat)

AB
(sterile hybrid)
(AB=14)

spontaneous chromosome doubling about 8000 years ago

AABB
(fertile tetraploid)
(AABB =28)

(AABB=28)
Triticum turgidum
(wild emmer)

X

(DD=14)
Triticum tauschii
(a wild relative)

(AABBDD=42)
Triticum aestivum
(a common bread wheat)

Case study

Human insulin

One of the earliest commercial uses of genetic engineering was in the production of human insulin to treat diabetics unable to produce enough of their own. Until the mid-1980s, all insulin was obtained either from dead cattle or from dead pigs. Such insulins are very similar to human insulin, but differ slightly in the order of their amino acids. Consequently it was hoped that the production of human insulin by genetic engineering would be a great improvement in the treatment of diabetes.

To a large extent this hope has been realised. Most of the diabetics who now inject human rather than bovine insulin (from cattle) or porcine insulin (from pigs) find it very satisfactory. However, some problems have resulted. In particular, it may be more difficult for a diabetic using human insulin to realise when his or her blood sugar levels are getting dangerously low. This is because the symptoms of low blood sugar levels are slightly different when human insulin has been injected than when bovine or porcine insulin has been, and may not be recognised by a diabetic used to bovine or porcine insulin.

Some of the diabetics who switched to human insulin died through failing to recognise these new symptoms. This is a reminder that genetic engineering is not the solution to every problem.

More recently scientists have carried out research on mice in an effort to find a better way of treating diabetes in humans. They have found that cells taken from the pituitary region of a mouse's brain can be genetically engineered to produce insulin. If these cells are packed into tiny fibres, the fibres can be inserted in a mouse. Here they function as a sort of artificial pancreas. The hope is that when the technology has been perfected on mice, it will allow scientists to make similar artificial pancreases for people with diabetes.

Questions

1 What are the disadvantages of using bovine or porcine insulin to treat diabetics?

2 Why have some people died during a result of switching to genetically engineered human insulin?

3 What problems might be encountered in scaling up production of genetically engineered human insulin from test-tube to commercial scale?

4 The researchers working on artificial mice pancreases chose the pituitary as a source of cells because it is relatively easy to grow mice pituitaries in tissue culture. List the conditions that would have to be controlled for mice pituitary cells to grow successfully in culture.

5 Is it right to use mice for research such as this? Try to argue both sides of the case.

6 Discuss the feasibility of inserting the human insulin gene directly into the DNA of a person with diabetes.

5 | Control the transfer of energy

Our lives are entirely dependent upon ample, reliable and flexible sources of energy. Currently our energy supplies are dominated by fossil fuels (such as natural gas, oil and coal) and nuclear fuels. To make the best use of these finite supplies of energy we must use them efficiently and effectively. This includes the transfer of energy. Everything we do involves the transfer of energy – maintaining rail and road transport, moving fuels (whether gaseous, liquid or solid) from one place to another, heating and lighting houses, hospitals and factories, and so on.

Figure 5.1 *Safety features built into this car will help prevent serious injury to its passengers.*

The Elements

 Controlling transport, page 210

Element 5.1 Control transport of objects
To control the transport of people, vehicles and other objects you need to:
- explain why their transport needs to be controlled and describe the factors which affect their motion
- determine changes in their motion
- describe the safety features for controlling their motion.

Figure 5.2 *We often take the flow of water and other effluent from our houses for granted. However, the pipes and channels must be carefully designed to ensure their effectiveness.*

Element 5.2 Control fluid flow

To control the flow of a fluid you need to:

- identify whether it is flowing in a tube or channel, or if it is flowing freely
- describe devices to measure its continuous flow and measure its rate
- describe how its flow can be controlled.

 Controlling fluid flow, page 223

Figure 5.3 *Warmth is essential to human survival. Our clothing and our dwellings are constructed to ensure that we stay warm in winter and cool in summer.*

Element 5.3 Control thermal energy transfer

To control thermal energy transfer you need to:

- describe how the transfer of thermal energy from secondary sources (electrical, gas, oil) can be controlled
- describe the cause of a change in temperature of an object
- design and construct a system for controlling an object's temperature
- explain how an automatic feedback system works.

 Controlling thermal energy transfer, page 236

Controlling transport

Why control transport?

The transport of an object from one place to another involves the use of forces. Those forces can damage the object as well as transport it. Scientists can predict the size and direction of forces on objects when they are transported. This knowledge can then be used to design safe and effective transport systems.

Assignment trigger

Fragile eggs

Eggs have to be transported from the farm to the table. But eggs are notoriously fragile.

How is this done without breaking the eggs?
How can the strength of an egg be determined?

If a practical assignment is developed, it is essential that a risk assessment is made and checked by your teacher/lecturer.

Could lead to possible assignments relating to Unit 5.

Acceleration

▶ Quantifying motion, page 221

▶ Newton's laws of motion, page 222

Acceleration is the rate of change of velocity. Forces are always needed to accelerate objects. Motion of objects from one place to another requires the transfer of energy.

Transporting an object involves changing its speed or **accelerating** it. Look at Figure 5.4a. The satellite atop its launch rocket has a mass of 100 kg. Gravity tugs down on it with a force of about 1000 N. When the rocket is ignited, the satellite is accelerated upwards at a rate of 50 ms^{-2}. The resultant force F needed to do this is calculated as follows.

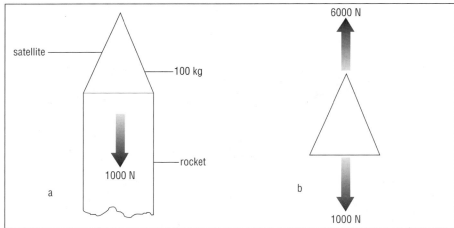

Figure 5.4a Gravity pulls down on the satellite with a force of 1000 N...

Figure 5.4b but the rocket pushes up with a force of 6000N to accelerate the satellite upwards.

$$F = ?\,N \qquad\qquad F = ma$$
$$m = 100\,kg$$
$$a = 50\,ms^{-2}$$
$$\text{Therefore} \quad F = 100 \times 50$$
$$\text{or} \quad F = 5\,000\,N$$

Figure 5.4b shows the forces acting on the satellite during launch. All of the forces must add up to 5000 N, so the rocket must push upwards with a force of 6 000 N. Unless the satellite has been designed to withstand this force, it will be damaged.

1 A jet pilot has a mass of 75 kg. On take-off, he is accelerated horizontally at 40 ms^{-2}. Show that the force needed to do this is four times his own weight.

Slowing down

What happens to the contents of a vehicle when it suddenly slows down and stops? Provided large enough forces can act on them, the contents also stop.

Imagine the driver of a car going along at a steady 15 ms^{-1}. She slams on the brakes and manages to stop the car in 3.0 s. How big a force is needed to ensure that she stops as well? Start off by calculating the *impulse* needed. The driver's mass is 50 kg. (Note that Δx is the symbol for a change of x. The prefix Δ (delta) attached to a symbol always means a change in the quantity which the symbol represents.)

$$\Delta p = ? \, \text{Ns}$$
$$m = 50 \, \text{kg}$$
$$\Delta v = 15 - 0 = 15 \, \text{ms}^{-1}$$
$$\Delta p = m \times \Delta v = 50 \times 15 = 750 \, \text{Ns}$$

Then calculate the average force needed:

$$F = ? \, \text{N}$$
$$F = \frac{\Delta p}{\Delta t}$$
$$\Delta p = 750 \, \text{Ns}$$
$$\Delta t = 3 \, \text{s}$$
so $$F = \frac{750}{3}$$

therefore $$F = 250 \, \text{N}$$

 Force, page 219

That force comes from the seat belt (see Figure 5.5) which she is wearing. Its value is about half her weight (500 N). If she wasn't wearing the seat-belt, she would continue to move forwards at a speed of 15 ms^{-1} until she met something else (such as the steering wheel or the windscreen) which could provide a force of 250 N to decelerate her.

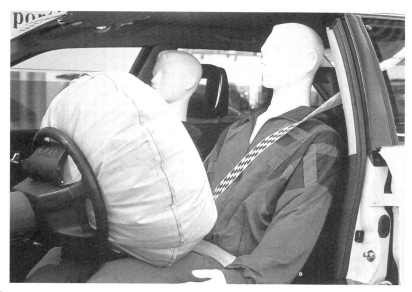

Figure 5.5 A seatbelt can provide the force needed to reduce safely the speed of a car driver to zero. The steering wheel can do the same job, but not without damaging the driver.

 2 The mass of a typical car is 1000 kg. A car going at 30 ms^{-1} (about 70 m.p.h.) can be stopped in 6.0s. Show that the brakes need to exert an average force of 5.0 kN.

Energy, page 222

Assignment trigger

Motorbikes

You may enjoy riding motorbikes. Your parents or guardians may be less happy about it.

What are the dangers of riding motorbikes?
What precautions can be taken by yourself and by the manufacturers?

If a practical assignment is developed, it is essential that a risk assessment is made and checked by your teacher/lecturer.

Could lead to possible assignments relating to Units 2 and 5.

Energy efficiency

Moving things from one place to another involves the use of energy. They need to be given *kinetic energy* to get them moving. More energy needs to be transferred during the motion to counteract the effects of *friction*. Any uphill component of the motion requires the transfer of some energy to *potential energy*. Finally, when the destination is reached, the kinetic energy must be safely transferred to heat energy.

Distance-to-fuel ratio

The energy input for a road vehicle is most conveniently measured as the volume of fuel consumed. The efficiency of the vehicle can then be evaluated by finding out the number of kilometres that vehicle can travel per litre of fuel.

For example, suppose that a car on a level motorway travelling at $30\,\text{ms}^{-1}$ uses up 5 litres of fuel for every 40 km it moves. Its *distance-to-fuel ratio* is then $\frac{40\,\text{km}}{5\,\text{litres}} = 8\,\text{km litre}^{-1}$.

Factors which affect motion

When you need to assess a transport system, there are three major questions to ask. How much energy does it use? How fast can it get objects up to speed? What is their speed? The answers depend on forces acting on the object, the **power** of the transport system and the amount of drag and **friction**.

Force

Figure 5.6a shows the two forces acting on the car when it is at rest before you push it. Gravity tugs downwards with a force of 5000 N; this is the *weight* of the car. The road is squashed by the car on top of it and exerts a 5000 N upwards force, the *reaction force*. The resultant force on the car is 0 N, so its motion does not change.

The power of a vehicle and the friction on it determine its acceleration and top speed.

Force, page 219

Quantifying motion, page 221

Newton's laws of motion, page 222

Energy, page 222

Figure 5.6a *The downwards tug of gravity is balanced by the upwards reaction force from the road .....*

Figure 5.6b *but if the forwards push is larger than the friction, the car will move forwards faster and faster.*

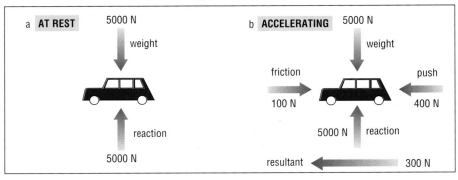

Two more forces come into play when you push the car. Figure 5.6b shows the forces acting while you are accelerating the car. You have applied a 400 N force forwards and *friction* in the car wheels provides a 100 N force backwards. The resultant force of 300 N *accelerates* the car forwards. It goes faster and faster.

Power

The power of a car fixes its maximum acceleration. Here is an example. An 800 kg car has a maximum engine power of 24 kW. Estimate how long it will take to get the speed from zero to 60 km/h on a level road.

The first step is to convert 60 km/h into a speed in ms^{-1}.

$$\Delta x = 60\,000 \text{ m}$$
$$v = ? \text{ ms}^{-1}$$
$$\Delta t = 60 \times 60 = 3\,600 \text{ s}$$
$$v = \Delta x/\Delta t = 60\,000/3\,600$$

Therefore $v = 16.7 \text{ ms}^{-1}$

The next step is to calculate how much work the engine will have to do on the car to get its speed up to 16.7 ms^{-1}. This will be the kinetic energy of the car.

$$KE = ? \text{ J}$$
$$m = 800 \text{ kg}$$
$$v = 16.7 \text{ ms}^{-1}$$
$$KE = \tfrac{1}{2} mv^2 = 0.5 \times 800 \times (16.7)^2$$

Therefore $KE = 112 \text{ kJ}$

If we ignore work done by the engine against friction, we can now calculate an estimate for the acceleration time.

$$P = 24 \text{ kW}$$
$$E = 112 \text{ kJ}$$
$$t = ? \text{ s}$$
$$P = E/t$$

So $24 = 112/t$

Therefore $t = 112/24 = 4.7 \text{ s}$

In practice, the car will take longer than this to reach 60 km/h. This is because not all of the energy transferred by the engine becomes kinetic energy of the car. Some becomes converted to heat energy because of friction.

Q 3 Show that a 200 kg motor bike with an engine power of 4 kW can accelerate from rest to 40 km/h in about 3 s.

Friction

The amount of *friction* increases as a vehicle speeds up. So the vehicle eventually reaches a speed where the friction force exactly balances your 400 N push. As you can see from Figure 5.7, this leaves a resultant force of 0 N. The vehicle stops accelerating. It keeps on moving at a constant speed in a straight line as long as your push exactly balances friction.

Maximum speed

The maximum speed of a vehicle travelling horizontally is set by the combined effects of *drag*, *friction* and *power*.

At low speeds, *rolling friction* dominates. This is due to surfaces moving against each other in the wheel bearings, drive shaft and gear box. It increases slowly with speed. At higher speed, *wind resistance* (or drag)

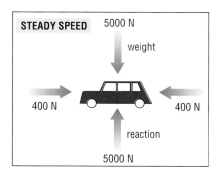

Figure 5.7 When a car is going at a steady speed, the forwards push from the engine is exactly balanced by the friction pushing backwards. The resultant force is zero.

213

dominates as it rises rapidly with speed. The wind resistance can be approximately calculated with the formula $F = fDAv^2$. Since the power of a car moving at a steady speed v is given by $P = Fv$, the two formulae can be combined as follows.

$$P = Fv, \qquad F = fDAv^2$$

Therefore $\quad P = (fDAv^2)v$

or $\quad P = fDAv^3$

This can be used to estimate the top speed of a vehicle. For example, suppose a van has a shape factor of 0.5, is 3 m wide and 2 m high, and is moving through air of density 1.2 kgm^{-3}. What is its top speed if its maximum engine power is 120kW?

$$
\begin{aligned}
P &= 120\,000 \text{ W} \\
f &= 0.5 \\
D &= 1.2 \text{ kgm}^{-3} \\
A &= 2 \times 3 = 6 \text{ m}^2 \\
v &= ? \text{ ms}^{-1} \\
P &= fDAv^3
\end{aligned}
$$

So $\quad 120\,000 = 0.5 \times 1.2 \times 6 \times v^3$

or $\qquad v^3 = \dfrac{120\,000}{(0.5 \times 1.2 \times 6)}$

Therefore $\qquad v = 32 \text{ ms}^{-1}$

You can check for yourself that this is about 70 m.p.h. It is only an estimate because the value of the shape factor changes slightly as the speed changes.

 4 A car which is 1.1 m high and 2.0 m wide has a shape factor of 0.25. If its top speed is 130 km/h, show that its maximum power is 31 kW.

Investigating motion

Laboratory techniques
Investigations into the motion of objects in the laboratory can involve measurements of force, velocity and acceleration.

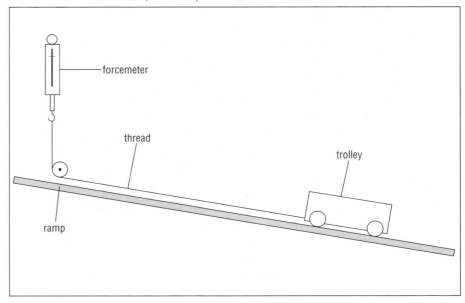

Figure 5.8 Using a forcemeter to measure the size of the gravitational force pulling the trolley along the plane

Force

Figure 5.8 shows a forcemeter in use. It uses the extension of a spring to measure the vertical force on the hook. Note the use of the pulley and thread. They change the direction of the force being measured, so that it is vertical. Forcemeters only give a correct reading when they are vertical.

Velocity

Laboratory measurements of velocity involve timing how long it takes an object to travel a known distance. Timers which can be turned on and off by electrical signals are ideal for this.

Force, page 219

Quantifying motion, page 221

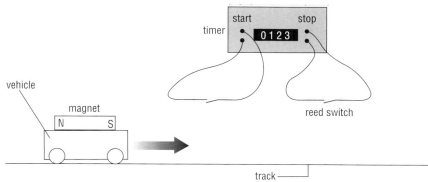

Figure 5.9 *How reed switches can be used to measure the speed of a vehicle.*

One arrangement is shown in Figure 5.9. It uses reed switches to sense the presence of the vehicle. The switches are placed a known distance apart in the path of the vehicle. A magnet stuck on the vehicle closes each switch for a moment when the vehicle passes it.

When the first switch is closed, the timer starts to count. When the vehicle passes the second switch, the timer stops. Its display shows how long the vehicle took to get from one reed switch to the other. It is then a simple matter to calculate the velocity of the vehicle.

Acceleration

The easiest way of measuring acceleration in the laboratory is with a comb, light gate and computer.

Figure 5.10 *Light gates and a computer being used to measure the acceleration of a vehicle as it travels down an inclined plane.*

The apparatus is similar to that shown in Figure 5.10. The comb is a piece of U-shaped card which projects from the top of the vehicle. The light gate consists of an infrared emitter and detector placed so that the comb can pass between them. The computer is connected to the detector, via an interface, so that it can time how long the comb takes to pass through the light gate.

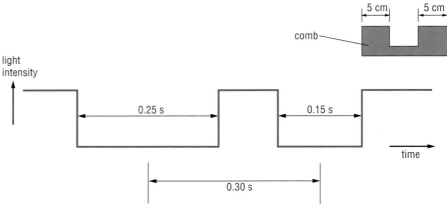

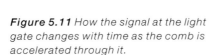

Figure 5.11 *How the signal at the light gate changes with time as the comb is accelerated through it.*

The graph of Figure 5.11 shows a typical signal at the detector when an accelerating vehicle passes through the light gate. Here are the calculations that the computer would perform to find the acceleration.

Start off by calculating the initial velocity.

$$v = ?\,\text{ms}^{-1}$$
$$\Delta x = 5\,\text{cm} = 0.05\,\text{m}$$
$$\Delta t = 0.25\,\text{s}$$
$$v = \frac{\Delta x}{\Delta t}$$

Therefore $\quad v = \frac{0.05}{0.25}$

or $\quad v = 0.20\,\text{ms}^{-1}$

Then calculate the final velocity.

$$v = ?\,\text{ms}^{-1}$$
$$\Delta x = 5\,\text{cm} = 0.05\,\text{m}$$
$$\Delta t = 0.15\,\text{s}$$
$$v = \frac{\Delta x}{\Delta t}$$

Therefore $\quad v = \frac{0.05}{0.15}$

or $\quad v = 0.33\,\text{ms}^{-1}$

Finally, calculate the acceleration.

$$a = ?\,\text{ms}^{-2}$$
$$a = \frac{\Delta v}{\Delta t}$$
$$\Delta v = 0.33 - 0.20 = 0.13\,\text{ms}^{-1}$$
$$\Delta t = 0.30\,\text{s}$$
$$a = \frac{0.13}{0.30}$$

Therefore $\quad a = 0.43\,\text{ms}^{-2}$

Figure 5.12 *A car speedometer*

Figure 5.13 *The lines drawn on this tachograph disc are a form of velocity-time graph for the lorry it came from.*

Field techniques

Investigations of motion outside the laboratory usually involve measurements of velocity. Values of distance and acceleration can then be calculated from these measurements.

Velocity

Most road vehicles can be fitted with a speedometer. These use a variety of techniques to obtain an electrical signal whose size is proportional to the speed of rotation of a wheel in contact with the ground (see Figure 5.12).

A record of how that signal changes with time can be obtained with a suitable computer or a chart recorder. The result is a velocity-time graph. An example is shown in Figure 5.13.

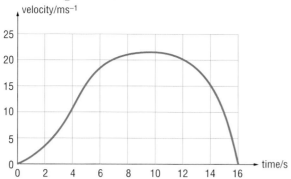

Figure 5.14 An example of a velocity-time graph. The object starts from rest, speeds up to a steady speed and then suddenly slows down to a stop again.

Distance

The distance gone by an object is the area under its velocity-time curve. For example, look at the graph Figure 5.14. The number of squares under the curve is about 21. Each square is worth 5 ms⁻¹ × 2 s= 10 m. So the total distance travelled was 21 × 10 = 210 m.

Acceleration

The acceleration of an object is given by the gradient of its velocity-time curve. If you look at Figure 5.15, you can see that the velocity changes by 20 ms^{-1} in the first 4.0 s. The initial acceleration of the vehicle was therefore $20 \text{ ms}^{-1}/4.0 \text{ s} = 5.0 \text{ ms}^{-2}$.

Safety features of vehicles

Any vehicle which transports people must be able to stop without damaging them. Many of the safety features of a modern car have been devised by scientists with the help of Newton's Laws of Motion.

Crumple zones

Suppose that a car moving at 10 ms⁻¹ collides with a very solid wall (see Figure 5.16). A 70 kg passenger in the car has to lose a lot of momentum and kinetic energy during the collision. Let's consider the momentum first.

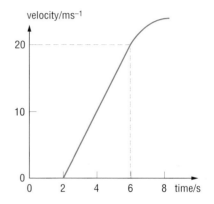

Figure 5.15 Velocity-time graphs can be used to measure acceleration. The speed increases by 20 ms⁻¹ in the first 4.0 s, so the initial acceleration is 5 ms⁻².

A safe vehicle ensures that the rate of change of momentum in an accident is as low as possible. It also provides somes means of safely transferring the kinetic energy of its passengers.

 Newton's Laws of Motion, page 222

$$p = ? \text{ Ns}$$
$$m = 70 \text{ kg}$$
$$v = 10 \text{ ms}^{-1}$$
$$p = mv$$
$$\text{So} \quad p = 70 \times 10$$
$$\text{Therefore} \quad p = 700 \text{ Ns}$$

Figure 5.16 A car crumples when it collides with a solid object.

The car will not stop instantly when it hits the wall. It will crumple, changing shape to absorb the car's kinetic energy. Suppose that the front of the car crumples by 0.5 m. Since its average speed during the impact is $\frac{(10 \text{ ms}^{-1} + 0 \text{ ms}^{-1})}{2} = 5 \text{ ms}^{-1}$, you can calculate the time of the impact.

$$\Delta x = 0.5 \text{ m}$$
$$v = 5 \text{ ms}^{-1}$$
$$\Delta t = ? \text{ s}$$
$$v = \frac{\Delta x}{\Delta t}$$

so

$$5 = \frac{0.5}{\Delta t}$$

or

$$\Delta t = \frac{0.5}{5}$$

Therefore $\Delta t = 0.1 \text{ s}$

Now you can find out the force needed to bring the passenger to a halt.

$$F = ? \text{ N}$$
$$\Delta p = 700 \text{ Ns}$$
$$\Delta t = 0.1 \text{ s}$$
$$F = \frac{\Delta p}{\Delta t}$$

so

$$F = \frac{700}{0.1}$$

Therefore $F = 7000 \text{ N}$

You can check for yourself that if the car had only crumpled by 5 cm instead of 50 cm then the force would have been ten times larger!

 5 A car driver has a mass of 80 kg. His car slams into a bridge at 15 ms⁻¹. If the car crumples by 1.5 m, show that the driver's seatbelt exerts a force of 6 kN on him, extracting 9 kJ of kinetic energy from him.

Seatbelts

The force of 7000 N needed to stop the passenger comes from his seatbelt. It also has to absorb much of the passenger's 3.5kJ of kinetic energy. It does this by stretching and breaking some of its fibres; this is why a seatbelt should always be replaced after a serious accident.

Air bags

A seatbelt will always stretch in a collision. This not only allows the person's kinetic energy to be safely transferred, it further increases the impact time. There is a danger in a high speed collision that the driver's seatbelt will stretch so much that she hits the steering wheel. An air bag fitted to the wheel can provide extra protection.

Figure 5.17 An air bag inflates automatically and rapidly when the car is suddenly decelerated. It applies the decelerating force for the driver over a much larger area than the steering wheel can. The lower pressure makes it less likely that the driver will be seriously injured.

Helmets

Riders of bicycles and motor-bikes need helmets to protect their heads. If the bike stops suddenly, the rider usually carries on moving, often head-first.

The helmet reduces the pressure of the impact of any subsequent collision by spreading the force over the whole head. The inner lining of the helmet squashes up, increasing the impact time and thus reducing the force needed to stop the rider. Finally, the helmet can absorb some of the rider's kinetic energy by permanently changing its shape. It is for this reason that a helmet should always be thrown away after an accident!

Assignment trigger

Road safety

Different safety regulations apply to car drivers and to lorry drivers.

What are these differences?
What safety features are built in to their vehicles?
How are safety features tested?

If a practical assignment is developed, it is essential that a risk assessment is made and checked by your teacher/lecturer.

Could lead to possible assignments relating to Units 2 and 5.

Force

Forces alter the motion of objects. Their size is measured in units of newtons (N). Their direction is usually shown in diagrams as an arrow. (See Figure 5.18.)

Components

It is always possible to replace a single force *F* with two other forces acting at right angles to each other. These are known as components of the original force. The sizes of these components depend on their directions.

Look at Figure 5.19. The force *F* acts at an angle θ to the horizontal. Its vertical component is *F*sinθ and its horizontal component is *F*cosθ.

Mass and weight

The mass of an object is measured in kilograms (kg). Its value tells you how much material the object contains. The mass of an object can only be altered by adding bits to it or by cutting bits off.

The weight of an object is the force of gravity on it. It is related to the mass of the object and the local strength of gravity.

> weight (N) = mass (kg) × gravity (Nkg^{-1})
> $W = mg$

The value of *g* (pronounced 'little gee') is approximately 9.8 Nkg^{-1} on the surface of the Earth. Its value changes by a few per cent as you move from one place on the Earth to another. Its value on the Moon is only 1.6 N kg^{-1}.

Friction

When an object rests on a surface, two forces act on the object. The reaction force is at right angles to the surface. The reaction force will

> Forces change the velocity of an object. They have a size and a direction. Weight and friction are forces.

Figure 5.18 *A rock on Earth with a mass of 10 kg is tugged down by gravity with a force of 98 N.*

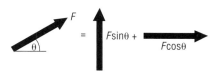

Figure 5.19 *A single force* F *can be treated as the sum of its two components* Fsinθ *and* Fcosθ *which act at right angles to each other.*

▶ Factors which affect motion, page 212

always be equal and opposite to the component of the object's weight at right angles to the surface.

Limiting friction

Friction acts along the direction of the surface.

If the object is not moving, then the friction acts against other forces parallel to the surface. Its largest (limiting) value is given by the formula:

$$\text{limiting friction (N)} = \text{coefficient of friction} \times \text{reaction (N)}$$
$$F_l = \mu R$$

The value of the coefficient of friction only depends on the nature of the surfaces in contact. Once the object is moving, the friction remains approximately fixed at the limiting value.

 6 A box sitting on the floor has mass of 40 kg. If the coefficient of friction between the box and the floor is 0.7, show that a force of just over 280 N will be needed to make the box slide along the floor.

Wind resistance

The wind resistance (or drag) on a vehicle can be approximately calculated by using the formula:

$F = fDAv^2$
F is the wind resistance (N)
f is the shape factor of the vehicle
D is the density of the air (kgm^{-3})
A is the vehicle's cross-sectional area (m^2)
v is the speed of the vehicle (ms^{-1})

The value of the shape factor is fixed by how easily air can flow past the vehicle. A streamlined vehicle allows air to flow past with the minimum of turbulence, giving a low value for the shape factor (see Figure 5.20). A football has a shape factor close to 1.0. The shape factor of a javelin is much smaller.

Figure 5.20 *Investigating how air travels past a car at high speed. Jets of smoke, or streamers, are blown towards the car in a wind tunnel. If the air travels smoothly past the car, its shape factor will be low.*

 7 Things falling freely through the air reach a maximum speed (their terminal velocity) when air resistance equals their weight. If a girl of mass 50 kg falling through air of density 1.2 kgm^{-3} is 1.5 m high and 0.3 m across, show that her terminal velocity is 30 ms^{-1}. Assume a shape factor of 1.0.

Assignment trigger

Windmills
Windmills can be used to capture wind energy.

What determines their design, location and separation?
How can the wind speed be measured in specific locations?

If a practical assignment is developed, it is essential that a risk assessment is made and checked by your teacher/lecturer.

Could lead to possible assignments relating to Unit 5.

Quantifying motion

The distinction between **speed**, **velocity** and **acceleration** must be borne in mind when calculating values for each.

> **Velocity is the rate of change of position in a given direction. Acceleration is the rate of change of velocity.**

Speed

The speed of an object is how far it travels in one second.

$$\text{speed (ms}^{-1}) = \frac{\text{distance travelled (m)}}{\text{time taken (s)}}$$

$$v = \frac{\Delta x}{\Delta t}$$

Velocity

The velocity of an object is a vector. This means that it has a magnitude and a direction. The magnitude is the speed of the object. The direction is the direction of the object's motion.

Changes of velocity can be worked out with the help of vector diagrams. An example is shown in Figure 5.21.

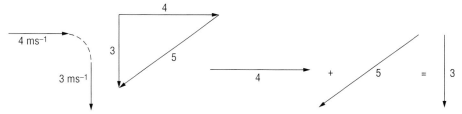

Figure 5.21 *Using a vector diagram to calculate the change of velocity of an object going round a corner. The speed only changes by 1 ms⁻¹, but the velocity changes by 5 ms⁻¹ because it is a vector.*

Speed is *not* a vector. It does not change if the direction does. However, velocity can change if only the direction changes. So an object going in a circle at a constant speed has a continually changing velocity.

Acceleration

Acceleration is the rate at which an object's velocity is changing. If it is negative, the object is slowing down or decelerating.

$$\text{acceleration (ms}^{-2}) = \frac{\text{velocity change (ms}^{-1})}{\text{time taken (s)}}$$

$$a = \frac{\Delta v}{\Delta t}$$

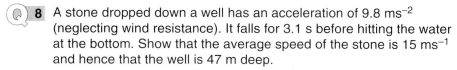

Q 8 A stone dropped down a well has an acceleration of 9.8 ms⁻² (neglecting wind resistance). It falls for 3.1 s before hitting the water at the bottom. Show that the average speed of the stone is 15 ms⁻¹ and hence that the well is 47 m deep.

Newton's Laws of Motion

These three laws are the secret to understanding the physics of motion.

First Law

If the resultant force on an object is zero, then its velocity does not change.

Second Law

The resultant force on an object is the product of its mass and its acceleration.

$$\text{force (N)} = \text{mass (kg)} \times \text{acceleration (ms}^{-2})$$
$$F = ma$$

Third Law

When two objects interact, they exert equal and opposite forces on each other.

Momentum

Momentum is a very useful concept for dealing with crashes and collisions. Momentum is mass times velocity. Heavy, fast-moving things have a lot of momentum.

$$\text{momentum (Ns)} = \text{mass (kg)} \times \text{velocity (ms}^{-1})$$
$$p = mv$$

Newton's Laws of Motion can be rewritten in terms of momentum. The First Law says if the resultant force on an object is zero, its momentum does not change. The Second Law says that the resultant force on an object is equal to the rate at which its momentum is changing.

$$\text{force (N)} = \frac{\text{momentum change (Ns)}}{\text{time taken (s)}}$$
$$F = \frac{\Delta p}{\Delta t}$$

The rate of change of momentum of an object (its impulse) is equal to the resultant force on it. The total momentum of interacting objects does not change. Any work done on an object transfers energy to it. That energy can be kinetic, potential or heat.

Impulse

The change in momentum of an object (Δp) is sometimes called its **impulse**. Newton's Third Law says that when two objects interact with each other, they have equal and opposite impulses. In other words, they can exchange momentum with each other, but the total momentum cannot change. It is conserved.

Energy

All transport systems rely on the use of fuel. The concept of energy is the key to understanding how to make the best use of that fuel.

Work and energy

Work has a special meaning in science. When a force moves along the direction in which it is pushing, that force does some work. Work is measured in units of joules.

$$\text{work (J)} = \text{force (N)} \times \text{distance (m)}$$
$$E = Fd$$

Whenever work is done on an object, that object gains some energy. The energy gained is always equal to the work done.

Q 9 A car at 30 ms^{-1} stops in about 60 m when the brakes are applied. If the brakes exert a force of 5 kN on the car, show that 300 kJ of heat energy is transferred to the brake drums.

Potential energy

Any object which is moved away from the surface of the Earth gains energy at the same time. That energy is called gravitational potential energy, often called just **potential energy**. As an object moves towards the Earth, it loses potential energy.

potential energy gained (J) = mass (kg) × gravity (Nkg^{-1}) × height increase (m)
$$PE = mgh$$

 10 A typical bath holds 100 kg of water. Show that a bathful of water on the second floor of a house (9.0 m above ground level) has 9 kJ of potential energy.

Kinetic energy

Forces applied to objects can make them speed up. Work done accelerating an object increases its kinetic energy.

kinetic energy (J) = × mass (kg) × velocity^2 (ms^{-1})
$$KE = \tfrac{1}{2}mv^2$$

 11 A sprinter can travel 100 m in 10 s. If her mass is 65 kg, show that her maximum kinetic energy is 3.3 kJ.

Heat energy

Vehicles are stopped safely with the help of friction. Brake pads are squeezed onto the rotating wheels, transferring their kinetic energy into heat energy. In this way, all of the kinetic energy of a vehicle can be transferred into heat energy, bringing the car to a halt.

Power

The power of a device is the rate at which it can transfer energy. Power is measured in watts.

power (W) = $\dfrac{\text{energy (J)}}{\text{time (s)}}$
$$P = \frac{E}{t}$$

There is an alternative formula for power in terms of the velocity of a vehicle and the driving force required to keep it moving at that velocity. (The resultant force on a vehicle moving at a steady velocity is zero.)

power (W) = force (N) × velocity (ms^{-1})
$$P = Fv$$

 12 Human beings have a maximum continuous power of about 100 W. Show that they can do about 3 MJ of work in an eight hour day.

Controlling fluid flow

Fluids can be used to transport energy, chemical reagents, heat and other forms of energy.

Why control the transport of fluids?

There are several reasons why we need to control the flow of **fluids**. Here they are.

Transporting energy sources

Oil is extracted from the rocks deep underground wherever it can be found. Quite often, this is far away from where people would like to use the oil. Pipes are widely used to transport crude oil from the well-head to the nearest port. The oil can then be pumped onto a tanker and transported across the sea to where it is going to be used.

Natural gas is another example of an energy source which is a fluid. Liquid fuels (such as petrol and alcohol) can be safely transported in containers carried on lorries or trains. They don't have to be moved down pipes. Gases, however, have to be compressed when transported by lorry or train. This is because they have a low density. The compression increases their density, so that a container-load contains a reasonable quantity of gas. Compressed gases are difficult and dangerous to handle, so the best way to move gases from one place to another is along pipes (see Figure 5.22).

Figure 5.22 *Pipes used for transporting hazardous gases*

Chemical processing

Much industrial chemistry involves the controlled mixing of fluids. A large chemical works is instantly recognisable by the pipes which carry the chemicals from one place to another (see Figure 5.23). The manufacture of materials on a large scale in such factories demands very fine control of the rate at which chemicals flow down tubes into reaction vessels.

Figure 5.23 *Just a few of the many hundreds of pipes at a typical chemical works*

Heat transfer

Fluids are widely used to move heat energy from one place to another. Central heating systems use heated air or water to transfer heat energy from an energy source (such as natural gas or electricity) to the interior of buildings.

Hydraulic and pneumatic machinery

Hydraulic machines use compressed oil to transfer energy from a pump to a piston or other type of actuator. Pneumatic systems do the same thing, but use compressed air as the working fluid.

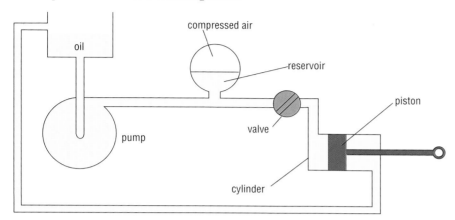

Figure 5.24 illustrates the basic principles behind hydraulic machinery. A **pump** keeps the oil in the reservoir at a high pressure. This can be let through a **valve** to a piston, forcing it from one end of the cylinder to the other. The low pressure oil at the other side of the piston is forced out of the cylinder, back to the pump. Other valves can be used to reverse the process.

Figure 5.24 A very basic hydraulic system

Flowing fluids are controlled with pumps and valves.

Drainage

Managing water resources is very important for our well-being. Water pours down on us regularly from the skies. We don't want it in our buildings, so we arrange channels and pipes to catch rainwater and feed it safely to reservoirs or allow it to sink safely into the ground. The ability to control the flow of water down rivers is vital for irrigating crops and averting floods.

Assignment trigger

Rain water

Sewers are used to remove rain water from roads during storms. If the water flows too slowly sewage can overflow into streets and houses.

How does the design of a sewer affect the rate at which sewage can flow down it?
How could you model a sewer and measure the rate of flow?

If a practical assignment is developed, it is essential that a risk assessment is made and checked by your teacher/lecturer.

Could lead to possible assignments relating to Unit 5.

Methods of controlling fluid flow

The rate at which a fluid flows through a system can be controlled in two ways. You can put obstructions in its path, or you can adjust the pressure which is pushing it through.

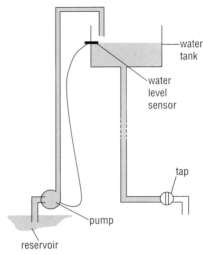

 Figure 5.25 *The water sensor switches on the pump every time that the level of water in the tank gets too low. This ensures that the water pressure in the tap remains constant.*

Driving pressure, page 231

Pressure

Figure 5.25 shows how a pump can be used to control the supply of drinking water in a town. The pump forces water from the reservoir to a large tank at the top of a hill overlooking the town. A sensor switches on the pump whenever the water in the tank is below a certain level. This ensures that each of the water taps in the town have a fixed pressure of water inside them. No matter how many taps are opened, the water gushes out of them at the same rate.

Types of pump

Most large-scale pumps for liquids are *centrifugal* ones. The liquid is fed in at the centre of a spinning chamber. As the liquid starts to spin round with the chamber, it is flung outwards at high pressure. An example of one in action is shown in Figure 5.26.

Figure 5.26 *A centrifugal pump from a fire-fighting vehicle*

Peristaltic pumps are used when the fluid must not be contaminated by the pump. As you can see from Figure 5.27, the fluid is contained in a flexible plastic pipe which passes underneath a set of rollers. These force the fluid through the pipe. Peristaltic pumps are always used for handling blood and other biologically sensitive liquids.

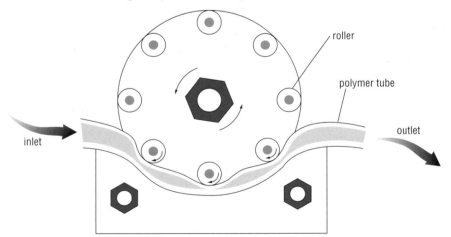

Figure 5.27 *Pumping blood without contaminating it. The blood in the polymer tube is never in contact with the rollers which push it along.*

The pressure of a gas is raised with a *compressor*. Figure 5.28 illustrates a refrigerator compressor. It is basically a piston in a cylinder, with an arrangement of valves to ensure that the low pressure gas enters the system and high pressure gas leaves it.

Figure 5.28 *The compressor from a refrigerator*

Variable pressure

The rate at which a pump can force fluid through a pipe depends on the rate at which the pump transfers energy. So the speed of flow can be controlled by adjusting the electrical power delivered to the pump.

Figure 5.29 shows how the power of an electric pump can be controlled with a variable resistor. As the resistance is increased, there is less current through the motor, so it pumps the fluid round more slowly. An alternative method, which uses fixed resistors, is shown in Figure 5.30. Each setting of the rotary switch gives the pump a different power.

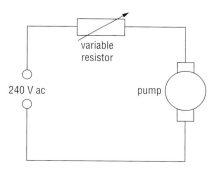

Figure 5.29 Using a variable resistor to control the output power of an electrical pump.

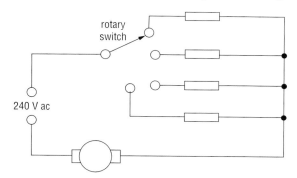

Figure 5.30 Each of the resistors has a different value. So each setting of the rotary switch results in a different pumping speed.

Valves

The simplest form of valve is a tap. As you unscrew it, more and more water is allowed to pour through. When it is screwed down tightly, no fluid can get through at all.

Figure 5.31 shows a solenoid valve. They allow electrical signals to control the flow of fluids in pipes (domestic washing machines contain several).

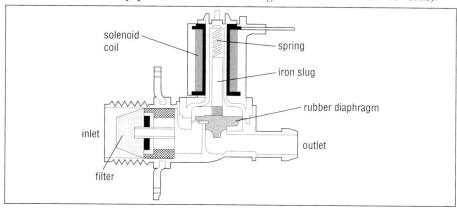

Figure 5.31 A solenoid valve

This is how the valve works. When enough current flows in the coil, the slug of iron is attracted into it, releasing pressure on the rubber diaphragm and allowing the liquid to get from one tube to the other. As soon as the current is turned off, the spring pushes the iron slug back and the flow of liquid is cut off.

Measuring fluid flow

The simplest way of measuring the rate at which a liquid flows down a pipe or a channel is with a bucket, a balance and a stopclock. The bucket is used to collect all of the liquid which flows out of the system in a fixed time. The balance is then used to weigh the contents of the bucket. This give you enough information to calculate the mass flow rate (the mass of liquid delivered per second).

For example, suppose that the bucket collects 12 kg of water per minute. The mass flow rate is then 12 kg/60 s = 0.20 kgs^{-1}.

Flowmeters

Unfortunately, the direct method outlined above only works in simple situations. For example, you can't use it to find the flow rate inside the pipes of a closed system such as a chemical works. Nor is it any use for finding the flow rate down a stream or river!

Turbine flowmeters

▶ Fluid flow, page 233

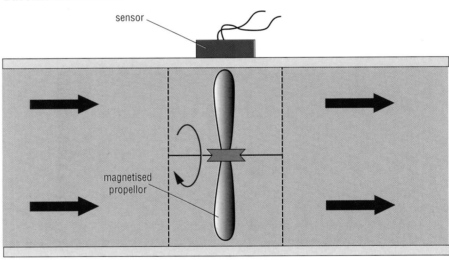

sensor

magnetised
propellor

Figure 5.32 *A turbine flowmeter*

Figure 5.32 shows a device which can be used to measure the volume flow rate of a liquid or gas through a pipe without needing to break it open. The turbine is a magnetised propeller which can rotate freely inside the pipe on low-friction bearings. As the fluid flows along the pipe, it turns the turbine round. A sensor placed outside the pipe (made from a non-magnetic material) detects the rotation of the turbine; the output is a series of pulses whose rate can be measured by an appropriate set of electronic circuits.

Turbine flowmeters need to be calibrated by the bucket, balance and stopwatch method outlined above. Their reading is sensitive to the density, viscosity and temperature of the fluid. They have the advantage of being able to measure flow rates without slowing the fluid down very much.

Venturi meters

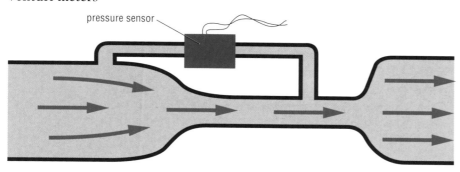

Figure 5.33 A venturi meter

A different sort of flowmeter is illustrated in Figure 5.33. It only works for liquids whose flow is not turbulent. As the liquid enters the venturi tube it is forced to speed up as it passes through the narrow region. The fast moving liquid is at a lower pressure than the slower moving liquid. If you can measure this pressure drop, the speed of the liquid in the tube can be approximately calculated with the following formula.

▶ Bernoulli's theorem, page 235

$v = A_v(2\Delta P/D(A_t^2 - A_v^2))^{\frac{1}{2}}$
where v is the speed of the liquid (ms^{-1}),
A_t is the cross-section area of the tube (m^2),
A_v is the cross-section area of the venturi (m^2),
ΔP is the pressure difference (Nm^{-2}) and
D is the density of the liquid (m^3).

13 Water (density 1000 kgm^{-3}) flows from a tube of diameter 5.0 cm to one whose diameter is 1.0 cm. If the pressure rises by 1.0 kPa as the water enters the narrow tube, show that its speed in the wide tube is 5.7 cm s^{-1}.

Orifice plates work on the same principle as venturi tubes. They consist of a plate with a hole in it (the orifice) which is inserted into the stream of fluid. The difference in pressure between the liquid inside and outside the orifice is a measure of the speed of the fluid in the system.

Pitot tubes

Another device which measures the speed of flow of a fluid is shown in Figure 5.34. It is called a Pitot tube. Like the venturi meter, it only works for liquids whose flow is not turbulent. It also assumes a constant density D. This is how it works.

The speed of fluid flow can be found by measuring the pressure change as fluids flow through gaps.

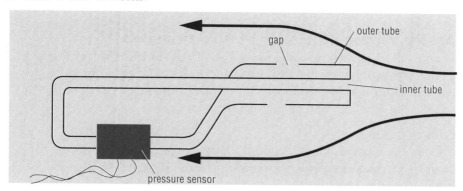

gap
outer tube
inner tube
pressure sensor

Figure 5.34 A Pitot tube

Two tubes, one inside the other, are connected to a pressure sensor. The open end of the inner tube points directly into the flow. The outer tube has gaps in it. The pressure sensor measures the difference in pressure between the fluids in the two tubes.

The fluid at the tip of the inner tube is static, at a pressure P. The gap in the outer tube is at a lower pressure, $P - \frac{1}{2}Dv^2$, because it is close to fluid with a speed v. The difference in pressure between the outer and inner tubes can be measured with a manometer or by some suitable electronic sensor.

 14 Pitot tubes are often used to measure the speed of aeroplanes. Show that for an aeroplane moving through air of density 1.2 kgm^{-3} at a speed of 150ms^{-1}, the pressure difference between the inner and outer tubes will be 13500 Nm^{-2}.

Wind speed

The simplest method of measuring the speed of the wind is with a rotating anemometer (see Figure 5.35). The rotating cups turn a small dynamo, producing a voltage which increases as the wind speed increases.

The hot wire anemometer is smaller and interferes less with the wind. It contains a grid of wires which carry an electric current. This heats up the wires, increasing their resistance. As the wind passes across the wires, it carries heat energy away. The faster the wind blows, the cooler the wires will become. Since the resistance varies with temperature, and the current depends on the resistance, an ammeter reading can be used as a measure of the wind speed.

Both types of anemometer need to be calibrated by mounting them on a vehicle moving through still air at a series of known speeds.

Figure 5.35 *An anemometer*

Assignment trigger

Windy cities

Large buildings tend to alter local wind currents considerably.

Why do leaves build up in a particular corner?
What other consequences are there?
Why is Chicago called the 'windy city'?

If a practical assignment is developed, it is essential that a risk assessment is made and checked by your teacher/lecturer.

Could lead to possible assignments relating to Unit 5.

> **The energy transferred to a fluid moving down a pipe is equal to the volume transferred $\times$ pressure drop.**

Assessing the efficiency of fluid transport

To move fluids from one place to another involves the transfer of energy. The kinetic energy of the fluid is continuously transferred into heat energy via friction of the moving fluid with itself and the walls of the system. An efficient system wastes as little energy as possible.

Energy input

The energy input needed for a fluid transport system is most easily measured if an electrical pump is used. The input power can then be calculated from measurements of the current and voltage of the pump. Figure 5.36 shows how the meters need to be connected. The power can be calculated with the formula $P = VI$.

$P = VI$ where P is the electrical power of the pump (W), V is the voltage drop across the pump (V) and I is the current through the pump (A).

For example, a pump which draws 5 A from a 12 V supply has a power of 12 V × 5 A = 60 W. It transfers electrical energy into other forms at a rate of 60 J per second.

Calculating energy transfer

You can calculate the amount of **energy transferred** by a liquid moving through a system if you know the pressure drop which is driving that liquid.

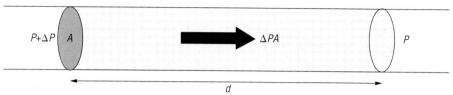

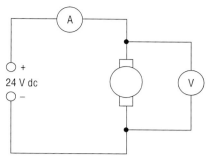

Figure 5.36 *Using an ammeter and a voltmeter to measure the input power of an electric pump*

Figure 5.37 *As a liquid moves along a tube, its pressure drops.*

Consider the simple system shown in Figure 5.37. The pressure drop from one end of the tube to the other is ΔP. The overall force pushing the liquid through the tube is therefore $\Delta P \times A$, where A is the cross-section area. To force liquid from one end of the system to another involves doing work $E = Fd = \Delta PAd$. But $V = Ad$, the volume of liquid being forced through. So $E = V\Delta P$. The energy needed to feed a given volume of water through a system only depends on the pressure difference across the ends of it.

For example, the pressure of water behind a domestic tap is typically $50\ \text{kNm}^{-2}$. (You can check for yourself that this is equivalent to a head of 5m of water.) How much energy has to be transferred for each litre of water delivered by the tap?

$$E = ?$$
$$\Delta P = 50 \times 10^3\ \text{Nm}^{-2}$$
$$V = 1.0\ \text{litre} = 0.001\ \text{m}^3$$
$$E = V\Delta P$$
$$= 0.001 \times 50\ 000$$
$$= 50\ \text{J}$$

Q 15 Draw a flow diagram to show the energy transfers involved in moving water from a reservoir to the kitchen sink.

Driving pressure

A fluid (liquid or gas) will only flow from one place to another if there is a pressure drop along the way. Each portion of fluid is pushed from high pressure to a lower pressure.

Force and pressure

Look at Figure 5.38. The shaded portion of fluid is subject to forces from the fluid on either side. The pressure of the fluid on the left hand side is P, acting on an area A. So the force pushing the shaded fluid to the right is PA.

> **Pressure is force per unit area.**
>
> $$\text{Pressure (Nm}^{-2}) = \frac{\text{force (N)}}{\text{area (m}^2).}$$
>
> **It can be measured with a manometer.**

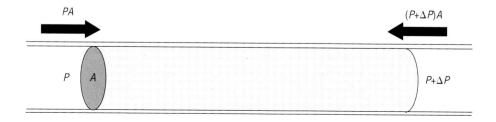

Figure 5.38 *The force which keeps the liquid moving against friction comes from the pressure drop along the pipe*

$$\text{pressure } (\text{Nm}^{-2}) = \frac{\text{force (N)}}{\text{area } (\text{m}^2)}$$

$$P = \frac{F}{A}$$

(The Pa (pascal) is an alternative unit for pressure. 1 Pa = 1 Nm^{-2}.)

The pressure on the right hand side is higher, $P + \Delta P$. So the force pushing the shaded fluid to the left is $(P + \Delta P)A$ or $PA + \Delta PA$. Since these forces are acting in opposite directions, the resultant force on the shaded fluid is ΔPA, pushing it to the left.

Pressure and height

The pressure in a liquid increases the further you are under the surface. This is because the pressure comes from the weight of the liquid above you.

$$\text{pressure } (\text{Nm}^{-2}) = \text{density } (\text{kgm}^{-3}) \times \text{gravity } (\text{Nkg}^{-1}) \times \text{vertical depth (m)}$$
$$P = Dgh$$

Gravity is often used as the driving pressure for making drinking water flow through domestic pipes. An example is shown in Figure 5.39. The tap is 3.0 m below the top of the water in the tank. Since the density of water is 1000 kgm^{-3}, you can use the above formula to calculate the pressure of water in the tap.

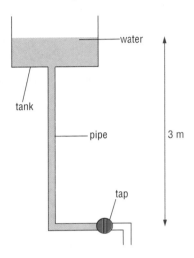

Figure 5.39 *The water in the tank exerts a pressure of 30 kPa on the tap.*

$$
\begin{aligned}
P &= ?\,\text{Nm}^{-2} \\
D &= 1000\,\text{kgm}^{-3} \\
g &= 10\,\text{Nkg}^{-1} \\
h &= 3.0\,\text{m} \\
P &= Dgh \\
  &= 1000 \times 10 \times 3 \\
  &= 30\,000\,\text{Nm}^{-2} \\
  &= 30\,\text{kNm}^{-2} \\
  &= 30\,\text{kPa}
\end{aligned}
$$

So when the tap is opened, there is a pressure drop of 30 kPa across it. This accelerates the water through the tap.

Manometers

Manometers are pressure meters. A liquid can be used to indicate its own pressure by letting it flow up a tube. Look at Figure 5.40. The venturi meter has two small outlets which lead to vertical glass tubes. Some of the liquid flowing through the meter moves up these tubes. As the liquid climbs up the tube, it exerts a pressure on the liquid in the pipe. Eventually, the pressure of the liquid in the tube exactly balances the pressure in the pipe and no more liquid flows into the tubes.

This means that the pressure drop ΔP in the meter can be measured by finding the difference in level of the liquid in the tubes. For example, suppose that the liquid is oil (density 800 kgm^{-3}) and the difference in levels is 25 cm.

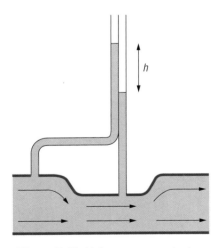

Figure 5.40 *Using a manometer to measure the pressure drop as a liquid flows through a venturi meter.*

$$
\begin{aligned}
\Delta P &= ?\,\text{Nm}^{-2} \\
D &= 800\,\text{kgm}^{-3} \\
g &= 10\,\text{Nkg}^{-1} \\
h &= 0.25\,\text{m} \\
P &= Dgh \\
  &= 800 \times 10 \times 0.25 \\
  &= 2\,000\,\text{Nm}^{-2}
\end{aligned}
$$

16 Mercury columns (density 13 550 kgm⁻³) can be used to measure atmospheric pressure (about 100 kPa). Show that atmospheric pressure can support a column of mercury which is 76 cm high.

Fluid flow

There are two ways in which fluids can flow. One (called **laminar flow**) is orderly and efficient. The other (**turbulent flow**) is chaotic and wasteful.

Laminar flow

In laminar flow, the pattern of movement in a fluid is steady, not changing with time. Figure 5.41 illustrates the behaviour of a fluid which has laminar flow. The streamlines show the path taken by various parts of the fluid as it travels down the pipe.

The streamlines have different lengths. The length of the streamline indicates the speed of the fluid at that point in the pipe. The speed is always zero for the fluid right next to the pipe. This is because there is friction between the pipe and the fluid. There is also friction between fluid following different streamlines, so the fastest moving fluid is always in the centre of the pipe.

Flow down pipes

The average speed of the fluid in a pipe is proportional to the pressure drop (assuming that the flow is laminar).

$$v = \left(\frac{r^2}{8\mu l}\right) \times \Delta P$$

where
- v is the average speed of the fluid (ms⁻¹),
- r is the radius of the pipe (m),
- l is the length of the pipe (m),
- μ is the viscosity of the fluid (kgm⁻¹s⁻¹) and
- ΔP is the pressure drop across the pipe (Nm⁻²).

> Laminar flow is steady and predictable. Turbulent flow is variable and unpredictable.

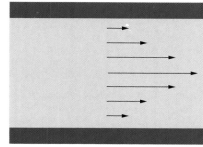
Figure 5.41 *Illustrating laminar flow in a liquid. The arrows show the path taken by different portions of the liquid in the same time.*

Table 5.1 Some typical values for the viscosity of various fluids at room temperature and pressure. (The viscosity of many fluids drops rapidly as the temperature is raised.)

Fluid	Viscosity/kgm⁻¹s⁻¹
Air	2×10^{-5}
Water	89×10^{-5}
Alcohol	106×10^{-5}
Petrol	60×10^{-5}

 17 Show that if all the dimensions of a pipe are doubled, the average speed of the fluid going through it is also doubled.

Speed and flow rate

The average speed of the liquid in a pipe can be used to calculate the flow rate. Figure 5.42 shows an example. A greenhouse has a tank of water which fills up with water which drains from the roof when it rains.

That water flows through a long pipe to the plants. If the end of the pipe is 2.0 m below the surface of the water in the tank, how much water is delivered to the plants in an hour?

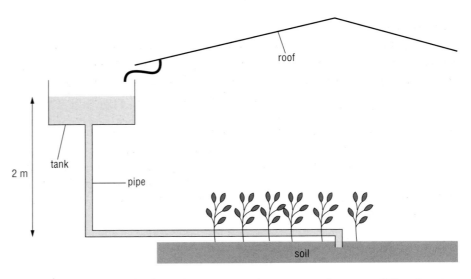

Figure 5.42 *A rainwater irrigation system for a greenhouse*

The first step is to calculate the pressure drop across the pipe. (The density of water is $1000 \, \text{kgm}^{-3}$.)

$$\Delta P = ? \, \text{Nm}^{-2}$$
$$D = 1000 \, \text{kgm}^{-3}$$
$$g = 10 \, \text{Nkg}^{-1}$$
$$h = 2.0 \, \text{m}$$
$$\Delta P = Dgh$$
$$= 1000 \times 10 \times 2.0$$
$$= 2 \times 10^4 \, \text{Nm}^{-2}$$

Now you can calculate the average speed v of the water. (The viscosity of water is about $1 \times 10^{-3} \, \text{kgm}^{-1}\text{s}^{-1}$.)

$$\Delta P = 2 \times 10^4 \, \text{Nm}^{-2}$$
$$r = 1.0 \times 10^{-3} \, \text{m}$$
$$l = 5 \, \text{m}$$
$$\mu = 1 \times 10^{-3} \, \text{kgm}^{-1}\text{s}^{-1}$$
$$v = ? \quad \text{ms}^{-1}$$
$$v = \left(\frac{r^2}{8\mu l}\right) \times \Delta P$$
$$= ((1.0 \times 10^{-3})^2/8 \times 10^{-3} \times 5) \times 2 \times 10^4$$
$$= 0.50 \, \text{ms}^{-1}$$

The volume of water which leaves the end of the pipe in each second can now be calculated. It will be a cylinder of radius 1 mm and length 0.5 m.

$$V = ? \, \text{m}^3$$
$$r = 1.0 \times 10^{-3} \, \text{m}$$
$$l = 0.5 \, \text{m}$$
$$V = \pi r^2 l$$
$$= \pi \times 10^{-6} \times 0.5$$
$$= 1.6 \times 10^{-6} \, \text{m}^3$$

Finally, you calculate the volume delivered per hour. It will be
$$1.6 \times 10^{-6} \, \text{m}^3\text{s}^{-1} \times 3600 \, \text{s} = 5.7 \times 10^{-3} \, \text{m}^3 \text{ or } 5.7 \text{ litres.}$$

Q 18 A hosepipe delivers water (density $1000 \, \text{kgm}^{-3}$) at a rate of 20 kg per minute. If the internal diameter of the hosepipe is 25 mm, show that the average speed of the water inside it is $0.7 \, \text{ms}^{-1}$

Turbulence

When the flow of a liquid through a pipe or channel is laminar, the pressure drop is proportional to the speed of the liquid. The liquid flows in a steady, ordered and predictable manner. As the speed of the fluid is increased, the flow will suddenly become turbulent. The behaviour of the liquid will become chaotic and unpredictable, with lots of circulating eddies and vortices. You can see these in a fast-flowing river or stream.

For a turbulent liquid, the pressure drop tends to be proportional to the square of the speed. So the pressure drop rises rapidly as the speed increases.

Provided that the speed of the fluid is small enough, the flow in a pipe will be laminar. The speed at which turbulence sets in can be estimated with the following formula.

$$v \approx 1000 \times \left(\frac{\mu}{Dr} \right)$$

For example, for water (density 1000 kgm^{-3}, viscosity $10^{-3} \text{ kgm}^{-1}\text{s}^{-1}$) flowing down a pipe of radius 1 cm, the flow is turbulent if the speed is below $1000 \times (\dfrac{10^{-3}}{(1000 \times 0.01)}) = 0.1 \text{ ms}^{-1}$.

Q 19 Show that petrol (viscosity $6 \times 10^{-4} \text{ kgm}^{-1}\text{s}^{-1}$, density 700 kgm^{-3}) flowing down a pipe of diameter 15 mm will become turbulent if its speed exceeds 100 mm s^{-1}.

Bernoulli's theorem

When a liquid has laminar flow, the rate at which the liquid's kinetic energy is transferred into heat energy is relatively small. Each portion of the liquid has two sorts of energy. It has strain energy because it is compressed. It also has kinetic energy because it is moving. So as the portion flows along, the sum of its kinetic and strain energy doesn't change. This was first expressed in algebraic form by Bernoulli.

The pressure of a fluid drops as it speeds up.

$$P + \tfrac{1}{2}Dv^2 = \text{constant as the liquid moves}$$

where P is the pressure of the liquid, D is its density and v is its speed. (The strain energy is fixed by P and the kinetic energy is fixed by $\tfrac{1}{2}Dv^2$.)

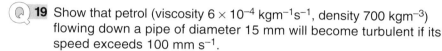

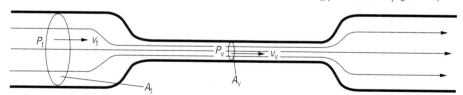

Figure 5.43 *Applying Bernoulli's theorem to a venturi meter*

Bernouilli's theorem is behind the design of venturi flowmeters. Look at Figure 5.43. As the liquid flows through the meter it has to speed up, so **its pressure drops**.

$$P_t + \tfrac{1}{2}Dv_t^2 = P_v + \tfrac{1}{2}Dv_v^2$$

The volume of liquid which passes through the tube per second is $A_t v_t$. Since we are assuming that the density of the liquid is constant, this is therefore the same as the volume which passes through the venturi meter per second which is $A_v v_v$.

$$A_v v_v = A_t v_t$$
$$\text{so} \quad v_v = v_t \times (A_t)/A_v$$

When this is combined with Bernoulli's theorem, you end up with an expression for the speed of the fluid in the tube in terms of the pressure drop ΔP between the tube and the venturi.

$$\Delta P = P_t - P_v = \tfrac{1}{2}D(v_v{}^2 - v_t{}^2)$$
$$= \tfrac{1}{2}Dv_t{}^2\left(\left(\frac{A_t}{A_v}\right)^2 - 1\right)$$

20 Find out how Bernoulli's theorem allows aeroplanes to fly.

Controlling thermal energy transfer

Controlling heat energy loss

After food and water, your most important need is heat energy. Unless your surroundings are at an appropriate temperature, you are not going to be comfortable. Indeed, if the temperature is too high or too low, you may not survive for very long!

If you wish to fix the temperature of something, then you have to control the rate at which heat energy enters and leaves it. Its temperature will only be stable if heat energy enters it as fast as it leaves it again.

Natural flow of heat energy

It is not possible to prevent an object from exchanging heat energy with its surroundings. Heat energy will always flow from a hot place to a colder one. The end result of this process is thermal equilibrium; the object ends up at the same temperature as its surroundings.

There are three ways in which heat energy can leave an object. Heat energy can be **conducted** through any solid contact with the object. **Convection** currents in fluids around the object can remove heat energy. Finally, the object can emit heat **radiation** from its surface.

Reducing conduction

The rate at which heat energy is conducted through a solid depends on its shape, size and thermal conductivity. All metals are good conductors. Nonmetals which are poor conductors of heat are called insulators.

Table 5.2 Values for the thermal conductivity k of various solid materials

Material	k/Wm^{-1}K^{-1}	Material	k/Wm^{-1}K^{-1}
Copper	400	Glass	1.1
Aluminium	200	Brick	0.7
Iron	60	Wood	0.15
Concrete	1.5		

The formula for calculating the rate of heat flow P through a solid is $P = kA\frac{\Delta T}{x}$. So if you need to reduce P, you need to keep the cross-sectional area A small and the length x large. The best way to do this is by suspending it from wires (see Figure 5.44).

21 Show that if you double all of the dimensions of a wire, the rate of heat flow through it is also doubled.

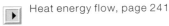
Objects lose heat energy by conduction, convection or radiation.

Heat energy flow, page 241

Figure 5.44 *The filament of a light bulb converts electrical energy into heat and light radiation. The rate at which it loses heat energy by conduction is reduced by suspending it from long thin wires.*

Reducing convection

Since convection takes place at the surface of an object, you can reduce this type of heat loss by having a small surface area. An object which is shaped like a sphere or cube will lose heat far less rapidly than one which is shaped like a plate or a plank.

The other way of reducing convection is to cover the surface of the object with a material which hinders heated fluids from rising away. Such materials (called lagging) contain many gaps in them which trap the fluid. For example, the clothes that you wear reduce the heat energy lost by convection from your body. The warmed air is trapped in the layers between the clothes. The clothes themselves are made of fluffy materials (wool, cotton and other woven fibres) which also trap air and prevent it from convecting away.

Reducing radiation

Black surfaces are the best emitters of heat radiation. If you want to reduce heat loss by radiation, go for shiny silvered surfaces. You also need to avoid a large surface area, since heat radiation is a surface effect.

 22 How do internal combustion engines transfer waste heat energy to the environment?

Assignment trigger

Temperature control

A variety of organisms need a carefully controlled temperature. For example, tropical fish, fermenting yeasts and ripening tomatoes.

Why do they require constant temperatures?
How could you control the temperature?
How could you monitor it?

If a practical assignment is developed, it is essential that a risk assessment is made and checked by your teacher/lecturer.

Could lead to possible assignments relating to Unit 5.

Transferring heat energy from energy sources

If you want to hold the temperature of an object above its surroundings, you need some way of **transferring heat energy** to it.

Electrical heating

> **Heat energy can be transferred to an object by three different mechanisms. It can be conducted through solids and liquids which are in contact with it. It can be carried by convection currents in liquids and gases around it. It can be transferred through empty space as heat radiation.**

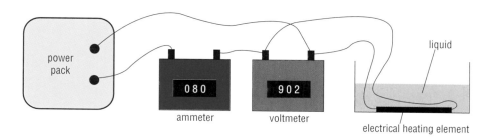

Figure 5.45 illustrates a scheme for delivering heat energy to an object at a known rate. It employs an electrical heating element which transfers electrical energy from the power supply into heat energy.

Figure 5.45 Using an electrical heating element to deliver a known amount of heat energy to a liquid

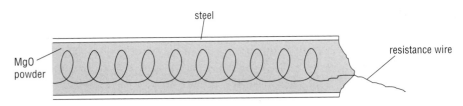

Figure 5.46 *The construction of a heating element*

The element is a resistor designed to allow heat energy to be rapidly conducted out of it. The best ones are lengths of wire packed in a metal cylinder. Magnesium oxide powder (a good conductor of heat) acts as an electrical insulator for the wire (see Figure 5.46). The voltmeter and ammeter readings allow the power of the heater to be calculated.

$$\text{power (W)} = \text{voltage (V)} \times \text{current (A)}$$
$$\text{or} \quad P = VI$$

Heat energy from an electrical element is normally convected away from it by a liquid. (In an immersion heater for example.) If the heat is to be transferred to the object by conduction, then the element needs to be shaped so that there is a large area of contact with the object. A thin layer of heat conducting paste is usually placed between element and object to improve the rate of heat flow between them.

Assignment trigger

Central heating
Central heating systems often use water to transfer heat energy.

Why is water used?
How is the water flow monitored?
How is it controlled?
How can the heat energy flow be determined?

If a practical assignment is developed, it is essential that a risk assessment is made and checked by your teacher/lecturer.

Could lead to possible assignments relating to Unit 5.

Figure 5.47 *A large boiler on the move. It is normally upright, full of liquid. Heat energy is introduced at the bottom and transferred to the rest of the liquid by convection currents.*

Flame heating

Many domestic central heating systems use wood, coal, oil or natural gas as their source of heat energy. When these fuels are burnt in air, they produce hot flue gases. Heat energy is transferred from the flue gases to water in a boiler. The heat energy can then be forcibly convected around the house by pumping the heated water through pipes to a series of radiators.

Radiant heating

If enough electric current flows through a piece of metal wire (the filament), most of the heat energy will leave as radiation. This can be directed towards an object with a curved mirror (see Figure 5.48). The object needs to have a large surface area which isn't a good reflector so that it absorbs the heat energy well.

A light bulb is a good source of heat radiation. The basic construction is shown in Figure 5.49. In order for most of the heat energy to leave the filament as radiation, the temperature of the filament needs to be as high as possible. (The rate of radiation is proportional to the fourth power of the temperature!) This means that the filament has to be made from a metal with a very high melting point; tungsten is the usual choice.

 23 Can you describe the many ways in which heat energy is transferred to food to cook it and keep it hot?

Assignment trigger

Space heating

There are various ways in which spaces can be heated or cooled.

What are they?
What are the advantages and disadvantages of the different methods?
How can you improve their efficiency?

If a practical assignment is developed, it is essential that a risk assessment is made and checked by your teacher/lecturer.

Could lead to possible assignments relating to Unit 5.

Designing a temperature control system

A closed-loop heating control system contains several parts. You need to think carefully about your choice of these parts. The information which follows should help.

Temperature sensors

There are several different types of temperature sensor.

Thermistors are resistors whose resistance changes rapidly with temperature. It usually falls as the temperature increases. When connected in series with fixed resistor (see Figure 5.50), the result is a voltage whose value rises with temperature.

Thermocouples are useful at high temperatures where thermistors would be damaged. Their output is a small voltage which increases with temperature. It needs amplifying before being fed into the comparator; a suitable op-amp circuit is shown in Figure 5.51.

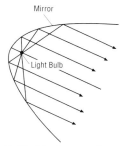

Figure 5.48 *The heat radiation from a light bulb comes out in all directions. A curved mirror can be used to make some of it go in one particular direction.*

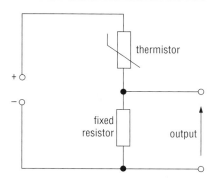

Figure 5.49 *A quartz-halogen light bulb*

▶ Temperature control systems, page 245

The temperature of an object can be stabilised by building a feedback loop around it.

Figure 5.50 *The output of this circuit is a voltage which rises as the temperature of the thermistor rises.*

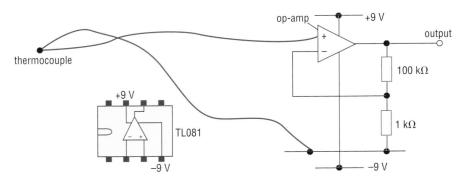

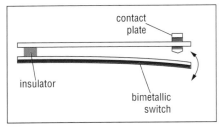

Figure 5.51 Using an op-amp to amplify the voltage from a thermocouple.

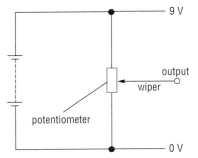

Figure 5.52 A thermostat

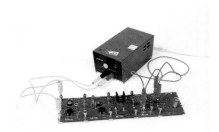

Figure 5.53a Using a potentiometer to generate a variable reference voltage........

Figure 5.53b .... which can be altered by rotating the knob.

Thermostats are mechanical devices which act as both sensor and comparator. The temperature sensor is usually a bimetallic strip. Its curvature varies with temperature (see Figure 5.52). This can be used to open and close an electrical switch. The temperature at which the switch opens can be adjusted by moving the contact plate.

Voltage references

Figure 5.53a shows how a potentiometer can be used to set up a reference voltage. The track terminals are connected to the 9 V and 0 V supply rails.

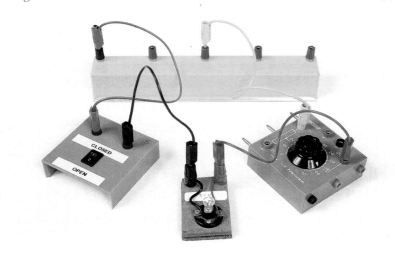

The voltage at the wiper can have any value between 0 V and 9 V, depending on the setting of the knob on top of the potentiometer (see Figure 5.53b).

Comparators

Figure 5.54 includes the circuit diagram of a general purpose comparator based on the LM311N integrated circuit. It is shown operating from supply voltages at 9V and 0 V, although it will be quite happy with a top supply voltage of 5V to 36V.

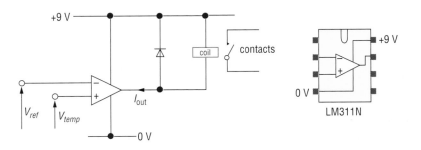

Figure 5.54 An op-amp and a relay can be used to switch an electrical heater on and off.

The output of the integrated circuit controls a relay. The relay coil has a resistance of 300 Ω, and it makes the contacts change over when the current in it is 40 mA. The contacts can handle currents of up to 10 A at voltages of up to 240 V. The diode protects the integrated circuit from voltage surges when it turns off the current in the coil.

Table 5.3 describes the behaviour of the comparator.

Table 5.3 Operating conditions for a comparator

Input conditions	Output conditions
$V_{temp} > V_{ref}$	$I_{out} = 0$ mA
$V_{temp} < V_{ref}$	$I_{out} = 40$ mA

 24 Design a system which will turn on a fan in the ceiling of a room if the temperature goes above 20° C.

Energy source controls

If your chosen source of heat energy is electrical, then it can be run directly from the relay contacts. Any device which operates from more than 20 V needs handling with care; don't attempt to skimp on safety.

Figure 5.55 is the circuit diagram for the control of an electrical water heater. Note the use of fuses, neon indicators and residual earth leakage circuit breakers. These all increase the level of safety; leave them out at your peril!

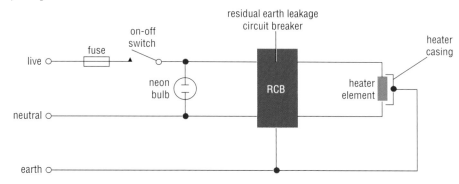

Figure 5.55 Electrical circuit diagram for an electrical heating element

If your source of energy is a fuel such as oil or gas, you will need to use a solenoid valve to switch the flow on and off.

Heater power

The heater power needs to be greater than the rate at which the object loses heat energy to its environment. If the heater power is too low, the object will never reach the desired temperature. So it is worthwhile reducing heat loss from the object to a sensible minimum.

 25 Discuss the various ways in which the heat energy lost by a house can be reduced.

Heat energy flow

There are three mechanisms by which heat energy can flow from one place to another.

Conduction

Conduction is the transfer of heat energy from one place in a material to

▶ Controlling heat energy, page 236

another, without any overall displacement of the material. The heat energy flow is *always* from high temperatures to low temperatures.

There are several factors which determine the rate at which heat energy is conducted. They are summarised in the following formula.

rate of heat transfer (W) = thermal conductivity $(Wm^{-1}K^{-1}) \times$ area (m^2)
$$\times \frac{\text{temperature drop (K)}}{\text{thickness (m)}}$$

or $\qquad P = kA\frac{\Delta T}{x}$

Convection

Convection occurs when heat energy is transferred by the movement of a fluid.

For example, hot water is widely used to transfer the heat energy from burning fuels to all of the rooms in a building. Central heating systems employ forced convection, where the heat energy is transferred by pumps from one place to another, regardless of any temperature change along the way.

Natural convection occurs in fluids (liquids and gases). When heat energy is conducted into a fluid, the fluid expands and its density decreases. This means that it immediately floats up on top of the denser cold fluid around it. The hot fluid rises up, forming a convection current which transports heat energy. Natural convection only allows heat energy to flow from high temperature to low temperature.

Figure 5.56 The chimneys of a steel works: convection put to work

Many domestic fuel combustion systems employ natural convection. The hot gases from the combustion process rise up through the boiler, before being convected up the chimney (see Figure 5.56). The upwards flow of hot gases provides a steady inflow of cold air for the burners.

Ⓠ **26** Victorian factories which burnt coal to boil water for steam engines had very tall chimneys. Why?

Radiation

All objects emit heat radiation. This is an electromagnetic wave, similar to light, which transfers heat energy when it is absorbed. The rate at which an object emits heat radiation, depends on several factors, including the temperature of its surroundings.

$$P = \varepsilon\sigma A(T_o^4 - T_s^4)$$
where P is the rate of heat loss (W),
ε is the emissivity of the object's surface,
σ is 5.67×10^{-8} (the Stefan-Boltzmann constant),
A is the surface area of the object (m^2)
T_o is the temperature of the object (K) and
T_s is the temperature of the surroundings (K).

The emissivity is a number between 0 and 1. It is close to 1 for blackened, rough surfaces. Shiny, reflecting surfaces have very small values for emissivity.

 27 A typical naked human being can be modelled as cylinder of diameter 0.4 m and height 1.6 m with an emissivity of 0.75. Show that he radiates heat energy at a rate of about 300 W when the surroundings are at 0 °C.

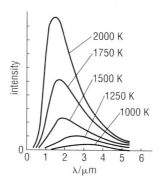

Figure 5.57 How the intensity and range of wavelengths emitted by a hot object depends on its temperature.

Colour

Heat radiation has a range of wavelengths. The graph of Figure 5.57 shows how the intensity of the radiation varies with wavelength at a number of diferent temperatures. The wavelength of the intensity peak is given by Wein's Law.

$$\lambda_m T_o = 2.9 \times 10^{-3} \text{ mK}$$
where λ_m is the maximum intensity wavelength (m)
and T_o is the temperature of the object (K).

Wavelengths between 400 nm and 680 nm can be seen by the human eye, so as the temperature of an object is raised, part of its radiation becomes visible. Hot objects start to emit appreciable amounts of red light when their temperature approaches 1 000 K.

Table 5.4 How the perceived colour depends on the wavelength of light

Wavelength (nm)	Colour	Wavelength (nm)	Colour
680–630	red	580–510	green
630–610	orange	510–420	blue
610–580	yellow	420–400	purple

The rate at which heat energy is transferred from an object can be calculated with the help of *U*-values. These take into account the thermal conductivity of a material, its emissivity and the rate at which it allows convection.

U-values

Calculations of the rate of heat flow through materials are simplified by the use of **U-values**. These take into account the thermal conductivity k of the material, its thickness x, and how easily heat energy is convected and radiated away from its surface.

$$\text{rate of heat transfer (W)} = U\text{-value (Wm}^{-2}\text{K}^{-1}) \times \text{area (m}^2)$$
$$\times \text{temperature drop (K)}$$

or $\qquad P = UA\Delta T$

A number of different U-values for typical building materials are given in table 5.5.

Table 5.5 *U*-values for typical building materials

Material	*U*-value/Wm^{-2}K^{-1}
Single window pane	6
Double glazed window	2
Tiled roof	2
Insulated tiled roof	0.5
Empty cavity brick wall	2
Foam cavity brick wall	0.5

Table 5.6 shows how these can be used to estimate the rate of heat loss from a typical single-glazed uninsulated house when the temperature inside is 20 K higher than outside. For example, the rate of heat loss from the walls is $2\,\text{Wm}^{-2}\text{K}^{-1} \times 120\,\text{m}^2 \times 20\,\text{K} = 4\,800\,\text{W}$.

Table 5.6

Structure	*U*-value	Area/m^2	Heat loss/W
Walls	2	120	4 800
Windows	6	40	4 800
Roof	2	50	2 000
Floor	2	50	2 000
		Total	13 600

Q 28 Show that the rate of heat loss from the house of Table 5.6 drops to only 3 800 W if it is fully insulated and double-glazed.

Heat energy and temperature

Whenever heat energy is transferred to an object, two things can happen: its temperature can rise, or it can change state.

The specific heat capacities and latent heats of a material allow you to calculate how much energy is needed to raise its temperature or change its state.

Temperature rise

The **specific heating capacity** (s.h.c.) of a material tells you how much its temperature will rise when you transfer heat energy to it.

heat energy transferred (J) =
mass (kg) × s.h.c. ($Jkg^{-1}K^{-1}$) × temperature rise (K)
or $\Delta Q = mc\Delta T$

Table 5.7 Typical values for the s.h.c. of various substances.

Substance	s.h.c./$Jkg^{-1}K^{-1}$	Substance	s.h.c./$Jkg^{-1}K^{-1}$
Aluminium	880	Water	4 200
Copper	380	Ethanol	2 400
Iron	440	Air	690
Perspex	1 500		

Change of state

There are two ways in which a substance can change state. It can turn from solid to liquid at its melting point. Or it can turn from liquid to gas at its boiling point. Both transformations require the input of heat energy. Any heat energy which is transferred during a change of state is known as **latent heat**.

latent heat (J) = mass (kg) × specific latent heat (Jkg^{-1})

For example, the specific latent heat of fusion of water is 330 000 Jkg^{-1}. So 5.0 kg of ice at 0°C needs 5.0 kg × 330 000 Jkg^{-1} = 1.65 MJ to convert it to water at 0°C.

Similarly, the specific latent of vaporisation of water is 2.26 $MJkg^{-1}$. So 5.0 kg of water at 100°C needs 5 kg × 2.26 $MJkg^{-1}$ = 11.3 MJ to convert it to steam at 100°C.

 29 Show that 10 kg of ice at 0°C needs 30.1 MJ of energy to convert it completely to steam at 100°C.

Temperature control systems

A temperature control system aims to keep the temperature of an object at some fixed value. There are two ways of doing this. **Open-loop** systems are cheap and easy to build, but deliver poor results. **Closed-loop** systems need more hardware, but have a much better performance.

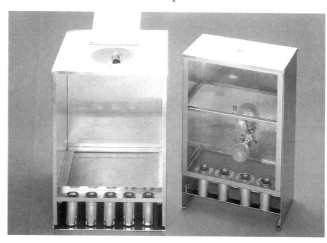

▶ Designing a temperature control system, page 239

Open-loop heating systems do not monitor their final temperature. Closed-loop systems automatically adjust their power to keep their temperature fixed.

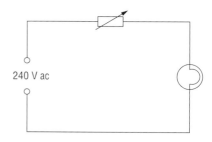

240 V ac

Figure 5.58 *The circuit diagram of a simple open-loop temperature control system for an insect cage (shown in the photograph).*

Open-loop control systems

A simple open-loop system is shown in Figure 5.58. The object (an insect cage) is kept at a temperature above the surroundings by the heat radiation from a light bulb. The power delivered to the light bulb can be controlled by a variable resistor.

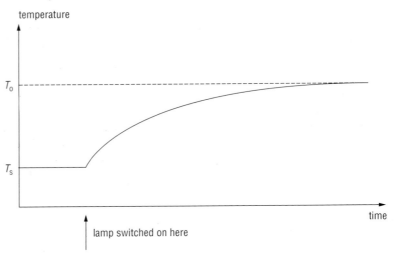

Figure 5.59 *The temperature of the cage rises exponentially until the rate of heat energy input is exactly matched by the rate of heat energy loss.*

The graph of Figure 5.59 shows what happens to the temperature of the cage when the light is switched on. It rises exponentially to a new value T_o. This value is fixed by the rate at which the lamp delivers energy to the cage P_{in} (the power of the lamp) and the way in which heat energy escapes from the cage.

The rate of heat loss from the cage is given by Newton's Law of Cooling.

$$P_{out} = C \times (T_o - T_s)$$
where P_{out} is the rate of heat energy loss (W),
C is a constant fixed by the object (WK^{-1}),
T_o is the temperature of the object (K) and
T_s is the temperature of the surroundings (K).

This takes account of conduction, convection and radiation from the object. The value of C depends on the precise way in which the heat is lost, the size and shape of the object and many other factors.

Q 30 How does the value of *C* change when the dimensions of an object are doubled?

Equilibrium temperature
Thermal equilibrium is reached when $P_{in} = P_{out}$.

$$P_{in} = C(T_o - T_s) \text{ or } T_o = T_s + \left(\frac{P_{in}}{C}\right)$$

So the final temperature of the object is determined by the power of the lamp. T_s can be set to any value you please by setting the lamp power P_{in} to the appropriate value.

However, the temperature will only be stable if the object's environment doesn't change. Any change in the way that convection currents rise off the object (such as forced ventilation from an open window) will alter the value of C. Furthermore, any change in the temperature of the surroundings T_s will alter the value of T_o.

Closed-loop control systems

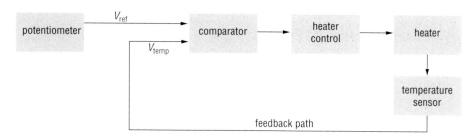

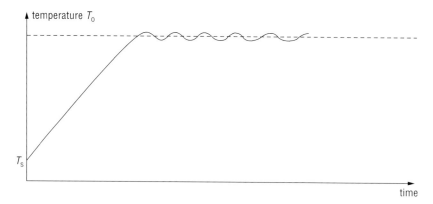

Figure 5.60 *The block diagram of a closed-loop temperature control system.*

A block diagram of a closed-loop control system is shown in Figure 5.60. This is how it works.

The temperature of the object T_o is measured by the sensor. The output of the sensor is a voltage V_{temp} whose value is proportional to T_s. The comparator compares V_{temp} with V_{ref}, the reference signal from the potentiometer. The comparator output operates the heater control.

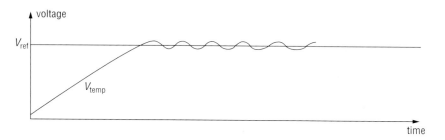

Figure 5.61 *What happens when a closed-loop temperature control system is turned on.*

The graphs of Figure 5.61 illustrate what happens when the system is switched on. T_o rises to start with because the comparator turns the heater on. Once T_o has reached the desired value, the comparator turns the heater off. The object now starts to lose heat energy to its surroundings by the normal processes of conduction, convection and radiation. The sensor signal V_{temp} eventually falls below the reference signal V_{ref} and the comparator turns the heater on once more.

Once the system has settled down, the value of T_o is only fixed by the value of V_{ref}.

Case study

STOPPING VEHICLES

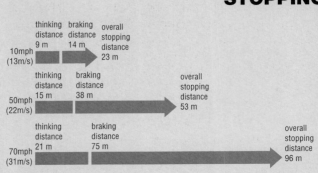

Illustration 1

The Highway Code contains a diagram which shows how the distance needed to stop a car depends on its initial speed (Illustration 1). This case study investigates the physics behind this data. Table 1 contains equivalent data expressed in convenient units. They apply to an alert driver in charge of a well maintained car on a level dry road.

Table 1

Speed /ms^{-1}	Thinking distance/m	Braking distance/m	Stopping distance/m
5	3.5	2.0	5.5
10	7.0	8.0	15.0
15	10.5	18.0	28.5
20	14.0	32.0	46.0
25	17.5	50.0	67.5
30	21.0	72.0	93.0

Thinking distance

The thinking distance d_t is how far the car moves while the driver moves his foot onto the brake pedal. A quick scan of the data should convince you that the d_t is proportional to the speed v; as you double one quantity, the other one doubles too. This pattern is easy to explain. Suppose that the reaction time of the driver is t_r.

Distance = speed × time, so $d_t = vt_r$.

You can check for yourself that the data in Table 1 implies that the reaction time of a typical driver is

0.7 s. Alcohol in the bloodstream, inexperience or old age can increase this figure dramatically.

Braking distance

The braking distance d_b is the distance travelled by the car once the brakes have been applied. Quite clearly, it is not proportional to the speed! Instead, d_b quadruples when the speed v is doubled. The braking distance is proportional to the square of the speed. This pattern arises because the act of braking a car really consists of transferring kinetic energy into heat energy via friction.

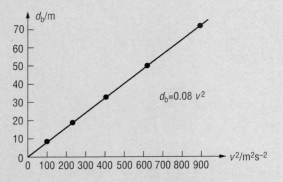

Illustration 2

Suppose that the car has a mass m. Its kinetic energy $\frac{1}{2}mv^2$ has to be transferred into some other form as the car is brought to a halt. When the brakes are applied, fibrous pads connected to the car body are squeezed hard against a steel disc connected to each wheel. Friction between disc and pad applies a force F on the car, slowing it down. If the car has four wheels, the total force slowing it down will be $4F$. The total work done by this force must equal the car's initial kinetic energy. Since work = force × distance, $4Fd_b = \frac{1}{2}mv^2$.

This argument suggests that $d_b = \left(\frac{m}{8F}\right)v^2$. So a graph of d_b against v^2 should be a straight line with a gradient of $m/8F$. Such a graph is shown in Illustration 2; its gradient is 0.080 kgN^{-1}.

Limiting friction

All road vehicles have the same stopping distance, regardless of their mass. This is implied in the fact that $m/8F = 0.080$ kgN^{-1}. In other words, $F = 1.56m$. Why should this be so?

Consider the act of braking. The size of F, the friction between pad and disc, only depends on the force squeezing them together R and the coefficient of friction . Indeed, $F = \mu R$. At first glance, F can be made as large as you like by increasing R. However, if F gets too large, the pads stick to the disc and the car skids. The wheels lock (stop rotating) and the car slides along the road. Kinetic energy is still transferred into heat energy via friction, but at a different place. This is a bad thing. Rubber is a poor conductor of heat energy. The surface of the tyre in contact with the road melts; the molten rubber acts as a lubricant, reducing the friction between car and road. Therefore a car with locked brakes has to travel a longer distance to transfer the kinetic energy than a car which isn't skidding.

So friction between tyre and road must always be great enough to force the disc and pad to slip against each other. The maximum friction force on each tyre only depends on the weight of car which it is supporting and the coefficient of friction. Therefore F must be proportional to m.

The Highway Code data suggests that the braking force from each wheel of an 800 kg car has a maximum value of 1.25 kN. The total braking force is therefore 5.0 kN. Since the weight of the car is 8.0 kN, the coefficient of friction between car and road is 5.0/8.0 = 0.63. This value arises from the properties of rubber tyres and road surfaces, not the size and shape of the vehicles which they support. This means that all vehicles which have rubber tyres need the same stopping distance, regardless of how many tyres they have or the load which they support.

Questions

1 Explain why a car needs a longer distance to stop if the road is wet.

2 Why should a car take longer to stop if its driver has a lot of alcohol in his bloodstream?

3 Describe and explain the features of a car which allow its occupants to slow down safely if there is a collision.

4 When a ship has to stop, its engines are put into reverse. How does the stopping distance of a ship depend on its mass, initial speed and power of its engines?

5 The friction between a boat and the water it floats in obeys an equation similar to that of wind resistance. Use this idea to describe how the stopping distance of a ship depends on its mass and speed if friction is the only mechanism for bringing it to a halt.

Case study

HEAT ENERGY AND LIFE

The complex chemical processes which keep you alive only work properly within a very narrow range of temperatures. Temperature regulation is one of your most pressing and persistent needs. Your body has to be kept at a temperature of nearly 37°C. If it is forced up or down by more than a few degrees, then death can ensue. So you need to take a lot of trouble over managing your body temperature. It is literally a matter of life or death.

Generating heat energy

Suppose that you are in a room which has a temperature of 20 °C. To keep your body 17 °C higher than the room, you have to generate heat at the same rate as you lose it to the rest of the room. Some of that heat energy is generated in your muscles each time that you use them. The fuel which is used by your muscles to do work is glucose ($C_6H_{12}O_6$). When it is oxidised in your muscles, only part of the chemical energy stored in the glucose can be converted into useful work. The rest becomes heat energy which is conducted through the muscle cells to the blood. The blood is then used to forcibly convect the heat energy to all the other parts of the body. Heat energy is also generated in many of the other chemical reactions which take place in the cells of your body. But however the heat energy is generated, it always comes from the chemical energy in the food which you eat. An adult human who is reasonably active needs a food intake of about 12MJ in 24 hrs. This corresponds to an average rate of heat energy loss of about 140 W.

To make efficient use of your food, you have to ensure that you only generate the minimum heat energy required. So you need to try and cut down the rate at which you lose heat energy to your surroundings. There are two ways in which you can cut down on the rate at which you lose heat energy. Wear clothes. Keep your environment hot.

Keeping heat energy

Clothes stop air from convecting heat energy away from your body. They trap the air which is close to your skin, forcing the heat energy to be conducted through the trapped air and cloth fibres. Air is a very bad conductor, so heat energy does not pass through it easily. The more air you trap in your clothes, the harder it is for the heat energy to conduct through it. Of course, forced convection by winds and draughts are to be avoided!

Many animals grow their own clothes. Hair, feathers, wool and fur are very good at trapping air and hindering convection.

Large is warm

Small animals have much more difficulty in regulating their temperature than large ones do. Elephants hardly notice a frosty night, but it can be enough to kill a small rodent. This is because the rate of heat loss is proportional to the surface area of an animal, but its ability to generate heat energy is proportional to its mass.

Suppose that an animal is modelled as a sphere of radius r. Its surface area A is therefore $4\pi r^2$. So the rate of heat loss P is Cr^2, where C is a constant whose value is fixed by the amount of fur and the temperature of the surroundings. The amount of chemical energy which the animal can store will be proportional to its mass. The mass of the animal m is $\left(\frac{4}{3}\right)\pi r^3 D$, where D is its density. So the total energy E is Kr^3. The length of time that the animal can survive without feeding is therefore $E/P = \left(K/C\right)r$. The smaller the value of r, the shorter this time will be.

You can estimate how small you have to be for heat energy loss to be a real problem as follows. A naked human being survives about a month without food. That is about 25 days. A sphere of water which has a radius of 25 cm has the same mass (70 kg) as an average human being. So $K/C \approx 25/25 = 1$ day/cm. So any animal whose size is much less than 1 cm will have difficulty surviving a cold night without food!

Feedback loops

The temperature of your body is actively controlled by negative feedback. The main temperature sensor is in your brain. This sends nerve messages to the rest of your body if you get too hot or too cold.

For example, suppose that you get too hot. The blood vessels just under the surface of the skin get larger. This increases the flow of blood to the skin, convecting more heat energy to the surface of the skin. As its temperature rises, the rate at which heat energy is convected and radiated from the skin's surface increases. So you lose heat more rapidly than before.

Sweating is another automatic mechanism which is used to cool your skin. Glands in your skin can secrete water onto its surface. It takes 2.26 kJ of heat energy to convert one gram of water from a liquid to a gas. So as the water evaporates, it takes away heat energy from your skin. The rate of heat energy loss is proportional to the surface area of an animal, but the amount of heat to be lost will be proportional to its mass. The larger an animal is, the less effective sweating will be unless extra surface area is created. This is probably why elephants have evolved such large ears!

If your brain detects that your temperature is too low, a number of different mechanisms are brought into play. Firstly, the blood vessels just under the surface of your skin contract, slowing down the convection of heat energy to the skin. So the skin cools down, reducing the rate of heat energy loss. Secondly, your metabolic rate increases; the rate of chemical reactions, particularly in your liver, increases. Thirdly, if your temperature drops far enough, you start shivering. This is an involuntary spasmodic contraction of muscles which converts chemical energy into heat energy.

Of course, if all of these do not generate enough heat energy to stop your brain temperature dropping below 35°C, you develop hypothermia. The feedback processes stop working. Your temperature continues to fall, you go into a coma and will eventually die unless someone else has the presence of mind to heat you up again!

Questions

1 When a chicken is taken from the freezer and left in the kitchen to defrost, the time taken to defrost depends on several factors. List them and explain their importance. If it takes six hours to defrost a chicken, how long will it take to defrost a mammoth?

2 Describe how the surface coating of animals is adapted to the temperature of their environment.

3 Describe the feedback loop used to keep food in a refrigerator at a constant temperature. Discuss the need to insulate a refrigerator. Are large refrigerators more efficient than small ones?

4 Describe the mechanisms by which long-distance runners lose heat during a race. Why do they have to be careful about their water intake during a race? Why are marathon runners often wrapped in shiny foil blankets at the end of a race?

5 In general, eskimos are round and short, whereas natives of countries near the Equator are often tall and thin. Explain why these characteristics may help people to survive better in their environment.

Case study

METER MEASURES OIL FLOW AT THE BOTTOM OF THE SEA

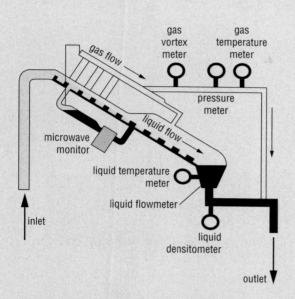

One of the greatest problems facing oil companies in exploiting remote under-sea reserves is measuring the quantity of oil in the fizzing mixture of hydrocarbon gases, oil, water and sand that bubbles out of the well. The oil industry is striving to develop measuring devices for this so-called multi-phase fluid that can sit on the seabed and be operated by remote control.

Later this month, the National Engineering Laboratory (NEL), at East Kilbride in Scotland, will open what it believes is the first laboratory in the world for testing and calibrating multiphase oil production equipment.

There are already 640 remote oil wells located on the seabed around the world. Fluid from these wells flows in multiphase form over distances of up to 20 kilometres to platforms on the surface. The oil, water and gas are separated on the platforms before the products are sent ashore.

Siting the well on the seabed dramatically reduces the cost of developing small fields close to existing platforms. But new technology is needed to operate wells further from platforms. Measuring the composition of the multiphase fluid as it comes out of the well is necessary because the fluids from different wells in a field are often combined into a common pipeline to be pumped to the platform. When the technical problems are overcome, oil companies could site wells up to 50 kilometres from platforms.

NEL's multiphase laboratory consists of a recirculation loop in which oil, water, air and nitrogen are mixed in a pipeline before passing through the meter under test. The system is designed to simulate the very irregular flow found in multiphase pipes. The consistency of the fluid can vary from a homogeneous mixture with small gas bubbles to

massive liquid slugs accompanied by large gas bubbles.

After passing through the meter under test, the gas, oil and water are separated. The flow rate of each stream is measured and compared with multiphase meter reading.

Oil engineers have investigated a wide range of measurement techniques for multiphase fluids, including homogenising the fluid, or probing it with radiation, sound or microwaves. Perhaps the most advanced research is being carried out by the oil company Texaco.

Texaco's prototype subsea metering system (SMS) was installed on the company's Tartan platform in the summer of 1989. Over 150 test runs were performed using production from different wells at various flow rates. Tests were completed earlier this year after problems with foaming were overcome. The SMS is expected to be installed on the Highlander subsea well this autumn for trials on the seabed.

The SMS consists of a separator vessel, which is a pipe inclined at an angle. The fluid cascades down the pipe under gravity over a series of baffles. The halting flow over the baffles helps separate the gas bubbles, which then rise to the top surface of the tube and pass out through an outlet. A small amount of the fluid is channelled off to measure how much of the liquid is water. This part of the meter probes the liquid with microwaves. Texaco will not divulge the workings of this part of the meter.

Once separated, various measurements are made of the gas and liquid flows. Data from the various sensors in the meter is sent to a computer on the platform which then estimates the flow rates of the different parts of the fluid. Finally, the liquid and gas flows are recombined at the outlet of the meter and pumped on to the platform.

Texaco is aiming for an accuracy of 5 per cent with the SMS. This is good enough for managing wells but an accuracy of nearer 1 per cent will be needed for commercial purposes.

Questions

1. Explain why a venturi meter cannot be used to measure accurately the flow of a multiphase fluid.

2. Describe the devices which could be used to measure the liquid flow rate in the SMS.

3. Explain why the SMS has to measure the pressure and temperature of the gas phase.

4. Describe how natural gas from the North Sea oilfields is piped ashore, stored and delivered safely to the customer.

5. There are several fluids which are passed from one place to another in a large building. State what they are and why they need to be moved around. Describe how they are moved around the building and how their flow is controlled.

6 | Control reactions

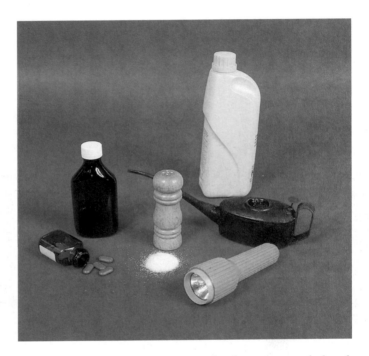

Figure 6.1 *Controlling chemical reactions enables the products we use to be produced in the most efficient manner.*

Many products which we use in our everyday lives are made by chemical reactions. To ensure that the reactions yield the correct products in the highest possible yield, scientists control and alter the conditions under which the reactions take place. As well as considering the major products from a reaction and their yields, scientists must audit the materials, energy and costs of a process carefully. In addition, scientists must examine carefully the economic, social and environmental consequences of using reactions in a production process.

The Elements

Element 6.1 Propose control strategies for reactions

Your first task is to apply theoretical ideas to control the reactions which you are studying. To do this you will need to:

- explain the need to control a reaction
- identify what affects the course of the reaction and how changes in conditions can achieve the desired effect (rate or equilibrium position)

252

- propose conditions which meet the need to control a reaction.

Element 6.2 Monitor and control reactions

To monitor a reaction and control the reaction to give the required products you will need to:
- identify the conditions which affect the course of a reaction and changes in the reaction mixture which can be monitored
- explain the choice of measurement method and monitor the changes in properties which occur during the reaction
- describe the effects of changes in conditions on the course of a reaction.

Element 6.3 Manage industrial processes

For any industrial process you must determine the quantities and costs of materials used, assess the effectiveness of the measures used to control the process and assess the social and environmental consequences of production. To do this you will need to:
- identify the reactions involved
- determine the quantities and costs of the materials and energy used in the process
- explain how effective the measures taken are in controlling the process
- assess the social and environmental consequences of production.

 Controlling reactions, page 268

Monitoring reactions, page 262

Managing industrial processes, page 274

Figure 6.2 Most industrial processes used to manufacture substances are automated.

Reactions and the need for control

Any chemical reaction must be controlled. You need to know how much product is being produced, how much starting material is being used up and the speed at which these processes are occurring. The reactions which you will be asked to control will be affected by changes in temperature and in the concentration of the reactants, and may be affected by the use of catalysts, the particle size of any solids involved, and, in the case of gaseous reactions, by pressure.

The substances whose production you will be asked to monitor will include both organic and inorganic compounds. The monitoring techniques which you will be asked to use will cover changes in the following:

- temperature
- concentration of substances
- absorption of light
- volumes of gases.

Reactions are not confined to the laboratory. Once a substance has been produced in the laboratory on a gram scale, the reaction must be scaled up if the product is to be manufactured on a tonne scale. Scaling up chemical reactions involves considering the reactions involved, the modifications necessary to both the chemicals and the method, and the implications of the production process on the community, economy and environment.

Types of chemical reaction

Chemical reactions may involve simple compounds (inorganic or organic) or complex ions. Biological reactions are chemical reactions which involve biological compounds, often occurring in an organism, and catalysed by enzymes. For example, the fermentation of sucrose to give ethanol and carbon dioxide is a chemical reaction catalysed by the enzymes in yeast.

Elements, compounds and mixtures, page 13

Phases

Substances are **solid**, **liquid** or **gaseous**. These are called states of matter or **phases**. Reactions which occur between substances in the same phase are said to be *homogeneous*. If more than one phase is present the reaction mixture is said to be *heterogeneous*. Aqueous solutions are a particular example of the liquid phase.

> There are three phases: solid, liquid and gaseous.

Q 1 Which of the following reaction mixtures are homogeneous and which heterogeneous? (a) Cu^{2+}(aq) and Zn(s), (b) H_2(g) and O_2(g), (c) Al(s) and Cl_2(g), (d) NH_4Cl(s) and $Ca(OH)_2$(s)

Endothermic and exothermic reactions

All chemical reactions either take in or give out energy as the reaction proceeds. Often this energy is transferred as heat energy, which causes the temperature of the reaction mixture either to drop or to rise.

Changes which occur with the release of heat energy are called **exothermic**. The energy transferred can cause a rise in the temperature of the surroundings.

Changes which occur with the absorption of heat energy are called **endothermic**. The energy absorbed can cause a fall in the temperature of the surroundings.

> An exothermic reaction releases heat energy (the surroundings get hotter).
> An endothermic reaction absorbs heat energy (the surroundings become cooler).

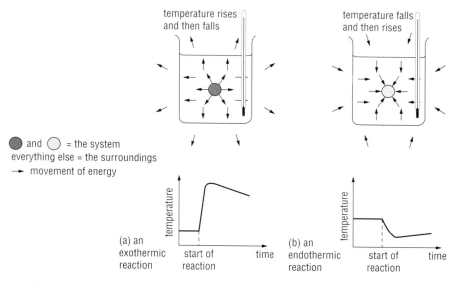

temperature rises
and then falls

temperature falls
and then rises

● and ○ = the system
everything else = the surroundings
→ movement of energy

(a) an
exothermic
reaction

start of
reaction

time

(b) an
endothermic
reaction

start of
reaction

time

Figure 6.3 *The temperature changes associated with exothermic and endothermic reactions can be recorded over time intervals.*

If the energy changes take place at constant pressure then the heat energy changes are known as enthalpy changes and are given the symbol ΔH. For an exothermic reaction, ΔH is written as a negative number. For an endothermic reaction, ΔH is positive.

Chemical equilibrium

Many chemical reactions go to completion. For example,

- copper(II) carbonate decomposes completely to copper(II) oxide and carbon dioxide when heated:

$$CuCO_3(s) \rightarrow CuO(s) + CO_2(g)$$
copper(II)   copper(II)   carbon
carbonate   oxide   dioxide

- aluminium reacts with chlorine when heated to give aluminium chloride:

$$2Al(s) + 3Cl_2(g) \rightarrow Al_2Cl_6(s)$$
aluminium   chlorine   aluminium
                                chloride

- hydrochloric acid reacts with sodium hydroxide to give sodium chloride:

$$HCl(aq) + NaOH(aq) \rightarrow NaCl(aq) + H_2O(l)$$
hydrochloric   sodium   sodium   water
acid   hydroxide   chloride

However, many reactions do not go to completion. No matter how long they are left under a particular set of conditions, they never produce the theoretical yields. In these reactions, products are formed and then react with one another to re-form starting materials. The reaction mixtures contain both starting materials and products which are continually reacting to form one another. When such 'forward and back' reactions are occurring at the same rate, the state of the reaction is called **dynamic equilibrium**.

To denote that the reaction is an equilibrium the arrow used in the reaction is $\rightleftharpoons$ and not $\rightarrow$. For example,

$$N_2(g) + 3H_2(g) \rightleftharpoons 2NH_3(g)$$
nitrogen hydrogen   ammonia

▶ Establishing a position of equilibrium, page 261

In a dynamic chemical equilibrium the forward and back reactions occur at the same rate. Products react to form reactants at the same rate as reactants react to form products.

$$CH_3COOH(l) + C_2H_5OH(l) \rightleftharpoons CH_3COOC_2H_5(l) + H_2O(l)$$

ethanoic acid   ethanol   ethyl ethanoate   water

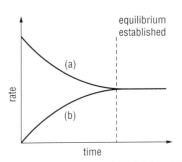

(a) rate of decomposition of $N_2O_4(g)$: $N_2O_4(g) \rightarrow 2NO_2(g)$

(b) rate of formation of $N_2O_4(g)$: $2NO_2(g) \rightarrow N_2O_4(g)$

Figure 6.4 *Dynamic equilibrium is reached when the forward and back reactions occur at the same rate.*

By changing reaction conditions it is possible to:
- **increase or decrease the rate of reaction**
- **increase or decrease the yield of products, by changing the position of equilibrium.**

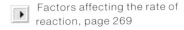 Factors affecting the rate of reaction, page 269

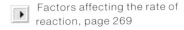 Factors affecting the position of equilibrium, page 272

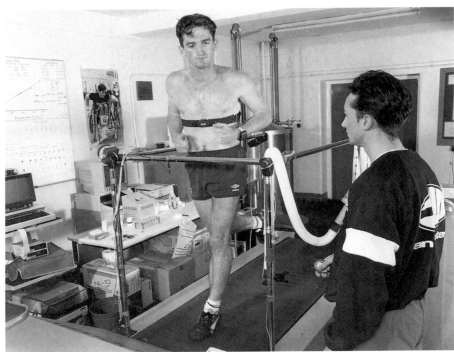

Figure 6.5 *This athlete is running at the same speed but in the opposite direction to the moving belt of the tread-mill. The two are in dynamic equilibrium.*

The need to control reactions

Chemical change often needs to be controlled in different ways. We may wish to speed up or slow down a reaction. In the case of a reaction in a state of equilibrium, we may want to change the position of equilibrium in order to increase or decrease the yield of products.

Often we want to speed up chemical change. For example, in an industrial process the goal is usually to obtain high yields of pure product in the shortest possible time. However, sometimes conditions which increase the rate of a reaction give a low yield of product. To achieve higher yields, a slower reaction rate must be accepted. As with so many things, choosing reaction conditions is often about *compromise*.

Assignment trigger

Industrial processes

Biotechnological and chemical industries make a huge range of products. Modern society makes huge demands for these products.

What are the major industries?

What materials do they use?

What do they produce?

How do scientists control production?

What regulations must be obeyed?

If a practical assignment is developed, it is essential that a risk assessment is made and checked by your teacher/lecturer.

Could lead to possible assignments relating to Units 4 and 6.

Figure 6.6 *Some chemical reactions need to be slowed down. Rusting is a good example. If this oxidation reaction occurs too quickly it can be very damaging!*

Q 2 List some chemical reactions involving substances you find around the home which need to be made faster.

For some reactions it is important to maintain constant reaction conditions. The rate of a chemical reaction increases with temperature. If this reaction is exothermic, the heat produced will increase the rate, producing more heat more quickly, increasing the rate even more, and so on. The danger of a runaway reaction getting out of control is easy to see. The temperature of an exothermic reaction can be maintained by cooling while the temperature of an endothermic reaction can be maintained by heating.

Enzymes are biological catalysts. They play key roles in our body chemistry and also in many industrial biotechnology processes. Their effectiveness often depends on maintaining a particular, constant pH and temperature. The pH is usually maintained by using a *buffer solution*.

▶ Maintaining constant pH, page 274

Assignment trigger

Body chemicals

The body is a highly sophisticated chemical plant. It produces countless chemicals essential to life.

What types of chemicals are produced?
What types of chemical reactions are involved?
How do the conditions under which these chemicals are made in the body and in the laboratory differ?

If a practical assignment is developed, it is essential that a risk assessment is made and checked by your teacher/lecturer.

Could lead to possible assignments relating to Units 6 and 7.

The course of chemical reactions

All chemical reactions follow particular courses which you need to be able to describe, understand and quantify.

Reaction pathways

The pathway of a chemical reaction can be represented by a reaction profile. For any reaction to occur the activation energy must be supplied to the reaction. This energy barrier must be overcome regardless of whether the reaction is exothermic or endothermic. The activation energy (given the symbol E_a) can be shown on energy profile diagrams.

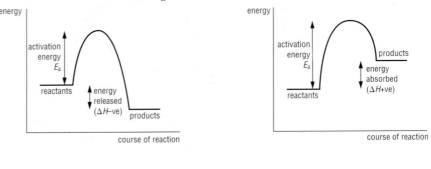

(i) reaction profile for a single step exothermic reaction

(ii) reaction profile for a single step endothermic reaction

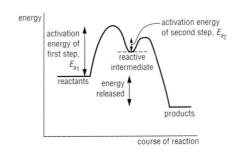

(iii) reaction profile for a two-step exothermic reaction

Figure 6.7 *A reaction profile shows how the energy of a reaction changes during the course of the reaction. These profiles represent typical one-step and two-step pathways.*

Q 3 Draw a reaction profile for a two-step endothermic reaction.

Molecules collide with each other but not all collisions lead to a reaction. Some molecules collide but do not have enough energy to react. Only molecules which collide with an energy greater than the activation energy are able to react. They are said to overcome the energy barrier to reaction and are said to undergo an *effective collision*.

As the temperature is raised the molecules have more energy. When molecules collide at higher temperatures more of them have sufficient energy to overcome the energy barrier, so more reactions occur.

Figure 6.8 *Distribution of energy among molecules at two different temperatures. At the higher temperature more molecules have energy greater than the activation energy.*

Figure 6.9 *In a single step reaction the reactants are turned into products without an intermediate being formed. An example is the hydrolysis of 2-chlorobutane.*

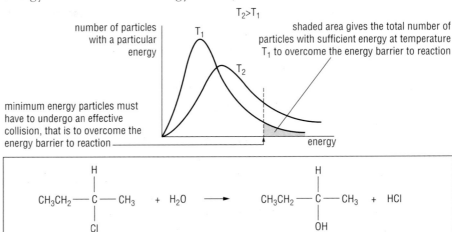

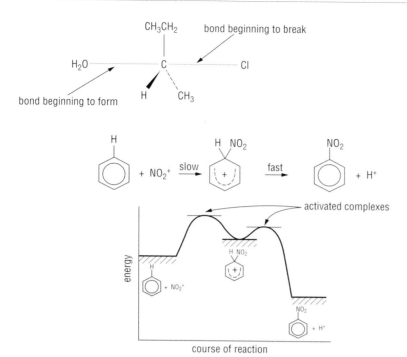

Figure 6.10 In the hydrolysis of 2-chlorobutane a transition state (or activated complex) is formed in which the H_2O has started to form a bond to the carbon and the bond between the carbon and the chlorine has started to break. Transition states cannot be isolated.

Figure 6.11 In a two-step reaction, reactants are turned into products via a reactive intermediate. An example is the nitration of benzene. The intermediate has both the incoming nitro group and the outgoing hydrogen attached to a carbon atom of the benzene ring.

Rate of reaction

How fast a reaction occurs (the **rate of reaction**) depends on the temperature, the concentration of the reagents and occasionally on the pressure and the activity of catalysts. In heterogeneous reactions where two phases are involved the particle size of a solid can be an important factor.

▶ Factors affecting the rate of reaction, page 269

Rate of reaction = change in concentration of reactant or product/time taken for change. Units are usually mol dm^{-3} s^{-1}.

The rate of reaction is determined experimentally. It is expressed in terms of either decreasing concentration of reactants or increasing concentration of products with time. For example in the decomposition of hydrogen peroxide to give oxygen and water

▶ Monitoring reactions, page 262

$$2H_2O_2(aq) \quad \rightarrow \quad 2H_2O(l) \quad + \quad O_2(g)$$
$$\text{hydrogen peroxide} \qquad \text{water} \qquad \text{oxygen}$$

The rate of reaction could be expressed in terms of the decrease in concentration of hydrogen peroxide with time or the increase in the volume of oxygen produced with time.

From experimental measurements it is possible to determine a rate equation for a reaction. This shows how the rate depends on the concentration of the reactants. For the general reaction:

$aA + bB \rightarrow$ products,

where a and b represent the number of moles of each reactant as shown in the balanced equation for the reaction, the rate equation is:

rate of reaction = $k[A]^m[B]^n$

where k = a constant (the *rate constant*),

$\quad\;\; [A]$ = concentration of A,

$\quad\;\; [B]$ = concentration of B,

$\quad\;\;\; m$ = the *order of reaction* with respect to A, and

$\quad\;\;\; n$ = the *order of reaction* with respect to B.

m and n are determined by experiment. They are often, but not always, integers and could be zero. The sum of the powers m and n is known as the *overall order of the reaction*. The values of m and n are not related to the balanced equation for the reaction, except by coincidence.

Table 6.1 Rates of reaction

For a reaction of the type X → products, the rate equation is of the form:	
rate of reaction = k[X]^n	where [X] = concentration of X
if $n = 0$ (zero order),	doubling [X] does not affect the rate
if $n = 1$ (first order),	doubling [X] doubles the rate
if $n = 2$ (second order),	doubling [X] increases the rate 4-fold

Consider the reaction between hydrogen and iodine

$$H_2(g) + I_2(g) \rightarrow 2HI(g)$$

The **rate equation** is: rate of reaction = $k[H_2]^m[I_2]^n$

From experiments you would find that if you kept the concentration of iodine constant and doubled the concentration of hydrogen, the rate of reaction would doubled. Therefore $m = 1$ and the reaction is said to be *first order* with respect to hydrogen. Similarly if the hydrogen concentration is kept constant and the iodine concentration doubled, the rate again doubles. Therefore $n = 1$ and the reaction is said to be first order with respect to hydrogen.

The overall order of reaction = $m + n = 1 + 1 = 2$. Another example may help.

Potassium ethanedioate, $K_2C_2O_4$, is oxidised to carbon dioxide, CO_2, by mercury(II) chloride, $HgCl_2$.

$$2HgCl_2(aq) + K_2C_2O_4(aq) \rightarrow 2KCl(aq) + 2CO_2(g) + Hg_2Cl_2(s)$$

The rate equation is: rate of reaction = $k[HgCl_2]^m[K_2C_2O_4]^n$

Here are the results of three experiments to investigate the rate of this reaction.

Table 6.2

	[HgCl$_2$(aq)] /mol dm^{-3}	[K$_2$C$_2$O$_4$(aq)] /mol dm^{-3}	Rate/ mol dm^{-3} s^{-1}
Experiment 1	0.0836	0.202	8.66×10^{-6}
Experiment 2	0.0836	0.404	34.64×10^{-6}
Experiment 3	0.0418	0.404	17.32×10^{-6}

Comparing experiments 1 and 2, the concentration of $HgCl_2$ remains the same and so changes in rate must be caused by increasing the concentration of $K_2C_2O_4$. Doubling its concentration gives a four-fold increase in rate. Therefore $n = 2$.

Comparing experiments 2 and 3, the concentration of $K_2C_2O_4$ remains the same, so the rate change must be caused by differences in the concentration of $HgCl_2$. Doubling its concentration (from experiment 3 to experiment 2) gives a two-fold increase in rate. Therefore $m = 1$.

The overall order for the reaction = $m + n = 1 + 2 = 3$.

There is often more than one step in a chemical reaction. The slowest one, the one with the highest activation energy, determines the overall

> The rate equation for a reaction shows how the rate depends on the concentration of the reactants. For the general reaction:
> $$aA + bB \rightarrow \text{products}$$
> the rate equation is:
> rate of reaction = $k[A]^m[B]^n$

rate and is said to be the *rate determining step*. For example, in Figure 6.7 (iii) the second step is the rate determining step.

 4 From experiments, the rate of reaction of iodine with propanone in the presence of hydrogen ions was found to be first order with respect to hydrogen ions and propanone and zero order with respect to the iodine. (a) Write the rate equation for the reaction. (b) What is the overall order of the reaction?

Establishing a position of equilibrium

Consider the esterification reaction between ethanoic acid and ethanol:

$$CH_3COOH(l) + CH_3CH_2OH(l) \rightleftharpoons CH_3COOCH_2CH_3(l) + H_2O(l)$$
ethanoic acid   ethanol   ethyl ethanoate   water

In the presence of an acid catalyst the reaction of ethanol and ethanoic acid is a dynamic equilibrium. At equilibrium the reaction mixture contains ethanoic acid, ethanol, ethyl ethanoate and water.

The equilibrium mixture can be formed from ethyl ethanoate and water or from ethanoic acid and ethanol. No matter which pair is used the same equilibrium mixture ratios will be formed. The activation energy for the reactants turning into products and products turning into reactants can be overcome from either direction (see Figure 6.12).

Eventually you can establish a situation whereby reactants are converted into products at the same rate as products are converted into reactants. While the reactants and products continue to react, the concentration of each product or reactant remains constant.

Complete reaction or no reaction

The reaction can be considered to have gone to completion if in the equilibrium mixture the products are present in a vast excess. On the other hand if the reactants are in large excess in the equilibrium mixture then the reaction has hardly taken place at all.

Homogeneous and heterogeneous equilibria

The equilibrium is called a **homogeneous equilibrium** if all of the reactants and products are in the same phase, that is, all gases, all liquids or all in solution. A **heterogeneous equilibrium** has two or more phases present.

Position of equilibrium

There is a mathematical **relationship** between the concentration of the **reactants** and **products** in a homogeneous equilibrium mixture. If the reaction is

$$aA + bB \rightleftharpoons cC + dD$$

then

$$\frac{[C]^c[D]^d}{[A]^a[B]^b} = \text{a constant at a given temperature}$$

where:
[A] is the concentration in mol dm^{-3} of A in the equilibrium mixture
[B] is the concentration in mol dm^{-3} of B in the equilibrium mixture
[C] is the concentration in mol dm^{-3} of C in the equilibrium mixture
[D] is the concentration in mol dm^{-3} of D in the equilibrium mixture

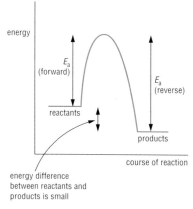

energy

E_a (forward)

E_a (reverse)

reactants

products

course of reaction

energy difference between reactants and products is small

Figure 6.12 In an equilibrium, the activation energy for both the forward and back reactions can be overcome. The energy difference between reactants and products tends to be small. This profile represents a one step reaction in which the forward reaction is exothermic.

Examples of homogeneous and heterogeneous equilibria:
Homogeneous equilibria
$N_2(g) + 3H_2(g) \rightleftharpoons 2NH_3(g)$
$I_2(aq) + I^-(aq) \rightleftharpoons I_3^-(aq)$
Heterogeneous equilibria
$Ca(OH)_2(s) + aq \rightleftharpoons Ca^{2+}(aq) + 2OH^-(aq)$
$ZnO(s) + CO(g) \rightleftharpoons Zn(s) + CO_2(g)$

The relationship between concentrations of reactants and products in a homogeneous equilibrium mixture for the general reaction
$aA + bB \rightleftharpoons cC + dD$ **is**
$\frac{[C]^c[D]^d}{[A]^a[B]^b}$ **= a constant at a given temperature**

The constant is called the **equilibrium constant**, K_c, where c indicates concentration. The larger the value of K_c, the greater the proportion of products in the equilibrium mixture. The smaller the value of K_c, the greater the proportion of reactants in the equilibrium mixture. The value of K_c only tells how far the reaction has gone *not* how fast it has got there. For the reaction

$$PCl_5(g) \rightleftharpoons PCl_3(g) + Cl_2(g)$$

$$K_c = \frac{[PCl_3(g)][Cl_2(g)]}{[PCl_5(g)]} \qquad \text{Units} = \frac{\text{mol dm}^{-3} \times \cancel{\text{mol dm}^{-3}}}{\cancel{\text{mol dm}^{-3}}}$$

The units of K_c in this case are mol dm^{-3}.

At 300°C the value of K_c for this reaction is 2.3×10^5 mol dm^{-3} which means that at equilibrium at this temperature the products are in excess.

Q 5 The equilibrium constant for the reaction between hydrogen and nitrogen to form ammonia is about 2.73×10^8 mol^{-2} dm^6 at 25°C and 1 dm^3. If the mixture contains 0.012 moles of hydrogen and 0.003 moles of nitrogen, how many moles of ammonia are present?

In heterogeneous equilibria the meaning of the concentration of a solid is a problem. It can usually be assumed that the concentration of solid remains constant. This assumption simplifies the mathematical calculation of the equilibrium constant. For the reaction

$$aA(s) + bB(aq) \rightleftharpoons cC(g) + dD(aq)$$

$$K_c = \frac{[C(g)]^c[D(aq)]^d}{[A(s)]^a[B(aq)]^b}$$

Rearranging this equation,

$$K_c [A(s)]^a = \frac{[C(g)]^c [D(aq)]^d}{[B(aq)]^b}$$

assuming the concentration of solid A remains constant, then $K_c[A(s)]^a$ is also a constant, which we can call K.

Therefore $K = \dfrac{[C(g)]^c [D(aq)]^d}{[B(aq)]^b}$

So for the equilibrium set up when calcium carbonate is heated in a sealed tube

$CaCO_3(s)$	$\rightleftharpoons$	$CaO(s)$	$+$	$CO_2(g)$
calcium carbonate		calcium oxide		carbon dioxide

$K = [CO_2(g)]$ because the calcium carbonate and calcium oxide are solids. The units for K for this reaction are mol dm^{-3}.

Q 6 Write the equilibrium expressions (with the correct units) for the following reactions:
(a) $Ca(OH)_2(s) \rightleftharpoons Ca^{2+}(aq) + 2OH^-(aq)$,
(b) $2CO(g) + O_2(g) \rightleftharpoons 2CO_2(g)$

Monitoring reactions

Monitoring a reaction involves measuring two aspects: the *conditions* (such as temperature) and the *results of the reaction* – the amounts of reactants and products. These measurements can provide information about rate and position of equilibrium of the reaction.

When monitoring how conditions affect a reaction it is important to change only one variable at a time. For example, do not change both the concentration of one of the reactants and the reaction temperature. If you do and the yield of product changes you will not know the cause – temperature, concentration or both.

Reaction conditions

Reaction conditions which may be measured include temperature, pressure, pH, surface area of a solid reactant and initial concentration of reactants. The presence and nature of a catalyst can be recorded.

Amounts of reactants and products

You must determine changes in the concentration of a reactant or a product. What matters is that the substance is either consumed (if it is a reactant) or formed (if it is a product) in the reaction. The substance chosen is one which is easy to analyse.

If the rate of a reaction is being monitored, then changes in amount of a reactant or product must determined at different time intervals.

If the position of equilibrium is being monitored, then equilibrium concentrations of a reactant or product must be determined. Provided all initial concentrations and the equation for the reaction are known, the equilibrium concentrations of all the other components can be determined.

Sampling a reaction mixture

Sometimes it is possible to monitor a reactant or product directly. For example, if a substance is coloured, visible spectroscopy or colorimetry can be used to determine concentration. This is a **non-invasive** technique since the reaction mixture is not interfered with. Other non-invasive techniques include pH measurement, conductivity and changes in volume (for gaseous reactions). Samples need not be withdrawn from the reaction for analysis, but if they are they may be returned to the reaction mixture afterwards.

For many reactions a sample of the reaction mixture must be withdrawn to analyse for one of the reactants or products. This is an **invasive** technique. When the sample is taken, the reaction in the sample must be stopped or the rate slowed down to as close to zero as is possible. This process is known as *quenching*. The time at which the concentration

> **There are two aspects to monitoring a reaction:**
> - **conditions under which a reaction occurs**
> - **the amounts of reactants and products in a reaction mixture at any one moment (concentrations of reactants and products at a particular time).**

▶ Analytical techniques, page 50

> **Reaction mixtures may be analysed by invasive or non-invasive techniques.**

Figure 6.13 In the acid catalysed formation of ethyl ethanoate from ethanol and ethanoic acid, the reaction mixture is quenched by cooling in ice. The reaction is monitored by determining the concentration of the ethanoic acid by titration with sodium hydroxide.

of one of the reaction components is determined is when the reaction mixture is quenched, not when the sample was withdrawn.

Common quenching techniques include:

- diluting the mixture
- removal of any catalyst used in the reaction
- cooling the sample rapidly.

Techniques for monitoring a reaction

Each variable in a **reaction** can be **monitored** by a number of different techniques.

Temperature

The simplest way to measure temperature is to use a thermometer. Various thermometers are available. They differ in range and precision. It is important to choose one which meets the needs of the job.

An increasingly common technique is to use an electronic temperature probe. One end of the probe is put into the sample and the leads are plugged into a recording instrument. Once calibrated, the display on the monitor indicates the temperature.

> A reaction can be monitored by following changes in:
> - temperature
> - volume (for reactions involving gases)
> - concentration (for example by chemical analysis or conductivity)
> - pH.

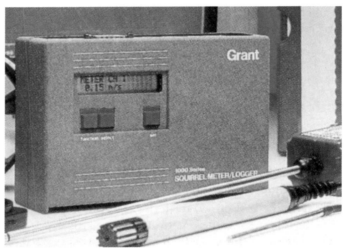

Figure 6.14 A temperature probe can be interfaced with a computer. Data may be collected and stored without anyone being there to read the monitor. This is called data-logging. Automated data collection is particularly useful when lots of data are required in a very small time or over an extended period of time.

Whatever technique is used to record the temperature it is important that the true value is measured. This involves ensuring that the bulb of the thermometer or the end of the probe is in good contact with the reaction mixture. Stirring ensures that the liquid is at a uniform temperature and that no 'hot or cold spots' have been formed.

Volume

Two types of reaction can be usefully monitored by volume measurement:

- homogeneous gaseous reactions
- reactions in which a gas is evolved.

Knowing the volume of a gas enables the amount of substance present to be determined, at a fixed temperature and pressure. This is given by the ideal gas equation:

$$PV = nRT$$

where P = pressure / N m^{-2},
V = volume / m^3,
n = number of moles,
R = gas constant (8.314 J K^{-1} mol^{-1}),
T = temperature / K

For example, to calculate the volume of 0.5 mole of an ideal gas at $100\,°C$ and $5 \times 10^4\,Nm^{-2}$

$$
\begin{aligned}
\text{using } PV &= nRT, \\
V &= nRT/P \\
V &= ?\,m^3 \\
P &= 5 \times 10^4\,Nm^{-2} \\
n &= 0.5\,\text{mole} \\
R &= 8.314\,J\,K^{-1}\,mol^{-1} \\
T &= (273 + 100)\,K \\
\text{Hence } V &= 0.5 \times 8.314 \times 373/5 \times 10^4\,m^3 \\
&= 0.0310\,m^3
\end{aligned}
$$

7 What volume would 1 mole of an ideal gas occupy at 25°C and 101 000 Nm^{-2}?

Although not exactly true, the ideal gas equation is a very good approximation when the temperature and pressure are around normal conditions. You are most likely to use it for reactions in which a gas is evolved. The change in volume can be recorded using a large graduated gas syringe or other graduated glassware such as a burette.

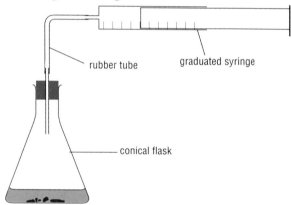

rubber tube   graduated syringe

conical flask

Figure 6.15 *This apparatus can be used to monitor the course of reaction in which a gas is evolved. Some approximate calculations are needed before the reaction is carried out to ensure that a syringe of an appropriate size is selected.*

Consider the reaction between magnesium and dilute hydrochloric acid:

$$
\underset{\text{magnesium}}{Mg(s)} + \underset{\text{hydrochloric acid}}{2HCl(aq)} \rightarrow \underset{\text{magnesium chloride}}{MgCl_2(aq)} + \underset{\text{hydrogen}}{H_2(g)}
$$

Initially, no gases are present. Hydrogen is produced as the reaction proceeds. The increase in the volume is directly related to the amount of hydrogen produced. It is important that the gas is not soluble in the solvent used for the reactants or the reactants themselves to any significant degree. If the gas is soluble then the volume which is measured will be less than that released by the reaction and will lead to anomalies in the results. At the start of a reaction the gas will dissolve hence a smaller volume will be recorded. As the reaction proceeds any solvent present becomes saturated, no more gas will dissolve and the true volume is recorded.

Concentration

The concentration of a component in a sample from a reaction mixture can be determined by the usual quantitative analytical methods. Acid-base and redox titrations are two common methods.

The concentration of a coloured reactant or product can be monitored with a spectrophotometer or a colorimeter.

Chemical tests, page 50

Spectroscopy, page 51

Quantitative chemical tests, page 62

Colorimetry, page 68

Conductivity

Conductivity is the measurement of the conduction of electric charge. For solutions of ions, the conductivity depends on:

- the concentration of ions
- the nature of the ion.

If ions are produced or consumed during a reaction then the reaction can be monitored using a conductivity cell and a meter.

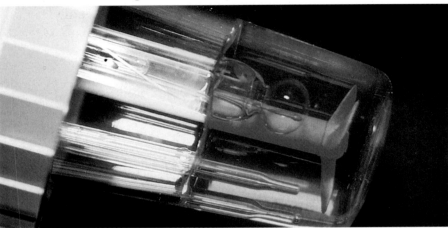

Figure 6.16 Most common conductivity cells have a glass outer case protecting two platinum electrodes which are immersed in the liquid. They are held in a fixed position in the cell. Special attachments allow other devices, such as stirrers, to be immersed in the solution at the same time.

As with colorimetry and spectroscopy or spectrophotometry, calibration graphs of conductivity against concentration must be obtained first. To determine the rate of a reaction, conductivity measurements are made at time intervals. These can be recorded manually, or by using a chart recorder or a computer. The measurements are converted into concentrations using the calibration graph.

pH

pH is a measure of the hydrogen ion concentration:

$pH = -\log[H^+(aq)]$ where $[H^+(aq)]$ = concentration of hydrated hydrogen ions (also called oxonium ions) / mol dm^{-3}

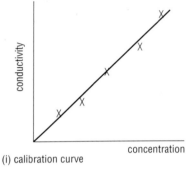

(i) calibration curve

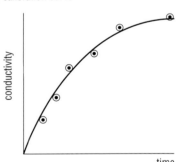

(ii) changes in conductivity with time

Figure 6.17 The rate of hydrolysis of 2-chloro-2-methylpropane can be monitored by conductivity measurements since ions are produced as a result of the reaction:
$(CH_3)_3CCl(aq) + H_2O(l) \rightarrow$
$(CH_3)_3COH(aq) + H^+(aq) + Cl^-(aq)$
An ethanol/water mixture is used as solvent because the halogenoalkane is not soluble in water.

Table 6.2 Concentration of hydrated hydrogen ions and pH

[H$^+$(aq)] / mol dm^{-3}		pH
0.1	(1×10^{-1})	1
0.01	(1×10^{-2})	2
0.001	(1×10^{-3})	3
0.0001	(1×10^{-4})	4
0.00001	(1×10^{-5})	5

You can use the 'log' button on your calculator to convert concentration to pH – but remember the minus sign. The calculator button marked '10^x' does the reverse calculation, to convert pH to concentration.

Q 8 Calculate the pH of the following solutions:
(a) 0.2 mol dm^{-3} HCl(aq), (b) 0.1 mol dm^{-3} H$_2$SO$_4$(aq)

9 What are the concentrations of the following solutions:
(a) hydrochloric acid of pH 4.2, (b) sulphuric acid of pH 5.1?

A pH meter comprises an electronic voltmeter connected to an electrochemical cell which measures the hydrogen ion concentration. The voltmeter is marked in pH units. Calibration of the pH meter against a buffer solution of known pH is essential because the pH of a solution is dependent on the temperature as well as the concentration of the hydrogen ions. After each measurement the probe should be washed with distilled or deionised water and stored with the bulb wet.

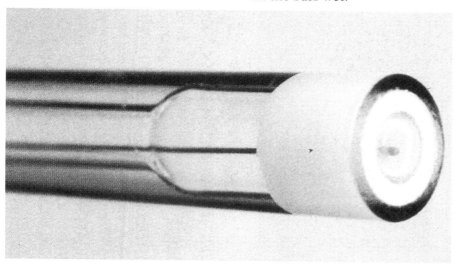

Figure 6.18 *A pH electrode. The electrochemical cell is in the form of a glass probe. It is usually stored in a buffer solution. Before use the pH meter should be calibrated by putting the probe into a buffer solution of known pH.*

Assignment trigger

Water softeners

Depending on where you live the water supplied to your home may vary from soft to hard.

What causes hard water?
How can it be removed?
One way to soften water is by using an ion exchange material.
How does an ion exchange material work?
Can it last for ever?

If a practical assignment is developed, it is essential that a risk assessment is made and checked by your teacher/lecturer.

Could lead to possible assignments relating to Unit 6.

Analysing the data

Data on how the concentration of a reactant or product varies with time can be analysed in various ways. A graph of temperature against time can be plotted by hand or by using a data plotting program on a computer. Graphs of concentration against time are invariably curves (called rate curves).

The gradients of tangents to the curve gives us the rate of reaction at various times during the reaction. These tangents become less steep as time goes by, indicating that the reaction is slowing down as it proceeds. All reactions do this because the rate of a reaction depends on the concentration of the reactants. As the reactants are used up the rate falls.

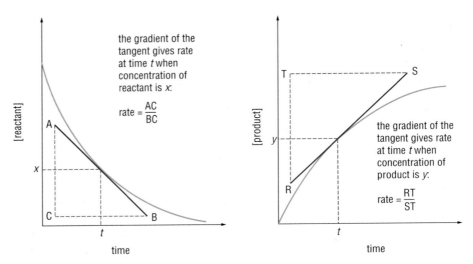

the gradient of the tangent gives rate at time *t* when concentration of reactant is *x*:

$$rate = \frac{AC}{BC}$$

the gradient of the tangent gives rate at time *t* when concentration of product is *y*:

$$rate = \frac{RT}{ST}$$

Figure 6.19 A graph of concentration with time is a curve for nearly all reactions. The gradient of a tangent to the curve gives the rate of reaction at that point in the reaction. The gradient is negative for the disappearance of a reactant and positive for the appearance of a product.

Comparing rates

Rates of reaction can be compared by determining initial rates of reaction. The initial rate is found by drawing a tangent to the curve at the beginning of the reaction (time = 0) and calculating the gradient. The steeper the curve the faster the rate.

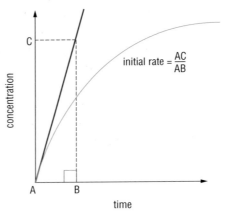

initial rate = $\frac{AC}{AB}$

Figure 6.20 The gradient of this tangent gives the initial rate of reaction. It is calculated as shown on the graph.

The effect of changing a variable can be determined by comparing the initial rate under different conditions. For example, the temperature can be changed, keeping all other factors constant. Comparison of the initial rates at different temperatures allows the effect of temperature on the rate of reaction to be determined. Similarly, the concentration of reactants can be changed or a catalyst used and the initial rates compared for each circumstance.

Q 10 The rate of decomposition of a gaseous molecule is given in the table:

Time /s	Volume of starting molecule /cm^3
0	500
60	250
120	125
180	62.5

Calculate the rate of reaction initially and after 120 s.

Controlling reactions

How fast and how far a chemical reaction goes can be controlled. Most reactions are affected by:

- changing the temperature
- the concentration of the reactants (including changes to the pressure of gases)
- particle size of solids
- the presence of catalysts.

Factors affecting rate of reaction

There are five main factors which are likely to affect the rate at which a reaction progresses: temperature, the concentration of the reactants, pressure, the presence of a catalyst and the size of any solid particles.

Temperature

Increasing the temperature increases the rate of any reaction and the value of the rate constant. When the temperature is increased the reaction mixture is given more energy. This means that more of the molecules will have sufficient energy to overcome the barrier to reaction. Decreasing the temperature has the opposite effect. It slows down the rate of reaction and decreases the value of the rate constant. As a crude rule of thumb, at room temperature, a reaction rate can double for each 10°C rise in temperature.

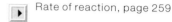 Rate of reaction, page 259

Concentration

Increasing the concentration of a reactant increases the rate of reaction. The higher the concentration, the more frequently the reacting molecules encounter each other so the higher the chances that they will react. As any reaction proceeds the reactants are used up so their concentration falls, hence all reactions slow down over time.

Pressure

Changing the pressure applies to reactions involving gases. Increasing the pressure – making the gases occupy a smaller volume – increases the effective concentration. Increasing the pressure, therefore, increases the rate of a reaction.

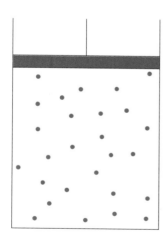 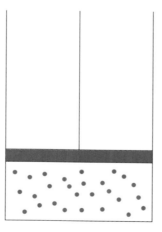

Figure 6.21 The closer reacting particles are to one another, the shorter the time between collisions, and therefore the faster the reaction. Both increasing concentration and increasing pressure have this effect.

Catalysts

The activation energy represents a barrier to the reaction proceeding. Catalysts provide an alternative pathway for the reaction which has a lower activation energy, hence they speed up a reaction. Although catalysts are involved in the reaction they are chemically unchanged at the end of the reaction.

 Reaction pathways, page 257

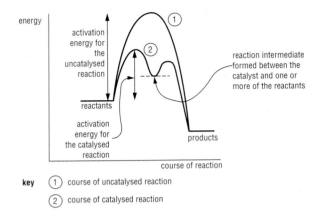

Figure 6.22 *A catalyst provides an alternative course of reaction with a lower activation energy. This means that a higher proportion of reacting molecules have sufficient energy to overcome the energy barrier to reaction.*

If the catalyst is in the same phase as the reaction then it is called a *homogeneous catalyst*. The reaction between ethanoic acid and ethanol to form ethyl ethanoate occurs extremely slowly even if the liquids are heated. However, a few drops of concentrated sulphuric acid dissolved into the solution act as a homogeneous catalyst and the reaction speeds up.

Heterogeneous catalysts are catalysts which are in a different phase to the reactants. The hydrogenation of alkenes with hydrogen is made possible by using a platinum catalyst (usually used as a fine powder mixed with carbon). The alkene is normally dissolved in a solvent and hydrogen is bubbled in; the catalyst does not dissolve but is present as a suspension. The platinum acts by providing a surface on which the alkene and hydrogen molecules can come together and react.

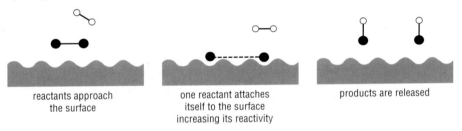

Figure 6.23 *In heterogeneous catalysis, the reactivity of a reactant can be increased by adsorption onto the catalyst surface.*

Enzymes are biological catalysts. Enzymes perform many vital functions in the body by enabling chemical reactions to take place at the much lower temperatures that are found in the body and at a much faster rate. Enzymes are responsible for most reactions which occur in the body, including the digestion of food and the production of energy.

It is possible to use enzymes to carry out chemical transformations. Fermentation, for example is used to make alcoholic drinks, vinegars and medicines such as penicillin.

Catalysts can be prevented from working by *inhibitors*. An inhibitor will stop the functions carried out by the catalyst, or in some cases slow down reactions which do not involve catalysts. The platinum catalysts used in the hydrogenation of alkenes are inhibited by the presence of sulphur. Sulphur attaches itself to the surface of the metal and occupies many of the sites which the alkene and hydrogen would have used. To avoid this the alkene and the hydrogen have to be sulphur-free.

Figure 6.24 *An inhibitor can block the adsorption of reactants on a catalyst surface.*

Enzymes can suffer from similar problems. The molecules on which enzymes act (the *substrates*) are unique. Enzymes only react with molecules of precisely the right shape. If an enzyme mistakenly reacts with an inhibiting substrate the substrate does not fall off, but blocks the enzymes from working further. The substance is called a *suicide substrate* and the enzyme is rendered inactive.

Assignment trigger

Delivering medicines

Drug delivery often needs to be controlled. This enables a more convenient dosage (for example, one a day) to be given to the patient and can reduce waste.

What methods are used to control drug delivery?
What is a time-release capsule?
How can the effectiveness of release systems be tested?

If a practical assignment is developed, it is essential that a risk assessment is made and checked by your teacher/lecturer.

Could lead to possible assignments relating to Unit 6.

Particle size

The effect of **particle size** on the rate of reaction can be important. The smaller the particle size the larger the surface area for the reaction to occur so the faster the rate of reaction. For example, small chips of calcium carbonate react with hydrochloric acid faster than large chips.

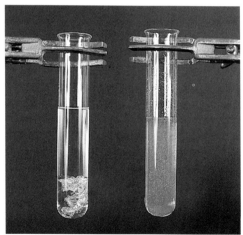

> **Factors which increase reaction rate:**
> - **increase in temperature (rate increases greatly)**
> - **increase in concentration of one or more reactants**
> - **increase in pressure (if gases are involved)**
> - **presence of a suitable catalyst**
> - **decrease in particle size (if one of the reactants is solid)**
>
> **A decrease in rate is brought about by the opposite changes.**

Figure 6.25 1 g of zinc dust has a greater surface area than 1g of zinc granules. It is for this reason that zinc dust reacts far more rapidly with dilute sulphuric acid than do zinc granules.

Q 11 From experiments the rate of reaction of iodine with propanone in the presence of hydrogen ions was found to be first order with respect to hydrogen ions and with respect to propanone. It is zero order with respect to the iodine. Assuming that the temperature is kept constant, what would be the effect on the rate of reaction of the following (a) doubling the concentration of propanone, (b) halving the concentration of iodine, (c) doubling the concentration of hydrogen ions and halving the concentration of propanone, (d) cooling the reaction mixture?

Catalytic convertors
Modern cars often have catalytic convertors.

Why are they fitted?
What materials are they made from?
What influences their design?
How are they tested?
Why has legislation made them more common?
In what other situations could catalysts be similarly beneficial?

If a practical assignment is developed, it is essential that a risk assessment is made and checked by your teacher/lecturer.

Could lead to possible assignments relating to Unit 6.

Factors affecting the position of equilibrium

The relationship between the relative amounts of reactants and products in a reaction can be influenced by a number of factors.

Temperature

Changing the temperature changes the value of an equilibrium constant and the position of the equilibrium (the relative amounts of reactants and products). The effect can be predicted if you know the enthalpy change for the reaction. The enthalpy change for an equilibrium always refers to the enthalpy change for the reactants turning into products, for example:

$$N_2(g) + 3H_2(g) \rightleftharpoons 2NH_3(g) \qquad \Delta H = -92.4 \text{ kJ mol}^{-1}$$

$$K_c = \frac{[NH_3(g)]^2}{[N_2(g)][H_2(g)]^3}$$

The data tells you that when nitrogen and hydrogen react to form ammonia 92.4 kJ mol^{-1} of energy are transferred by heating. This is an exothermic reaction, as shown by the negative sign.

The reverse reaction, whereby ammonia is converted into nitrogen and hydrogen takes in energy (it is endothermic) and ΔH for this reaction is +92.4 kJ mol^{-1}.

For this reaction, raising the temperature increases the rate of both the forward and reverse reactions. For reactions where the formation of the product is exothermic, the overall effect is to make the equilibrium constant smaller, i.e. it favours the formation of reactants.

The reaction of hydrogen and iodine is an example of the opposite type of equilibrium

$$H_2(g) + I_2(g) \rightleftharpoons 2HI(g) \qquad \Delta H = +82.4 \text{ kJ mol}^{-1}$$
hydrogen iodine   hydrogen iodide

$$K_c = \frac{[HI(g)]^2}{[H_2(g)][I_2(g)]}$$

Increasing the temperature favours the formation of hydrogen iodide.

Increasing the temperature raises the value of the equilibrium constant and by moving the position of the equilibrium to the right forms more product. Decreasing the temperature has the opposite effect, causing less HI to be formed and the equilibrium mixture will contain more reactants.

For an equilibrium reaction, an increase in temperature promotes the endothermic reaction (whether forward or reverse). A decrease in temperature promotes the exothermic reaction.

Concentration

Changing the **concentration of reactants** or products in a reaction at equilibrium alters the position of the equilibrium but does not change the value of the equilibrium constant. The equilibrium adjusts itself to restore the balance between the reactants and products.

For the equilibrium

$$I_2(aq) \quad + \quad I^-(aq) \quad \rightleftharpoons \quad I_3^-(aq)$$
iodine $\qquad$ iodide ions $\qquad$ triiodide ions

if you increase the concentration of $I^-(aq)$ the value of the equilibrium constant is unchanged. The position of the equilibrium moves to the right. More $I_3^-(aq)$ is formed. If you decrease the concentration of $I^-(aq)$ ions the position of the equilibrium moves to the left as $I_3^-(aq)$ ions dissociate. The value of the equilibrium constant is unchanged.

An increase in reactant concentrations or a decrease in product concentrations promotes the forward reaction. A decrease in reactant concentrations or an increase in product concentrations promotes the reverse reaction.

Pressure

For gaseous reactions at equilibrium where the volume of the products is different from the reactants, altering the pressure affects the position of the equilibrium but the value of the equilibrium constant remains unchanged.

For the equilibrium

$$N_2O_4(g) \quad \rightleftharpoons \quad 2NO_2(g)$$
dinitrogen $\qquad\qquad$ nitrogen dioxide
tetroxide

Increasing the pressure leaves the value of the equilibrium constant unchanged. The position of equilibrium moves to the left. More N_2O_4 is formed because this occupies the smallest volume. **Decreasing the pressure** moves the equilibrium to the right and more NO_2 is produced.

If there is no difference between the volumes of the gaseous reactants and products then changing the pressure has no effect on the position of the equilibrium. An example is the reaction:

$$H_2(g) \quad + \quad I_2(g) \quad \rightleftharpoons \quad 2HI(g)$$
hydrogen $\quad$ iodine $\qquad$ hydrogen iodide

An increase in pressure promotes the reaction which leads to a smaller number of gaseous molecules. A decrease in pressure promotes the reaction which leads to a greater number of gaseous molecules.

Catalysts

Catalysts do not affect either the value of the equilibrium constant or the position of the equilibrium. A catalyst does speed up the rate at which the equilibrium position is established.

Catalysts do not affect the position of an equilibrium.

Q 12 Methanol can be produced by the reaction of carbon monoxide and hydrogen:

$$CO(g) + 2H_2(g) \quad \rightleftharpoons \quad CH_3OH(g) \; \Delta H = -90 \text{ kJ mol}^{-1}$$

(a) Write the expression for the equilibrium constant
(b) What effect will each of the following have on the value of the equilibrium constant and the position of the equilibrium:
    (i) an increase in temperature;
    (ii) a decrease in pressure;
    (iii) the use of a transition metal catalyst?

Factors which affect equilibrium can be summarised by the statement:
If the conditions of a system are altered the position of equilibrium will move in the direction which reduces the effect of the imposed change.
This is a form of Le Chatelier's Principle (sometimes known affectionately as the 'Law of Cussedness').

Maintaining constant pH

Buffer solutions are used to maintain a constant pH. Buffers resist changes in pH when small amounts of acids or alkalis are added. Larger quantities overwhelm the buffer.

A buffer solution normally consists of a weak acid and the salt of that acid. Weak bases and their salts also act as buffers.

A weak acid (HA) dissolved in water does not dissociate fully. Instead an equilibrium is established:

$$HA(aq) \rightleftharpoons H^+(aq) + A^-(aq)$$

Any salt dissociates fully in water to give a solution of hydrated cations and anions.

The action of a buffer can be explained by considering an example, ethanoic acid and sodium ethanoate in water:

Sodium ethanoate:

$$CH_3COONa(s) + aq \rightarrow CH_3COO^-(aq) + Na^+(aq)$$
sodium ethanoate   water   ethanoate ions   sodium ions

Ethanoic acid:

$$CH_3COOH(l) + aq \rightarrow CH_3COOH(aq),$$

then: $CH_3COOH(aq) \rightleftharpoons CH_3COO^-(aq) + H^+(aq)$

In the mixture, $CH_3COO^-(aq)$ ions from the salt drive the equilibrium to the left and the dissociation of the acid is suppressed. This is now a buffer solution.

When $H^+(aq)$ ions are added to the buffer system, $CH_3COO^-(aq)$ ions from the salt combine with them to form $CH_3COOH(aq)$. When $OH^-(aq)$ ions are added they react with $H^+(aq)$ to form water. More $CH_3COOH(aq)$ then dissociates to produce $H^+(aq)$ and restore the equilibrium. The result of both actions is that the pH remains virtually unchanged following the additions.

A buffer solution resists changes in pH when an acid or alkali is added.

Assignment trigger

Acidity regulators

Contents of food products are shown on their labels.

What are the 'acidity regulators' shown on the labels of some foods.
What substances are acidity regulators?
How can they be made?
How can you test their effectiveness?
How is the use of regulators controlled?

If a practical assignment is developed, it is essential that a risk assessment is made and checked by your teacher/lecturer.

Could lead to possible assignments relating to Units 3, 4 and 6.

Managing industrial processes

The basic principles covered above are applied on a much larger scale in the chemicals industry, but the differences in scale require a different range of techniques to those used in the laboratory.

Batch and continuous processes

Industrial manufacture is carried out either as a **continuous process** or as a **batch process**. In a continuous process a dedicated manufacturing plant is built to carry out the preparation. It will be designed for one product on a large scale. Some plants are constructed from new while others are 'cut and carve'. These are old plants which are no longer required and are adapted to cope with the new process. To make it cost effective a continuous process will run 24 hours a day and 365 days a year. Examples of products made in this type of process include petrochemicals (chemicals obtained from crude oil or natural gas) and the chloro-alkali chemicals (sodium hydroxide and chlorine).

> **Substances can be manufactured by continuous processes or batch processes.**

Figure 6.26 A continuous reactor

Continuous processes require reactors which have been specially designed for the reaction. The reactors must cope with the reaction conditions and allow the reactants to be fed in and the products to be removed continuously.

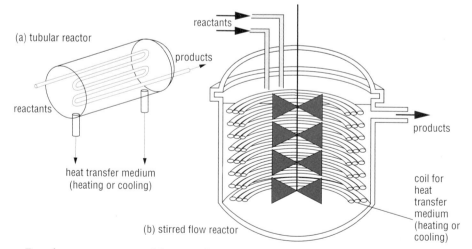

Figure 6.27 Liquid phase reactors in continuous processes tend to be of the tubular or stirred flow types. Tubular reactors consist of coiled tubing through which the reactants pass. The temperature of the reactor is controlled by cooling or heating jackets on the outside. A stirred flow reactor consists of a vessel in which the reactants are mixed by rotating paddles. The reactants can be added from the top, and the products removed either from the side or bottom.

Batch processing enables smaller amounts of materials to be produced. Rather than using equipment dedicated to one process, the equipment is assembled for the particular reaction concerned. The apparatus looks like a giant set of apparatus that would be found in any laboratory. Once the reaction is over the apparatus may be partially dismantled to isolate the product.

Although batch processing is more labour-intensive than continuous processing it is less capital-intensive, so the plant costs are lower. It is common to find pharmaceuticals and specialist chemicals such as dyes and pesticides (often called *fine chemicals*) being made by this method.

Q 13 Chemicals used as fragrances in the perfume industry are often expensive and used only in small quantities in perfumes. Do you think they are made by continuous or batch processing? Explain your answer.

Figure 6.28 *A batch reactor*

Energy is needed for heating, for lighting, and for the power to drive machinery and transport. It is expensive. Chemical engineers design chemical plants to keep energy consumption to a minimum.

Energy

Energy costs represent a major part of a chemical company's production costs, so a lot of effort is put into obtaining the most economical and reliable supply. Engineers seek to recycle energy whenever possible in the manufacturing processes to minimise wastage and reduce costs. Heat evolved in one part of the plant can be used for heating in another. Steam which is used for heating can be recycled. This is one reason why some large chemical plants have so many pipes criss-crossing the sites.

Figure 6.29 *Steam lines criss-crossing a chemical plant*

The industrial price of energy is negotiable. Some chemical plants have their own power stations to generate their own electricity. Others purchase electricity from one of the generating companies via the National Grid. Individual contracts are negotiated for the supply of electricity with generating companies, for example National Power, Powergen and Nuclear Electric. Additional electricity can be purchased from the 'pool'.

The prices of the 'pool' electricity depend on demand and capacity within the system. The prices are printed in the national newspapers.

	in England and Wales.				in England and Wales.		
	Provisional Price for Trading on 13.11.94	Final Prices for Trading on 16.10.94			Provisional Price for Trading on 14.11.94	Final Prices for Trading on 17.10.94	
1/2 hour period ending	Pool purchase price £/MWh	Pool purchase price £/MWh	Pool selling price £/MWh	1/2 hour period ending	Pool purchase price £/MWh	Pool purchase price £/MWh	Pool selling price £/MWh
0030	9.67	8.10	8.10	0030	9.22	8.12	8.12
0100	34.37	8.09	8.09	0100	9.89	8.07	8.07
0130	38.57	8.16	8.16	0130	9.89	8.13	8.13
0200	39.54	9.07	11.26	0200	9.89	9.10	11.03
0230	9.67	9.90	12.09	0230	9.89	9.70	11.64
0300	9.21	9.90	12.09	0300	9.21	9.70	11.64
0330	9.20	9.90	12.09	0330	9.20	9.70	11.64
0400	9.19	8.99	11.18	0400	8.22	8.13	8.13
0430	8.12	8.12	8.12	0430	8.21	8.13	8.13
0500	8.10	8.10	8.10	0500	8.21	8.12	8.12
0530	8.10	8.12	8.12	0530	8.14	8.40	8.40
0600	8.10	8.12	8.12	0600	8.14	8.40	8.40
0630	8.10	8.12	8.12	0630	9.21	9.16	11.09
0700	8.10	8.12	8.12	0700	9.24	19.22	21.15
0730	8.10	8.12	8.12	0730	30.37	21.86	23.95
0800	8.11	9.17	11.36	0800	31.79	34.24	36.68
0830	8.12	9.29	11.48	0830	31.79	42.01	44.49
0900	8.12	9.29	11.48	0900	31.84	42.30	44.87
0930	9.21	18.75	20.94	0930	43.42	33.71	36.14
1000	9.22	19.26	21.45	1000	43.44	33.88	36.35

Figure 6.30 Pool prices of electricity

14 What do you think makes the biggest demands on energy supplies in a chemical plant?

The supply of gas is also negotiated with a supplier, such as British Gas or one of the oil companies which operate in the North Sea. Coal and coke is purchased from a British mining company or on the world market.

The input costs of the energy and raw materials are offset by the price charged for the product. This is the way that companies make money for further research and development (R & D), as well as profits for their shareholders. The price of a product is determined by economists and market strategists. Like the cost of reactants, the price of the product will depend on the purity, cost of production, demand in the market place and the size of the order.

Co-products and by-products

By-products are produced as a result of carrying out a process and may be due to side reactions producing **side products**. In some reactions other products besides the one you want are made. These are called **co-products**.

In most cases it is preferable to minimise the by-products and co-products in a reaction. Many do not have a commercial value and they represent an added complication in the industrial process. They have to be isolated from the required product and may affect the efficiency of the process. A development chemist will aim to minimise the number and quantity of by-products and co-products when scaling up a laboratory preparation.

> In a chemical process, products other than the main product (the one that is the target of the process) are called side products. These may be by-products or co-products.

Planning a preparation, page 128

By-products

By-products of a process can be chemicals or energy. If the chemicals have a use then they can be sold. Sulphur is an impurity in crude oil and must be removed prior to the refining process. The sulphur could then be sold for use in the manufacture of, for example, sulphuric acid, and represents a source of extra revenue. Excess energy can be recycled or sold. Chemical plants with their own electric power stations can sell any excess capacity via the National Grid.

Figure 6.31 Sulphur, a by-product from the process of refining crude oil, is sold to other companies. It is often transported in bulk by tankers.

Co-products

Co-products are sometimes formed in a reaction. The larger the scale of the reaction the larger the amounts of co-products produced. Sometimes it is possible to find a use for these products. Chlorine is a valubable co-product from the industrial manufacture of sodium hydroxide. It is used in a wide range of industrial processes including the bleaching of paper.

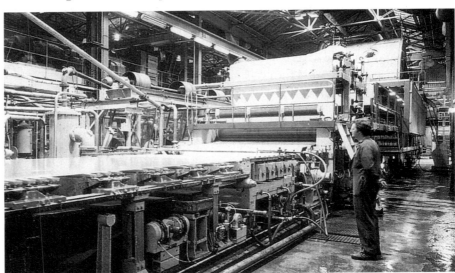

Figure 6.32 Chlorine is used in the bleaching of paper.

Balance between rate of reaction and yield

The efficiency of a reaction is measured in terms of the balance between the rate of reaction and the yield of product. This is an important consideration in industry: there is no point in getting a 100% yield if you wait for days for the reaction to go to completion.

The industrial production of ammonia is a good example of balancing yield and efficiency:

$$N_2(g) \; + \; 3H_2(g) \; \rightleftharpoons \; 2NH_3(g) \qquad \Delta H = -92.4 \, \text{kJ mol}^{-1}$$
nitrogen   hydrogen   ammonia

$$K_c = \frac{[NH_3(g)]^2}{[N_2(g)][H_2(g)]^3}$$

The lower the temperature, the higher the value of the equilibrium constant and the more ammonia is formed. However, the lower the temperature the slower the rate of reaction. While the low temperature favours a high yield of ammonia it is produced only at an extremely slow rate – too slow to make the process economical.

On the other hand the proportion of ammonia in the reaction mixture can be increased by raising the pressure and the rate at which the equilibrium is set up can be speeded up by using a catalyst.

The **compromise** is to use a temperature of 750 K, a pressure of about 200 times atmospheric and an iron catalyst containing potassium oxide and aluminium oxide as promoters. This gives a yield of about 14%.

Consequences of production

Industry makes products to meet consumer demand. The siting of a chemical plant depends on a number of factors. Bulk chemicals are often utilised near to their point of manufacture to reduce the costs of transport. Examples of this include the extraction of aluminium and the electrolysis of brine to produce sodium hydroxide.

The siting of a chemical plant has an impact on the local economy, and may contribute to the national economy and to international trade. It is often said that you can tell the economic state of a country by the amount of sulphuric acid it produced. Sulphuric acid is an acid, an oxidising agent and a solvent. It is used prolifically, and touches nearly every industrial process in one form or another, so its production is a measure of the underlying economic activity.

The siting of a plant in a town creates employment opportunities. People are required to work on the site. The cross-section of people will range from highly trained scientists, technicians and engineers to support staff such as secretaries, security guards, canteen staff and lorry drivers. The list of people is almost endless.

A factory also means that the local infra-structure will be affected. The site will need materials and services (gas, electricity, water, refuse disposal) and people will have to supply these needs. In turn the people who work on the site will need homes, shops and recreational facilities. It is often difficult to see the effect when a company opens up a site, but it is all too evident when a site closes down. The loss of 100 jobs on a site may lead to the loss of many times this number of jobs in local suppliers and support services.

The cumulative effect of a large number of chemical sites in one country adds strength to a nation's economy. Products can also be exported, leading to international trade.

Fine chemicals and pharmaceuticals are manufactured on smaller scales than bulk chemicals. Often the research and development is carried out in one country while manufacture is carried out elsewhere. The decision to manufacture in another country may be related to cheaper labour and manufacturing costs or a local Government may insist on the manufacturing being done locally before allowing access to the markets in that country. Most chemical and pharmaceutical companies are international with local offices or manufacturing sites all over the world. Research laboratories which often have expensive facilities and specialist staff tend to be concentrated on one or two sites.

> **Any industrial process aims to make the product quickly and with the highest possible yield. Sometimes conditions favour both. Sometimes, however, they are in conflict and a compromise has to be reached.**

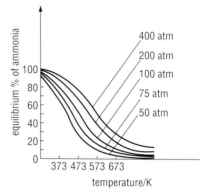

Figure 6.33 *Yield of ammonia at different temperatures and pressures*

> **A number of consequences of manufacturing a substance need to be considered:**
> • **economic issues**
> • **environmental issues**
> • **the health, safety and well-being of employees and the local community.**
> **Such consequences have an effect on both the local and the global scale. Both should be considered.**

Figure 6.34 *The expansion of BP's Grangemouth refinery 1934 – 1985*

Figure 6.35 *Strict adherence to Health and Safety at Work regulations is vital when working with chemicals.*

Health and Safety

All chemical and pharmaceutical products undergo rigorous testing. Pharmaceuticals are tested exhaustively to check that there are no side effects on humans. The tests look for any unexpected effects and inform the companies on the necessary dosage levels. Chemicals are also tested and any hazards noted.

In the laboratory every chemical which is to be used is assessed for its hazards so that the necessary precautions can be taken. Risk Assessments are now a standard part of everyday life. Employees who work on chemical sites are often subject to regular medical checkups. Employers have an incentive to monitor the health of their workforce. A healthy workforce will be more efficient! Most companies have monitoring programmes to ensure that high safety standards are maintained.

Environmental factors are important too. It is not in the best interest of a company to have a chemical plant adversely affecting the local community. Increasingly companies are building relationships with local communities to ensure that they are well informed about the company. Emissions from a chemical plant are monitored. Most sites monitor their own emissions. In the UK external regulators check to ensure that the regulations are obeyed. Emissions are monitored by the Environmental Protection Agency, which checks that discharges into the air, rivers and sea, as well as diposal in landfill sites, comply with regulations.

Some emissions from sites do not affect local communities alone: they also cross borders. The radioactive material which escaped from Chernobyl spread across Europe. The emissions of sulphur dioxide from power stations are the subject of controversy because the effects can be felt thousands of kilometres away. There is still considerable debate on what, if any, environmental impact emissions from the UK have had in other countries.

Figure 6.36 *Atmospheric pollution from an industrial plant*

Assignment trigger

Crumbling buildings

Many buildings are decaying.

Do some building materials erode more quickly than others?
What causes this erosion?
Why do some parts erode more rapidly than others?
Can the process be slowed down?
Can you model the process in the laboratory?

If a practical assignment is developed, it is essential that a risk assessment is made and checked by your teacher/lecturer.

Could lead to possible assignments relating to Unit 6.

Case study

SUNBLOCKS

Case Study

Many of us have suffered from sunburn. This happens when our skin is exposed to ultraviolet radiation from the sun. Excessive exposure can be more damaging and lead to melanomas – a form of skin cancer. Suntan lotions offer some protection.

Many suntan lotions contain organic compounds which absorb the damaging ultraviolet radiation. A common ingredient is 4-aminobenzoic acid. More recently, sunblocks have become popular. These are the creams that do not 'disappear' when rubbed on to the skin. Instead they look rather like warpaint! One advertising line for these products is to describe them as 'natural sunblocks' which contain 'no chemicals'. The active ingredients are titanium(IV) oxide, TiO_2, and zinc oxide, ZnO.

Illustration 1 *4-aminobenzoic acid*

Illustration 2 *This cricketer is protecting himself from harmful UV. The sunblock applied like warpaint may also have a psychological effect on the opposition!*

The usual starting point for the manufacture of TiO_2 is ilmenite. This is mainly iron(II) titanate(IV), $FeTiO_3$, but contains other materials depending on the location from which it is mined. Weathering, for example, causes some oxidation to iron(III) titanate(IV), $Fe_2Ti_3O_9$. The aim of the process is to remove all iron from the ore and obtain pure TiO_2.

The ore is stored under cover before being ground to a fine powder. The powder is mixed with sulphuric acid and heated by passing steam through the mixture. The reaction is highly exothermic:

$$FeTiO_3(s) + 2H_2SO_4(aq) \rightarrow Fe^{2+}(aq) + TiO^{2+}(aq) + 2H_2O(l) + 2SO_4^{2-}(aq)$$

$$Fe_2Ti_3O_9(s) + 6H_2SO_4(aq) \rightarrow 2Fe^{3+}(aq) + 3TiO^{2+}(aq) + 6H_2O(l) + 6SO_4^{2-}(aq)$$

Any iron(III) ions are now reduced to iron(II) ions using iron from recycled 'tin cans':

$$Fe(s) + 2Fe^{3+}(aq) \rightarrow 3Fe^{2+}(aq)$$

Any unreacted solids are left to settle (often aided by the used of flocculating agents). The hot solution is decanted and then allowed to cool to 30 °C so that iron(II) sulphate crystallises out. This is separated and the remaining solution concentrated by evaporation. Water is then added in a controlled way to precipitate TiO_2:

$$TiO^{2+}(aq) + H_2O(l) \rightleftharpoons TiO_2(s) + 2H^+(aq)$$

As the equilibrium sign in the equation indicates, the precipitation is incomplete. The solid is separated by filtration through poly(propene) filter cloths. Any remaining iron would discolour the final product and so is removed at this stage by washing the solid with dilute sulphuric acid (about 50 g dm^{-3}) containing titanium(III) ions. It is then slurried with water to remove the acid and filtered again.

The solid is finally dried in a rotary gas-fired calciner. As it passes through, the temperature of the solid is raised from 40 °C on entry to 1000 °C on exit. The dried TiO_2 is milled to produce particles of a desired size (dependent upon the intended use).

Illustration 3 *Rotary calciners are used to remove water and sulphuric acid from the titanium(IV) oxide.*

Various coatings may be applied depending on the intended use of the TiO₂. For example, a coating of aluminium oxide is produced by mixing a slurry of TiO₂ with a solution of aluminium sulphate and sodium hydroxide at a pH of 8. Similarly, coatings of silicon(IV) oxide and zirconium(IV) oxide can be applied using sodium hydroxide and solutions of sodium silicate(IV) and zirconium(IV) sulphate respectively.

The process gives a liquid waste which must be safely disposed of. The waste contains dissolved iron(II) sulphate, some titanyl sulphate and low concentrations of heavy metal ions (such as vanadium and chromium) which were present as impurities in the ilmenite. The effluent is pH 1 and contains around 18–20 g dm⁻³ of sulphuric acid.

Questions

1 Titanium(IV) oxide is an inert compound with a high refractive index. This makes it one of the whitest compounds known. It is manufactured by Tioxide UK. Each year over 100 000 tonnes are produced, about half of which is exported. Sunblocks do not account for all of this! What are the other uses of TiO₂?

2 Is the process batch or continuous? What raw materials are used and what are the products required and side products of the process?

3 What steps are taken to control the process and how could their effectiveness be determined?

4 What are the potential environmental consequences of manufacturing TiO₂? What measures might be taken to reduce these effects?

5 The reduction of iron(III) to iron(II) can be simulated in the laboratory using apparatus shown in Illustration 4. How can the rate of this reaction be determined and the factors which affect the rate investigated?

6 The hydrolysis of TiO^{2+}(aq) can also be carried out in the laboratory (Illustration 5). Devise a method to establish how the position of equilibrium can be affected so as to maximise the yield of precipitate.

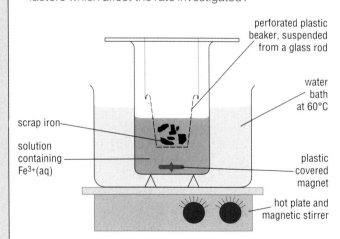

Illustration 4 *Reduction of iron(III) to iron(II)*

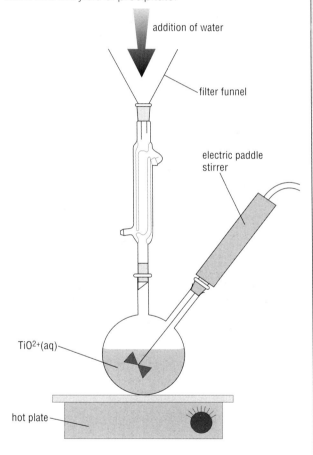

Illustration 5 *Hydrolysis of TiO^{2+}(aq)*

Case study

THE CONTACT PROCESS

Sulphuric acid is used in the manufacture of fertilisers, paints, pigments, detergents, fibres and plastics. It also finds many uses in the laboratory. As well as being an acid it can act as a solvent, oxidising agent and dehydrating agent.

All sulphuric acid is manufactured by the Contact process. The three key stages are:

1 formation of sulphur dioxide from sulphur (in some cases sulphur may already be in the form of sulphur dioxide, for example by roasting sulphide ores)
2 reaction between sulphur dioxide and oxygen to give sulphur trioxide
3 formation of sulphuric acid from sulphur trioxide and water.

The reaction between sulphur dioxide and oxygen is an equilibrium reaction.

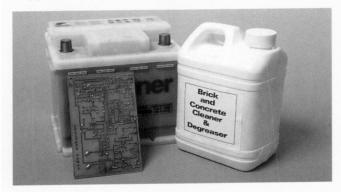

Illustration 1 *Some of the products made using sulphuric acid*

The equilibrium

The choice of reaction conditions for the Contact process is a good illustration of the way that the conditions chosen are often a compromise between the needs of equilibrium yield, reaction rate and cost.

The key reaction in the Contact process is:

$$2SO_2(g) + O_2(g) \rightleftharpoons 2SO_3(g) \quad \Delta H = -197.6 \text{ kJ mol}^{-1}$$

$$K_c = \frac{[SO_3(g)]^2}{[SO_2(g)]^2[O_2(g)]}$$

The equilibrium is affected by temperature, pressure and the use of catalysts. The effects are predicted in Table 1.

Table 1 Factors which affect the equilibrium

Factor	Position of equilibrium	Equilibrium constant
increase in temperature	moves to left	decreases
decrease in temperature	moves to right	increases
increase in pressure	moves to right	unchanged
decrease in pressure	moves to left	unchanged
adding catalyst	unchanged but established more quickly	unchanged

To achieve an increase in the yield of sulphur trioxide it is predicted that low temperature, high pressure and using a catalyst would be the favourable conditions.

Studies have shown that acceptably high yields of sulphur trioxide can be obtained by running the mixture at atmospheric pressure. Increasing the pressure would increase the amount of sulphur trioxide in the reaction mixture still further, but by avoiding high pressure, chemical companies save on the costs of expensive specialist high pressure reactors.

The establishment of the equilibrium is slow at room temperature, so a vanadium pentoxide catalyst and a reaction temperature of around 450 °C is used. The yield is over 90%. Notice that a fairly high temperature is used, even though this reduces the yield a little. The gain in rate makes the slight loss of sulphur trioxide acceptable.

Illustration 2 A Contact process plant in operation

Making sulphuric acid

The sulphur trioxide is converted to sulphuric acid by first dissolving the gas in 98% sulphuric acid. The final product (about 98.5% sulphuric acid) is diluted with more 98% sulphuric acid to give sulphuric acid of the required concentration. The heat evolved is removed by heat exchangers.

Illustration 3 If the sulphur trioxide is added directly to water an acidic mist is formed which is difficult to handle.

Questions

1 Copy Table 1 and add a fourth column headed 'Change in rate'. Complete the table by summarising the effect of the factors listed on the rate of the reaction.

2 Why is the Contact process a good example of compromise?

3 What would be the best theoretical conditions for the Contact process?

4 Is the manufacture of sulphuric acid a batch or a continuous process? Explain the advantages and disadvantages of the production method used.

5 Another very important industrial process is the manufacture of ammonia by the Haber process. Find out the reaction conditions which are used industrially and compare them with the ideal theoretical conditions.

6 It has been recognised that more sulphur-containing compounds are emitted from coal-burning power stations than are required for all the UK's sulphuric acid production. What are the implications of this?

7 | Human physiology and health care management

Left to itself, the human body manages pretty well most of the time. Given oxygen and the right diet, most newborn babies live for between fifty and ninety years. Sometimes, though, things go wrong for us. We may break a bone, catch an infection or develop some other disease. This unit is all about the knowledge and skills that scientists need to monitor and manage the human body. We shall look at how the human body can be studied and described, and at how management action can be taken to benefit our health, whether as individuals or as groups.

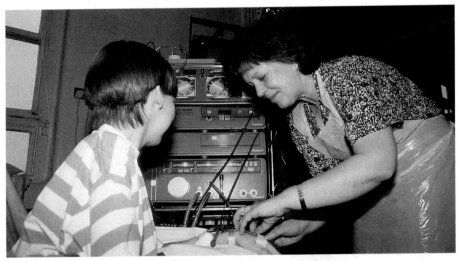

Figure 7.1 *This sixteen year-old's kidneys are not working properly. However, an artificial kidney machine can be used to perform their excretory function. In this way, scientists can 'manage' the human body.*

The Elements

Element 7.1 Establish the characteristics of mammalian organ systems in the maintenance of health

In order to see how mammalian organ systems contribute to the maintenance of health you need to:
- describe the roles of the main organ systems, such as the digestive and circulatory systems
- explain the relationship between the structures of organ systems and how they operate. We shall concentrate on the cardio-respiratory (heart, breathing and circulation) system

- use an optical microscope to analyse mammalian tissues and relate the visible features of tissues to their functions
- describe the functions of the major cell components.

Element 7.2 Monitor physiological changes in the human body

In order to study the cardio-respiratory system of the human body and see if it changes in any important respects, you need to:

- understand the principle of regulation
- carry out measurements to monitor physiological changes
- analyse data obtained from secondary sources, such as ECG traces and X-rays, and draw valid conclusions about a person's physiological state.

▶ Principles of regulation, page 323

▶ Monitor physiological changes in the human body, page 299

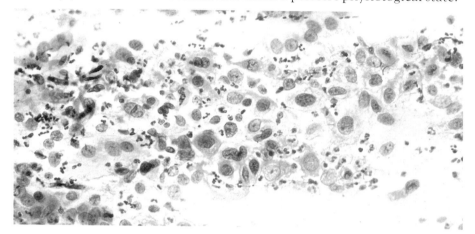

Figure 7.2 A range of instruments, including the optical microscope, can be used to obtain information about the functioning of organs, tissues and cells. This is a photomicrograph of a cervical smear. It shows cells scraped from the neck of the cervix. In this case there are large numbers of abnormal cells (stained in the photograph). These cells have large nuclei and indicate that the woman, unless treated, is at risk of developing cervical cancer.

Element 7.3 Prepare action plans for health care of people

Finally, you will need to be able to recommend action to be taken to help people, both individuals and groups, by:

- using physiological data to predict the consequences of changes in life style
- predicting the outcomes of particular methods of health care, such as exercise, diet and public health programmes
- evaluating these methods
- preparing action plans for people.

▶ Health care for individuals, page 288

▶ Healthcare for groups, page 296

▶ Evaluating healthcare, page 297

Figure 7.3 The exercise a person takes should be appropriate to their particular needs and abilities.

Health care for individuals

What is good health? No one, assuming they are alive, is totally unhealthy. At the same time, most of us have times in our lives when we feel pretty healthy, and other times when we feel less healthy. In a very real sense, health is a state of mind. There are no objective measures of precisely how healthy you are (see Figure 7.4). On the other hand, how healthy we are is connected with many of the physical measurements we shall go on to consider in this Unit. Physiological data can provide useful information about a person's health. For example, by and large, the lower your resting heart rate, the healthier you are.

Health is a personal sense of well-being. It is related to physiological measurements, but is more than these.

Figure 7.4 Aurelia Dobre, a top Romanian gymnast competing at the the Olympic Games. Gymnasts are often very healthy. However, some of them suffer lasting back damage or other injury as a result of their sport. Most sportspeople love their sport. A few come to hate it.

 Pulse rate, page 300

 1 How do each of the following affect your health:
(a) how physically fit you are,
(b) how much sleep you get,
(c) what you have eaten recently,
(d) your friendships,
(e) your family,
(f) your pets,
(g) your hobbies,
(h) how much money you have,
(i) stress,
(j) where you live,
(k) what you think about yourself?

Assignment trigger

Health

You are less likely to be happy if you are unhealthy.

What is health?
How do the major organ systems contribute to health?
What can you do to help to ensure that good health is maintained?

If a practical assignment is developed, it is essential that a risk assessment is made and checked by your teacher/lecturer.

Could lead to possible assignments relating to Unit 7.

Exercise

As a result of exercise, our body responds both in the short term, during the exercise itself, and in the longer term. We shall look at each of these in turn. The long-term effects of exercise are usually good for health, unless the exercise is carried to extremes.

Short-term changes

There are a number of **short-term changes** which can occur during or immediately after exercise:

- an increase in oxygen consumption (i.e. metabolic rate goes up)
- blood diverted from gut to actively contracting muscles
- a rise in body temperature
- an increase in pulse rate and volume of blood pumped each cardiac cycle (i.e. each time the heart beats)
- an accumulation of the three-carbon compound lactate as a result of the incomplete breakdown of glucose in respiration when there is insufficient oxygen (anaerobic conditions)
- the build up of an oxygen debt, to be paid off at the end of the exercise when extra oxygen is breathed in
- an increase in sweating and other ways of reducing overheating.

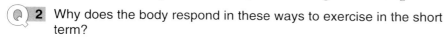 Functions of the cardio-respiratory system, page 316

Q 2 Why does the body respond in these ways to exercise in the short term?

Long-term changes

Long-term changes as a result of regular exercise include:

- a decrease in the resting heart rate
- an increase in the volume of blood pumped each cardiac cycle
- fatty deposits cleared from artery walls
- an increase in the vital capacity of the lungs
- an increase in the number of energy-producing mitochondria in muscle fibres
- an increase in the blood supply to muscles
- an increase in the synthesis of the oxygen-holding molecule myoglobin found in muscle
- an increase in the size (not number) of individual muscle fibres
- an increase in muscle strength, endurance and resistance to fatigue
- an increase in suppleness (especially with certain types of exercise, for example swimming and dancing)
- a feeling of well-being
- skin conditioning and tone may improve
- tendons, ligaments and bones are strengthened, reducing the risk of injuries.

Case study: Athletes sleep their way to the top, page 326

Q 3 Why does the body respond in these ways to exercise in the long term?

How much exercise?

How much exercise do you need to do to improve your health? The answer depends on what is meant by 'health'. If you want to develop your ability to exercise at maximum levels – for example because you want to be fitter for playing active sports – then you need to increase your **aerobic fitness** (hence the term 'aerobics'). Increasing aerobic fitness, so that you can run faster and for longer before getting exhausted, requires you to exercise at

Case study: Heart attacks, page 325

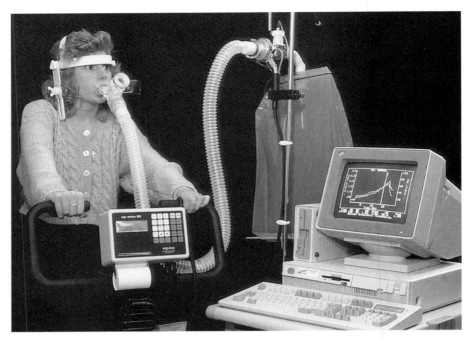

Figure 7.5 Maximum oxygen uptake can be measured using apparatus such as this. The air breathed out by the woman is collected in the plastic bag mounted on the stand. Its oxygen and carbon dioxide levels are then analysed.

 Pulse rate, page 300

Exercise has both short-term and long-term consequences. To improve aerobic fitness, exercise needs to be performed at 70% of maximum oxygen uptake for three periods of 20 minutes each week.

least three times a week for at least 15 minutes on each occasion at at least 70% of maximum oxygen uptake.

Determining maximum oxygen uptake requires specialised equipment (see Figure 7.5). However, measuring your heart rate (by measuring your pulse rate) provides a good approximation. Your maximum heart rate (in beats per minute) is approximately equal to your age in years subtracted from 220. So if you are 20 years old, to improve your aerobic fitness by exercise your heart rate will need to be at least 70% of 200, i.e. 140 beats per minute, for a period of 20 minutes three times a week.

The simplest way to determine your heart rate during training is to stop exercising, count the number of heart beats (or measure your pulse rate) for ten seconds and then multiply by six. You may find holding your breath for the ten seconds makes counting easier.

 4 What would be the disadvantage of measuring the heart rate during training by counting the number of heart beats for a full sixty seconds?

Assignment trigger

Exercise

Appropriate exercise is supposed to be good for your health.

What effect does exercise have on your body?
How can you determine the effects of exercise?
What different forms of exercise are there?
Which are the most beneficial for different types of people?

If a practical assignment is developed, it is essential that a risk assessment is made and checked by your teacher/lecturer.

Could lead to possible assignments relating to Unit 7.

Diet

It is an extraordinary thought that whatever you eat, your body can convert it into you. Whether you are a vegetarian, an omnivore, or, like an Inuit in the Arctic, you live off seal meat, the food you eat is digested and turned into you. Nevertheless, our diet is of significance. Too much or too little of certain things can have serious consequences.

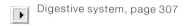 Digestive system, page 307

Deficiencies in the diet

A balanced diet contains proteins, carbohydrates, fats, vitamins, minerals, fibre and water in the right proportions. Problems arise if various items are eaten in inadequate amounts. A shortage of energy leads to continuous loss of body mass, starvation (sometimes referred to as marasmus) and eventual death. The energy provided by food is typically measured in kilojoules. The approximate quantities of energy needed each day by different categories of people are listed in Table 7.1. For an adult, fewer than about 5000 kJ a day eventually leads to death by starvation.

Table 7.1 **Approximate daily energy requirements for different categories of people. Note that the precise figures depend on the size of the person and on other variables.**

Type of person	kJ per day
Newborn baby	2000
Child 1 year	3000
Child 5 years	7000
Girl 12–15 years	9500
Boy 12–15 years	11 000
Woman 16–19 years	10 000
Man 16–19 years	12 000
Office worker (adult female)	9000
Office worker (adult male)	11 000
Heavy manual worker	15 000
Full-time athlete (female)	15 000+
Full-time athlete (male)	20 000+
Pregnant woman	10 000
Woman breast-feeding	11 000

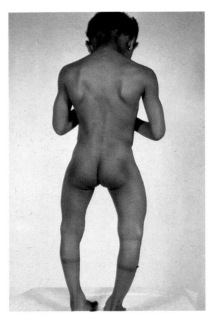

Figure 7.6 *Malformed legs resulting from rickets*

Health problems can result either from too much or from too little of certain things in the diet.

Blood pressure, page 301

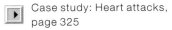
Case study: Heart attacks, page 325

Case study: Heart attacks, page 325

5 By what percentage do a woman's energy requirements increase when she is pregnant?

Anorexia nervosa is a condition in which a person doesn't eat enough even though they have access to food. 90-95% of all sufferers are female, usually in the 15–25 year age range. Often the anorexic is extremely interested in food but an obsession with her figure causes her to eat less and less and to lose more and more weight. In the UK probably one in 200 women aged 15–25 will suffer from the disease. There isn't a single cause, but expert counselling often reveals deep-seated psychological problems either with the person or with their family. Anorexics are often intelligent, well educated and come from well-off families. About 50% of treated anorexics recover within two to five years.

Insufficient protein gives rise to a condition known as *kwashiorkor*. An affected person is lethargic and weak. In addition, they may have a swollen abdomen caused by severe retention of fluid in their tissues (oedema).

Many vitamin deficiencies are known. Some of the more frequent are as follows:

- Vitamin A (retinol) deficiency can lead to night-blindness. This is because retinol is an essential component of the rods in our eyes.
- Vitamin B_1 deficiency results in beri beri.
- Vitamin C deficiency results in scurvy.
- Vitamin D deficiency can lead to rickets in children, a condition in which the bones remain soft (see Figure 7.6).

Finally, *fibre* or *roughage* in the diet helps prevent *bowel cancer*. Most people in the UK fail to get enough fibre in their diet. This is because many of us eat a diet that has not enough unprocessed plant matter in it. Fruits, vegetables and cereals are all good sources of fibre.

Excesses in the diet

In the last few decades our view of the significance of **diet** for the health of people in many countries, including the UK, has shifted. Rather than the important question being 'What is our diet short of?', it now tends to be 'What are we eating too much of?'

There is little doubt that most people in the UK eat too much sugar. The problem with this is that bacteria in our mouths convert the sugar to acid, causing tooth decay. Most people in the UK also eat too much salt (sodium chloride) which can cause high blood pressure.

The significance of too much animal fat in our diets is more controversial. It seems as though a high level of saturated fats in the diet is associated with an increased risk of coronary heart disease. A saturated fat is one which lacks any carbon-carbon double bonds in its structure. Such fats tend to be solids at room temperature and are found in animal fats (for example pork fat and lard). Fats with two or more double bonds in them (polyunsaturated fats) seem to be better for us. Such fats are liquids at room temperature and are found in many plants (for example, sunflower oil and olive oil).

Smoking

As you may well already know, the health consequences of tobacco smoking are almost wholly negative. About 100 000 people die in Britain each year as a result of smoking – and many more are debilitated. The only thing that can be said in favour of smoking is that many people who smoke say it calms them or gives them something to do with their hands. At the same time, most people who smoke want to give up. Unfortunately nicotine, the addictive chemical found in tobacco, is an extremely powerful drug. There are few substances known that are more addictive than nicotine.

Health consequences of smoking

Tobacco smoke contains a complicated mixture of chemicals. Its harmful effects are due to **tars**, **carbon monoxide** and **nicotine**.

Tars irritate the epithelial cells that line the gaseous exchange system. They paralyse and eventually destroy the cilia of the gaseous exchange system. These cilia protect our lungs by carrying mucus, with trapped dust and germs, away from the lungs, up to the throat where it is swallowed. Many smokers end up suffering from a chronic (i.e. long-lasting) disease called bronchitis. In bronchitis the bronchi and bronchioles become inflamed. The most obvious symptom is heavy coughing. Breathlessness results and the person becomes more susceptible to pneumonia and other diseases.

6 Suggest why bronchitis is associated with raised levels of pneumonia.

The other major effect of the tars in tobacco smoke is to cause a number of cancers including lung cancer (see Figure 7.7). Lung cancer is the most common cancer in Britain. Over 99% of the people who die from lung cancer in Britain have smoked cigarettes.

Carbon monoxide, CO, is a poisonous gas which binds almost irreversibly to haemoglobin in the red blood cells. As a result, the affected haemoglobin molecules are unable to carry oxygen. People who smoke have, typically, a permanent 5% reduction in the oxygen-carrying capacity of their blood. People who smoke are also much more likely to suffer from heart disease than are non-smokers. CO slows the growth of fetuses, so that babies born to mothers who smoke during pregnancy are significantly lighter, on average by around 200 g.

7 Why do you think CO slows the growth of fetuses?

The health consequences of smoking are almost entirely negative. The harmful effects of tobacco smoke are due to tars, carbon monoxide and nicotine.

Gaseous exchange system, page 314

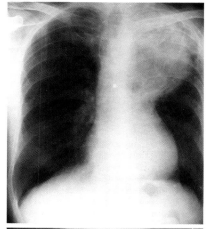

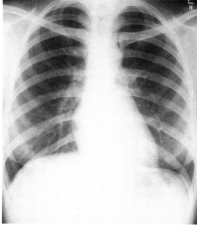

Figure 7.7 *(top) X-ray photograph of a person with lung cancer, (bottom) X-ray photograph of a healthy person without lung cancer. How would you describe the difference?*

Figure 7.8 *It has recently been discovered that inhaling other peoples' exhaled cigarette smoke (passive smoking) can damage your health.*

► Blood pressure, page 301

Few health problems are directly associated with nicotine, though it increases blood pressure and heart rate, putting extra stress on the circulatory system. Nicotine also causes the arterioles to constrict which, in rare cases, can lead to severe circulatory disorders, and even gangrene, in the limbs of smokers. The real problem with nicotine is that the withdrawal symptoms associated with giving it up are such that most people who smoke never succeed in stopping.

In recent years it has been found that even if you don't smoke yourself, inhaling other peoples' exhaled cigarette smoke, so-called *passive smoking*, can damage your health (see Figure 7.8).

Giving up smoking

Different people find that different approaches can help them give up cigarettes. Some people gradually manage to cut down by themselves. Others make pacts with friends. Nowadays various patches and gums containing nicotine are available to help. Leaflets are available from ASH (*Action on Smoking and Health*), 109 Gloucester Place, London W1H 4EJ.

Assignment trigger

No smoking

Smoking is banned increasingly in public places. Tobacco products carry Government health warnings.

What effects does smoking have on the body?
What are the benefits for the population as a whole of banning smoking?
Should the preferences of the many restrict the liberties of the few?

If a practical assignment is developed, it is essential that a risk assessment is made and checked by your teacher/lecturer.

Could lead to possible assignments relating to Unit 7.

Alcohol consumption can be measured in units. One unit equals 10 g of alcohol. A typical pint of beer contain two units; a glass of wine or a single whisky contains one unit. For an adult male, a weekly consumption of more than 21 units brings an increasing chance of damaging health; for an adult woman, more than 14.

► Assignment trigger: Health, page 288

Alcohol consumption

Small amounts of alcohol do no harm to your health. Indeed, recent research suggests that a glass or two of wine two or three times a week may even be good for your physical health. However, when drunk to excess alcohol has a number of serious effects on health. It's difficult to define what is meant by 'drunk to excess', but a useful measure of the amount of alcohol consumed is a **unit**. One unit of alcohol equals 10 g of alcohol. This is the amount that an adult's liver can break down in about an hour. If an adult male drinks more that about 21 units of alcohol a week, or an adult woman more than 14, they run an increasing risk of damaging their physical health. An average glass of wine or a single measure of a spirit such as whisky contains one unit of alcohol. A pint of typical strength beer or cider contains two units.

Each year in Britain about 100 deaths are the result of solvent abuse; another hundred are the result of illegal drugs such as heroin and cocaine. About 40 000 deaths result from alcohol consumption in Britain each year. In addition, tens of thousands of people each year are convicted of drink driving (see Figure 7.9).

The health consequences of alcohol

Alcohol (ethanol) is a small molecule with the chemical formula C_2H_5OH. Its fat-soluble and rapidly passes through the phospholipids in cell membranes. Because of this, alcohol is quickly absorbed from the stomach and small intestine. It is then carried to the liver. In the liver, ethanol is broken down to ethanal by the enzyme alcohol dehydrogenase. Most of the ethanal is then oxidised to release energy or converted to fat and stored.

 8 Suggest what the chemical formula of ethanal might be, given that it is produced by the action of alcohol dehydrogenase on ethanol (C_2H_5OH).

Many people find that alcohol makes it easier to relax. Alcohol reduces the activity of the brain and so is said to be a depressant. At low concentrations, typically 1 to 4 units, social restraint and judgement may be affected.

With the consumption of 5 to 8 units, motor skills become affected, so that it is difficult to walk in a straight line. The consumption over a short period of time (a few hours) of 10 units of alcohol can lead to memory impairment – you may not be able to remember the next morning precisely what you said or did. Consuming more than 12 units may lead to vomiting, a natural defence mechanism against poisoning.

The long-term consequences of high levels of alcohol consumption can include:
- increased levels of violence, especially against partners and children
- *cirrhosis* (damage to the liver)
- shrinkage of brain cells due to dehydration
- *strokes* as a result of small blood clots in the blood vessels that supply the brain
- hoarseness of the voice
- cancers of the mouth, throat, oesophagus and liver
- protein, mineral and vitamin deficiencies.

Alcohol can be addictive and the more someone is used to drinking, the more difficult it is to stop. Withdrawal symptoms can include:
- irritability
- shakiness
- insomnia
- sweating
- nausea
- panic attacks
- persistent shaking, a feverish pulse and visual hallucinations – a combination known as *delirium tremens* (DTs).

Giving up drinking

Various support agencies can help someone who wants to give up drinking, but is finding it difficult. The best known is Alcoholics Anonymous. Treatment relies on meeting regularly with others who are, or have been, dependent on alcohol. The members of the group talk among themselves, sharing their feelings and experiences. Giving up alcohol completely (abstinence) is usually the goal. Further details are available from *Alcohol Concern*, Waterbridge House 32–36 Loman Street London SE1 OEE,

Figure 7.9 *Driver being breathalysed to see if he is over the legal limit for the amount of alcohol in his blood– 80 mg per 100 cm³ of blood.*

Health care for groups

Groups are simply collections of individuals, and in one way health care for a group is simply health care for the individuals that comprise the group. However, it is worth keeping in mind that groups can be targeted by means of **public health programmes**. Such programmes may be designed, for example, to reduce the incidence of smoking or to cut coronary heart disease.

The most comprehensive package of public health programmes produced in the UK to date was unveiled in 1992. Called *The Health of the Nation*, it set specific targets for the health of people in England under five key areas:

- coronary heart disease and strokes
- cancers
- mental illness
- HIV/AIDS and sexual health
- accidents.

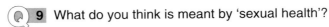 **9** What do you think is meant by 'sexual health'?

For example, the main targets under cancers are:

- to reduce the death rate for breast cancer in women invited for screening by at least 25% during the period 1990 to 2000
- to reduce the incidence of cervical cancer by at least 20% during the period 1990 to 2000
- to reduce the death rate for lung cancer under the age of 75 by at least 30% in men and by at least 15% in women during the period 1990 to 2010 (see Figure 7.10)
- to halt the year-on-year increase in the incidence of skin cancer by 2005.

> *The Health of the Nation* (1992) sets targets for health in England under the key areas of coronary heart disease and strokes, cancers, mental health, HIV/AIDS and sexual health, and accidents.

Case study: Heart attacks, page 325

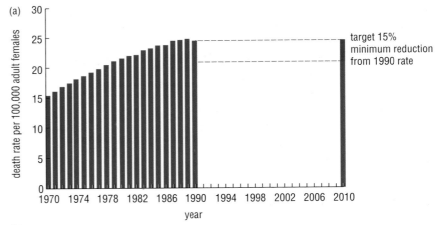

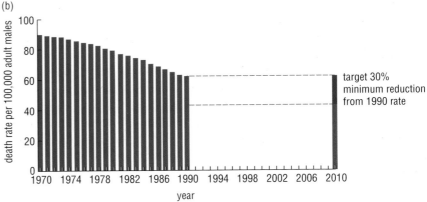

Figure 7.10 *Death rates for lung cancer in England from 1970 to 1990, together with UK government targets for the year 2010. Rates are calculated using a three year running average and using a procedure to remove differences across years in the age structure of the population.*
(a) Females aged under 75 years.
(b) Males aged under 75 years.

Figure 7.11 Alton College. Is this environment more or less attractive than where you work? How important is a good physical environment?

The main way in which the Government intends that the targets should be met, with the accompanying improvement in **people's health**, is through:

- Public policies: by policy-makers at all levels considering the health dimension when developing policies for things such as transport and education. This applies not only across Government but also in other public bodies and industry.
- Healthy surroundings: by the active promotion of healthy physical environments – in the home, in schools, at work, on the roads, at leisure, in public places (see Figure 7.11).
- Healthy lifestyles: by increasing knowledge and understanding about how the way people live affects their health, and enabling families and individuals to act upon this.
- High quality health services: by identifying and meeting the health needs of local populations and securing the most appropriate balance between health promotion, disease prevention, treatment, care and rehabilitation (see Figure 7.12).

People's health can be improved through appropriate public policies, healthy surroundings, healthy lifestyles and high quality health services.

Figure 7.12 A patient with a shoulder injury receiving physiotherapy from a nurse. Physiotherapy often plays an important part in rehabilitation.

Evaluating health care

To evaluate health care is to work out how effective it is. A number of different measures can be used to evaluate health care:

- Statistics can be used to measure changes in survival rates (for example in Figure 7.13).
- Questionnaires and interviews can be used to ask patients to state how they feel their health has changed as a result of their treatment.
- Financial criteria can be used to determine whether alternative treatments would have saved more lives or have led to greater patient satisfaction. For example, would shifting some of the money used for expensive heart transplant surgery into health education campaigns actually save more lives and lead to less suffering overall?

▶ Case study: Heart attacks, page 325

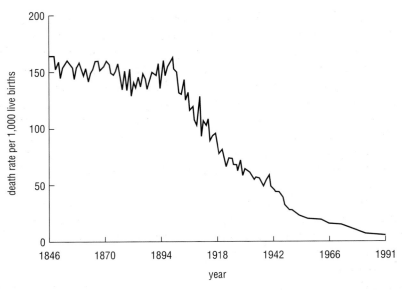

Figure 7.13 *Infant mortality (deaths in the first year of life) in England and Wales 1846 to 1991. During this period there has been a huge increase in infant survival as a result of improvements in sanitation, medicine and the standard of living.*

Just as there is no single perfect measure of health, so there is no single ideal way to **evaluate health care**. The traditional way to evaluate a new drug is to perform a *double blind trial*. In this, half the patients are given the new drug and half are given the old drug or, if no drug is available, an inert substance called a *placebo*. The important point is that neither the patients nor the doctors know who gets the new drug. Each patient is given a seemingly identical capsule with a number written on it. At the end of the period of treatment, each patient is examined to see how their health has changed. Only then do the doctors and patients find out who was given the new drug and who the old one or placebo. Statistics are then used to see whether the new drug is any better.

> **There is no single ideal way to evaluate health care. Statistical measures, patient opinions and financial analyses can all play a part.**

Q 10 Why is it important that neither the patients nor the doctors know who is being given the new drug and who the old one or the placebo?

Benefits and drawbacks of health care

Any method of **health care needs to be evaluated** as it may have drawbacks as well as benefits. The chief benefit, of course, is an improvement in health. However, this may need to be considered both in the short term and in the long term. Giving up cigarette smoking has few health benefits for the first few weeks; indeed, it can make you more irritable and stressed. The benefits only appear once the withdrawal symptoms have gone, and that can take months.

> **Health care needs to be evaluated as it may have drawbacks as well as benefits. These need to be considered in the long term as well as the short term.**

Drawbacks of a particular method of health care may include:
- the time the health care requires (for example time spent exercising to increase fitness)
- the financial cost of the health care (for example paying to use a swimming pool)
- the self-discipline and commitment required (for example to go on exercising three times a week).

The drawbacks can be considerable. Unless someone really wants to be healthier, they probably won't change their lifestyle in the way that's needed.

Management action for the human body

What can we do when something goes wrong with our bodies? Basically, there are two options. Either we learn to live with the shortcoming, or we can try to put things right. Sometimes, learning to live with one's shortcomings is the best approach. Isn't there something sad about a person who is terrified of getting wrinkles as they age, for example? However, it is often the case that either a change in our *behaviour* or treatment with *therapeutic drugs* can improve our health. ('Therapeutic' means 'healing'.) A *drug* is a substance that when taken into our body affects it in some way, without the substance simply being a food. A preparation of a drug in a form that can be taken is called a *medicine*.

To give a specific example. We saw earlier that there are a number of dangers associated with hypertension (high blood pressure). These dangers can be tackled in two main ways:

- A behavioural change in lifestyle. A person may need to lose weight, cut down on their salt or saturated fat intake, take more exercise, smoke fewer cigarettes or learn how to relax (see Figure 7.14).
- By taking appropriate medicines. A variety of medicines can be used to treat hypertension (see Figure 7.15).

We live in a society where many people assume that medicines are the answer to every medical problem. Often they aren't. On the other hand, it isn't the case that every medical condition can be treated by changes in behaviour alone. Often medicines can play a most valuable role.

Monitoring physiological changes in the human body

There are many ways in which doctors, nurses and other health care professionals monitor the workings of the human body. This is necessary to see whether everything is functioning as it should and, if it isn't, to allow the appropriate steps to be taken.

Monitoring the status of an organ system

Doctors and other health professionals have always examined their patients. During the last twenty years there has been a tremendous increase in the power and sophistication of the equipment and techniques used to monitor people's health (see Figure 7.16).

Figure 7.14 *High blood pressures often be reduced by simply taking more exercise and learning how to relax.*

▶ What can be learned from blood pressure readings?, page 301

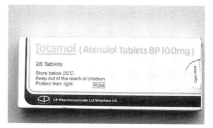

Figure 7.15 *A standard drug used to treat hypertension, and available on prescription.*

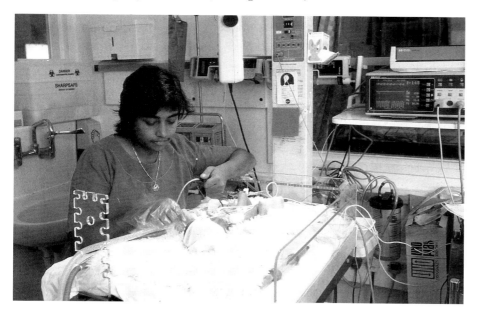

Figure 7.16 *A premature baby being attended by a nurse in intensive care. Special care baby units, operating theatres and intensive care units are filled with expensive examples of medical technology. So too, increasingly, are GPs' surgeries, sports clinics and even commercial fitness centres.*

Health can be monitored in a number of ways including recording physical data, seeing if pathogens are present and checking cells for signs of abnormalities.

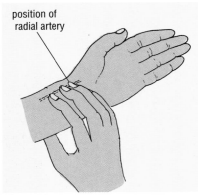

Figure 7.17 *Taking a pulse by feeling pulses of blood through the radial artery.*

▶ Arteries, veins and capillaries, page 316

By and large, the fitter a person is, the lower their resting pulse rate.

▶ Case study: Athletes sleep their way to the top, page 326

In the pages that follow we shall look at some of the ways in which health can be tested, checked and recorded. In the space available we shall concentrate on some of the techniques that involve the **monitoring** and recording of physical data. Other approaches include detecting the presence of **pathogens** or abnormal cells by visual screening (for example for pre-cancerous cells in a cervical smear) or through the use of antibodies (for example the test for HIV). Some of the techniques can be carried out in colleges and schools. However, if they *are* carried out, the results for individuals need to be interpreted with caution. Many factors can affect a measurement, and results outside the usual range often have a simple explanation and are of no medical significance. Other tests require specialised laboratory or hospital equipment, which means that for your study purposes you may need to obtain data from *secondary sources* rather than directly.

Pulse rate

Each time the heart contracts, the arteries carry a pulse of blood. This causes an alternating increase and decrease in the diameter of the arteries which can be felt in any large artery that lies close to the body surface. The technique involves the following steps:

- Compress a suitable artery so as to find the pulse. The point where the radial artery surfaces at the wrist is the most commonly used (see Figure 7.17). However, other arteries, including the common carotid artery in the neck, are also suitable.
- Count the number of pulses of blood over a fixed period of time, typically thirty or sixty seconds.
- Convert, if necessary, to pulses per minute.

Doctors and nurses often take someone's pulse. By and large, the lower the resting heart rate (or **resting pulse rate**), taken when a person is sitting or lying down, the fitter a person is. A typical resting heart rate for a person over the age of 16 is between 65 and 80 beats per minute. Lower than this and you're probably fitter than most people; higher than this and you're probably either rather unfit or unwell.

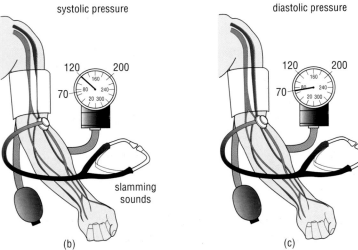

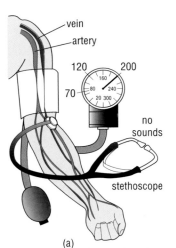

Figure 7.18 *Using a mercury sphygmomanometer to measure systolic and diastolic blood pressure, (a)When the inflation pressure of the cuff exceeds the systolic blood pressure, no blood flows through the cuff and no sound is heard through the stethoscope. (b) As the pressure in the cuff is gradually reduced, a point comes when blood pressure at the peak of systole is greater than the pressure in the cuff. At this point, a little blood squeezes through the artery and a slamming sound is heard through the stethoscope. (c) As the pressure in the cuff is reduced still further, a point is reached at which, even at diastole, blood flows continuously through the artery. When this point is reached, the slamming sound is replaced by a continuous 'woosh'.*

11 Why is a lower resting heart rate usually associated with greater fitness?

Blood pressure

The classic instrument used to determine a person's **blood pressure** is a **mercury sphygmomanometer**. This consists of a cuff, a small rubber pump with a regulation valve, and a mercury column (see Figure 7.18). The cuff is placed on the upper arm and inflated using the pump. The nurse or doctor listens with a stethoscope placed on the artery. As the cuff is deflated a sound is heard at the point at which blood can just force its way through the artery. This point corresponds to the systolic pressure. As the cuff is further deflated, this sound disappears when blood can flow continuously through the artery. This point corresponds to the diastolic pressure.

Operating a mercury sphygmomanometer is not all that easy. Considerable practice and expertise are required for readings to be taken accurately. Over the last few years a new range of electronic digital monitors have become available which do not rely on a stethoscope or other listening device (see Figure 7.19). They contain a cuff, an inflation bulb and the equipment to monitor and display systolic and diastolic blood pressures, and use a pressure sensor which detects the airflow from the cuff. The readings are then automatically displayed.

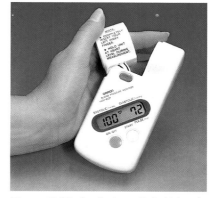

Figure 7.19 *A mikeless digital blood pressure and pulse rate monitor, which provides automatic inflation and deflation, and allows readings to be taken from an index finger.*

What can be learned from blood pressure readings?

Blood pressures are a measure of how hard the heart has to work to pump blood around the body. A person with too high a blood pressure is said to suffer from hypertension or **high blood pressure** (see Table 7.2). At least 15% of adults in Britain are thought to suffer from hypertension.

Table 7.2 World Health Organisation classification of adult resting blood pressures

	Systolic (mm Hg)	Diastolic (mm Hg)
Hypotension	Less than 100	Less than 60
Normal	100–139	60–89
Borderline	140–159	90–94
Hypertension	More than 159	More than 94

High blood pressure can be the result of many things, the most usual of which are:
- being very overweight
- smoking – nicotine causes temporary constriction of the arterioles;
- excessive saturated fat intake accompanied by insufficient exercise – cholesterol may become deposited on the insides of arteries, narrowing them
- certain kidney diseases
- stress
- high salt intake
- pregnancy.

Assignment trigger: Heart disease, page 305

Case study: Heart attacks, page 325

Blood pressures can be measured with a mercury sphygmomanometer or an electronic blood pressure monitor. Above a blood pressure of 140/90, the incidence of heart attacks and strokes increases substantially.

High blood pressure often goes undetected. However, its consequences may be serious, particularly if the condition persists for years. Insurance company statistics involving several hundred thousand people show that above a blood pressure of 140/90 – i.e. systolic blood pressure greater than 140 mm Hg, diastolic blood pressure greater than 90 mm Hg – the incidence of heart attacks and strokes increases substantially.

Vital capacity and other gaseous exchange measurements

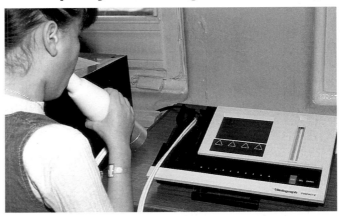

Figure 7.20 *11 year-old girl with a respiratory problem using a spirometer at Alder Hey Children's Hospital, Liverpool.*

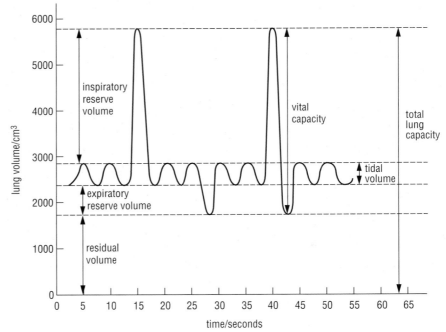

Figure 7.21 *An idealised recording from a spirometer showing the various lung capacities typical in a healthy adult. The residual volume is the volume of gas remaining in the lungs after breathing out as deeply as possible. It cannot be determined from a spirometer.*

A person's breathing capacities can be measured using a spirometer (see Figure 7.20). This instrument can be used to obtain the following readings (see Figure 7.21):

- **inspiratory reserve volume** – the maximum volume of air that can be breathed in *after* a person has taken a normal breath
- **expiratory reserve volume** – the maximum volume of air that can be breathed out *after* a person has breathed out normally
- **tidal volume** – the typical volume of air breathed in *or* out during a normal breath
- **vital capacity** – the sum of the inspiratory reserve volume, the expiratory reserve volume and the tidal volume

- **total lung capacity** – the sum of the vital capacity and the residual volume
- **breathing rate** – the number of inspirations (breaths) per minute.

Q 12 Which of these measures is also equal to the maximum volume of air that can be breathed in following an effort to breathe out as deeply as possible?

> A person's tidal volume is the volume of air they typically breathe in or out during a normal breath.

As the spirometer contains soda lime to absorb the carbon dioxide produced in respiration, by inhaling pure oxygen for a few minutes it can be used to measure the volume of oxygen uptake, and so determine a person's rate of oxygen uptake in $dm^3\ min^{-1}$.

Q 13 Explain how a person's oxygen uptake in $dm^3\ O_2$ per minute can be determined from the concentration of oxygen in inspired air, the concentration of oxygen in expired air, their tidal volume and their breathing rate.

The oxygen and carbon dioxide concentrations in a person's lungs or blood vessels can be monitored using gas and vapour analysers. These are widely used for patients undergoing surgery under general anaesthesia (see Figure 7.22). They allow an anaesthetist to ensure that the patient is receiving the right amount of oxygen for their brain and other organs.

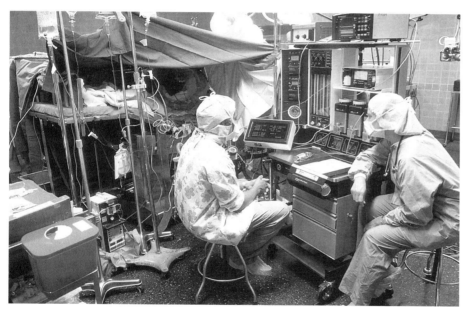

Figure 7.22 Anaesthetists monitoring gas and vapour analysers during an operation in the Bronx, New York.

Circulatory system, page 310

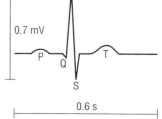

Figure 7.23 A typical electrocardiogram (ECG) from a healthy human showing electrical activity during a single heartbeat.

Electrical activity of the heart

The electrical activity of the heart can be monitored by means of an electrocardiogram (ECG). An ECG is obtained by placing electrodes at standardised positions on the body. A typical ECG trace showing the electrical activity during a single heartbeat of a healthy person is shown in Figure 7.23.

The value of recording an ECG is that an experienced health professional can tell a tremendous amount about the condition of a person's heart from it. Four ECGs are shown in Figure 7.24: one healthy, three unhealthy. Some cardiac problems in a patient may only be apparent when the person is active, for example, when climbing stairs. For this reason small, portable ECG recorders have been developed. A further approach is to utilise radio-telemetry. Here the patient carries a small radio transmitter which transmits

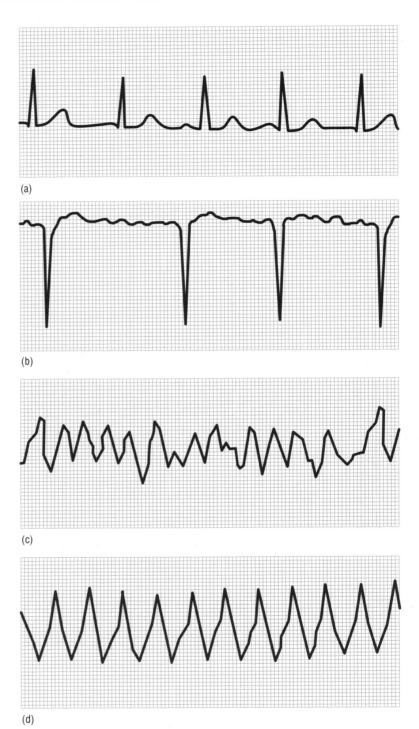

(a)

(b)

(c)

(d)

Figure 7.24 *(a) A normal ECG. (b) An ECG from a person with abnormally fast, unco-ordinated beating of the atria, a condition known as atrial fibrillation. (c) An ECG from a person with abnormally fast, uncoordinated beating of the ventricles, a potentially fatal condition known as ventricular fibrillation. (d) An ECG from someone whose ventricles are beating abnormally fast, a condition called ventricular tachycardia.*

the signals via a radio link back to a central recording device. Radiotelemetry has been used for patients where monitoring is still advisable but when the patient is not confined to bed.

Cholesterol levels

Cholesterol is a natural substance produced by the liver and serves a number of valuable functions in the body. However, health experts generally agree that a significantly increased blood cholesterol level can put you at increased risk of heart attack, heart disease, stroke and other cardiovascular diseases.

There are now a number of cholesterol tests which enable you to determine your own blood cholesterol level at home. (You will not normally be allowed to carry such a test out in your school or college without a special risk assessment.) A drop of blood is needed and, after a wait of a few minutes, the blood cholesterol level can be read off a quantitative scale. To decide whether the cholesterol level indicates a significant risk of cardiovascular disease, you first need to identify how many other risk factors you have. The following are considered to be risk factors:

- a family history of coronary heart disease
- smoking
- being overweight
- raised blood pressure
- high alcohol consumption
- lack of physical exercise
- stress
- diabetes.

The relationship between total blood cholesterol levels and the risk of cardiovascular disease is given in Table 7.3.

Table 7.3 Relationship between total blood cholesterol levels and the risk of cardiovascular disease. Other risk factors are described in the text.

Total cholesterol/mmol L^{-1}	No or one other risk factor	Two or more other risk factors
Up to 5.2	Within desirable limits	Low risk
5.2 – 6.5	Low risk	Medium risk
6.6 – 7.8	Medium risk	High risk
7.9 and over	High risk	Very high risk

Assignment trigger

Heart disease

The major killer in the UK is heart disease. Its incidence is higher than in any other country.

What is heart disease?
How can it be detected?
How can it be avoided?

If a practical assignment is developed, it is essential that a risk assessment is made and checked by your teacher/lecturer.

Could lead to possible assignments relating to Unit 7.

Case study: Heart attacks, page 325

X-ray photographs

From a medical point of view X-rays are useful because they pass through some materials more easily than others. In fact a quantitative relationship exists between the average atomic number, Z, of a material and the

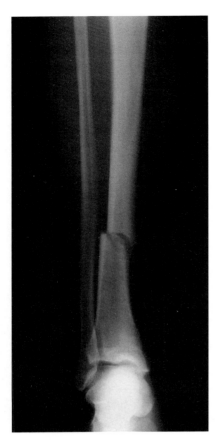

Figure 7.25 *X-ray of the lower leg, showing a fracture of the tibia. The tibia is the larger of the two bones in the lower leg; the smaller one is the fibula.*

penetration through that material by X-rays. (You may remember that Z, the atomic number, is equal to the number of protons in a nucleus.) As an approximate rule, the degree of penetration of an X-ray through a material is inversely proportional to the third power of Z. In other words:

$$\text{X-ray penetration} \, \alpha \, 1/Z^3$$

The average value of Z for fat is 5.9, for muscle 7.4 and for bone 13.9. As a result, X-rays are much more easily stopped by bone than by fat and muscle. This is why bone appears opaque on an X-ray – a most useful feature when it comes to seeing whether or not a bone is broken (see Figure 7.25). The differential penetration by X-rays of different kinds of tissues means that, to a skilled operator (a radiographer), an X-ray photograph can reveal the presence of cancerous tumours. In addition, a radiographer can tell from an X-ray whether a bone has been broken and, if so, how well it is healing.

Q 14 Suggest why the average value of Z for fat is less than for muscle or bone.

Blood cell counts

Traditionally blood cells, especially red blood cells, have been counted using a special light microscope slide called a **haemocytometer** (see Figure 7.26). This consists of a microscope slide with a central portion 100 μm (i.e. 0.1 mm) deep. Above this are squares 50 μm in length and width. The number of red blood cells in this little 'cell', 50 μm × 50 μm × 100 μm in size, can then be counted.

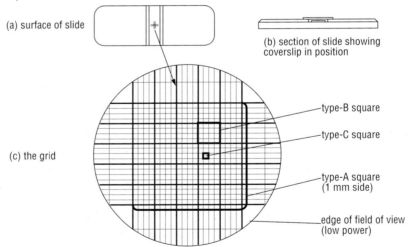

(a) surface of slide

(b) section of slide showing coverslip in position

(c) the grid

type-B square

type-C square

type-A square (1 mm side)

edge of field of view (low power)

Figure 7.26 *A haemocytometer, used for counting blood cells.*

Nowadays a number of automated cell counting techniques are also available. These are especially useful for monitoring the abundance of white blood cells as these are much rarer than red blood cells, and more difficult to see on a haemocytometer.

Unlike samples from most other tissues, blood samples are extremely easy to obtain under proper medical supervision, and blood cell counts have various uses. For example, a low red blood cell count may indicate a low iron intake, while an excess of white blood cells can be indicative of cancer of the white blood cells (leukaemia).

Blood cell counts measure the number of cells in a given volume of blood. They can be obtained using a haemocytometer or one of the newer automated cell counters.

Q 15 Why do you think leukaemia is associated with an increase in the number of white blood cells?

Concentrations of electrolytes in body fluids

For biological purposes, an electrolyte is an aqueous solution of an ion, such as $K^+(aq)$, $Ca^{2+}(aq)$ or $Cl^-(aq)$. Various techniques allow the concentrations of particular ions in blood or other body fluids to be determined. For example, ion selective electrodes can be used. These are electrodes that produce a voltage proportional to the concentration of a particular ion in the medium, such as hydrogen ($H^+(aq)$) or sodium ($Na^+(aq)$).

Roles of the main organ systems in mammals

The *cells* of which we and all multicellular organisms are composed build up into *tissues*. For example, cardiac (heart) muscle tissue is composed of identical cardiac muscle cells. At the next level up, an *organ* is composed of a number of different tissues. For example, the heart is an organ which contains both cardiac muscle tissue and nerve tissue. In turn, a number of associated organs together comprise an *organ system*. For example, the circulatory system includes the heart, arteries, veins, capillaries and certain nerves.

In common with other mammals, humans have seven main organ systems. We shall look briefly at each of these, emphasising their characteristics and roles.

The following are the main organ systems in mammals:
- digestive system
- excretory system
- reproductive system
- circulatory system
- endocrine system
- nervous system
- gaseous exchange system.

▶ Mammalian cells, page 321

▶ Mammalian tissues, page 318

16 Explain the difference between organ systems, organs, tissues and cells.

Digestive system

Our **digestive system** enables us to obtain the chemicals and energy we need from our food (see Figure 7.27). Without an adequate digestive system we would lose weight and eventually die through starvation. In the digestive system actions occur in the following order:
- **ingestion** – the passage of food into the body through the mouth
- **digestion** – the breakdown of food into smaller parts
- **absorption** – the movement of food from the gut to the blood and lymph systems
- **assimilation** – the incorporation of the products of digestion and absorption into the cells of the body.

Ingestion occurs in the mouth, or *buccal cavity*. Digestion also begins here. Swallowing results in a *bolus* of food being carried by a wave of muscular contraction called a *peristaltic wave* to the *stomach*. Eventually food is allowed into the first part of the small intestine, the *duodenum*, by relaxation of a muscular valve called the *pyloric sphincter*. In the duodenum many different enzymes act to catalyse the following reactions:
- starch and disaccharides → monosaccharides

The digestive system carries out ingestion, digestion, absorption and assimilation. The different regions of the gut are adapted to make digestion rapid and efficient.

▶ Diet, page 291

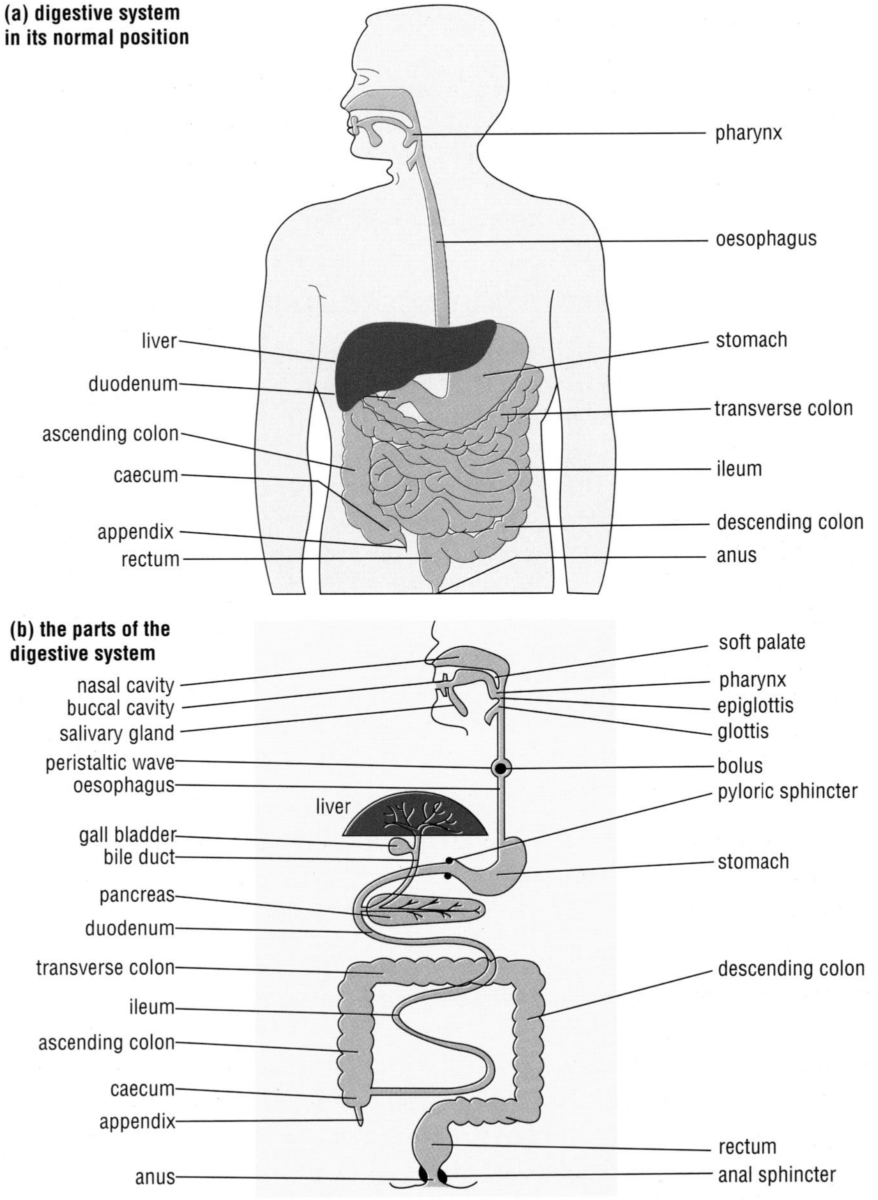

(a) digestive system in its normal position

pharynx
oesophagus
liver
duodenum
stomach
transverse colon
ascending colon
ileum
caecum
appendix
descending colon
rectum
anus

Figure 7.27 *The human digestive system consists of the human alimentary canal and associated organs. (a) The digestive system in its normal position. (b) Laid out diagrammatically. In the buccal cavity food is broken down into smaller pieces by the cutting and chewing actions of teeth. In addition it is moistened and partially digested by saliva which contains water, mucus and the enzyme salivary amylase which begins to digest starch. Food remains in the stomach at a pH of 1.5 – 2.0 for, typically, two to five hours. This very low pH helps in the rapid digestion of proteins to short polypeptide chains by the enzyme pepsin. Pepsin has an optimum pH of 1.5, and specialised cells in gastric glands in the stomach produce hydrochloric acid to generate these low pHs.*

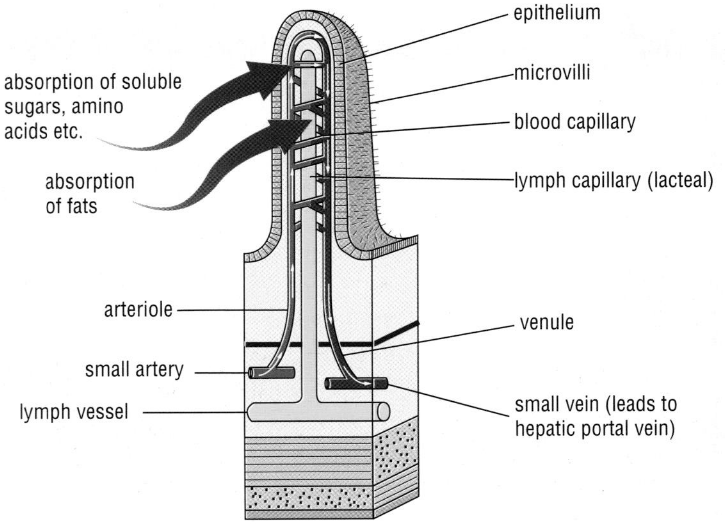

(b) the parts of the digestive system

soft palate
nasal cavity
pharynx
buccal cavity
epiglottis
salivary gland
glottis
peristaltic wave
bolus
oesophagus
pyloric sphincter
liver
gall bladder
bile duct
stomach
pancreas
duodenum
transverse colon
descending colon
ileum
ascending colon
caecum
appendix
rectum
anal sphincter
anus

epithelium
absorption of soluble sugars, amino acids etc.
microvilli
blood capillary
absorption of fats
lymph capillary (lacteal)
arteriole
venule
small artery
lymph vessel
small vein (leads to hepatic portal vein)

Figure 7.28 *The structure of a villus, showing its function in absorption.*

- proteins and polypeptides → amino acids
- fats → glycerol and fatty acids
- nucleotides → pentose sugars, organic bases and phosphoric acid.

The small molecules produced as a result of these reactions are chiefly absorbed across the wall of the *villi* of the *ileum* (see Figure 7.28). Villi provide a huge surface area for absorption, largely because their own surface has countless *microvilli* (see Figure 7.29).

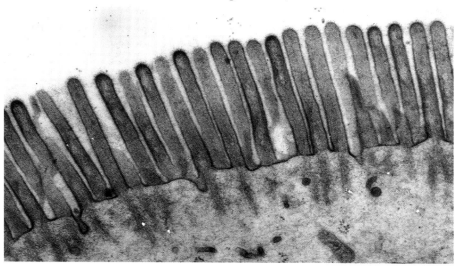

Figure 7.29 Microvilli on the surface of a villus in the ileum. Microvilli are tiny projections that can only adequately be seen under an electron microscope.

Q 17 Why do villi need a rich blood supply?

Finally, what remains of the food that was eaten enters the *colon*. Water is reabsorbed here. The mass of indigestible cellulose, dead epithelial cells and large numbers of bacteria is stored in the *rectum* before being expelled as *faeces*.

Excretory system

The removal from the body of the waste products of metabolism is known as **excretion**. We shall concentrate here on the excretion of nitrogenous wastes, such as **urea** ($CO(NH_2)_2$) and **ammonia** (NH_3). In the absence of

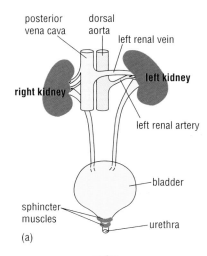

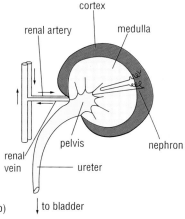

Figure 7.30 (a) The kidneys and associated structures of the mammalian urinary system. We have two kidneys. Each kidney receives blood via the renal artery. After blood has flowed through the kidneys it is carried from them via the renal vein. At the same time, substances which have been removed from the blood by the kidneys flow down the two ureters to the bladder. (b) The kidney seen in cross-section, together with a branch of the renal artery and renal vein.

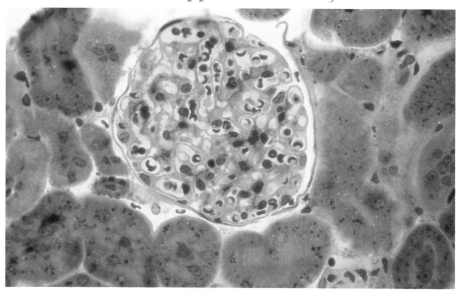

Figure 7.31 The glomerulus of one of the nephrons in a kidney. The glomerulus is where filtration in the nephron takes place.

The main products of mammalian excretion are urea, ammonia, carbon dioxide and bile pigments.

The kidney carries out nitrogenous excretion and osmoregulation.

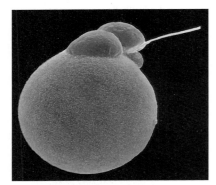

Figure 7.32 *A sperm fertilising an egg. Also present are three polar bodies – the functionless side products of the meiosis that gave rise to the egg. These polar bodies soon degenerate.*

How can Mendel's results be explained?, page 189

Respiration, page 323

nitrogenous excretion, our cells soon become poisoned by the accumulation of urea, which is toxic. However you should understand that other substances are excreted: for example the lungs excrete **carbon dioxide** (CO_2) and the liver excretes **bile pigments.**

In mammals, nitrogenous excretion is carried out by the **kidneys** (see Figure 7.30). The basic unit of the kidney is the **nephron** (see Figure 7.31). In addition to carrying out nitrogenous excretion, the kidneys are also responsible for the regulation of the concentrations of salts and water in the body. This is known as **osmoregulation**. Common experience should tell you that if you drink a large amount of fluid you will usually pass more urine within the next few hours. Similarly, if you eat some salty food you typically pass less urine over the next few hours. In both cases the kidneys do their best to maintain the concentrations of salts and water in the body at a constant level. If osmoregulation fails, the internal environment of the body is disrupted, and death can follow within twenty-four hours.

Reproductive system

The human **reproductive system** evolved originally to ensure that a woman's egg and a man's sperm can fuse to give rise to a fertilised egg, and so lead, eventually, to the birth of a baby. The reproductive system still, of course, serves this function, and this is what we shall concentrate on here. It is, fortunately, also the case that our reproductive systems, in particular the genitalia, can be a great source of pleasure. For many couples that pleasure can be separated from reproduction either through the use of contraceptives, or because the two people involved are of the same sex.

How are eggs and sperm produced?

A woman's eggs are produced in her ovaries, each of which is some 8 cm in length, 4 cm in width and situated at about hip level. The position of the ovaries is indicated on Figure 7.35. Within each ovary, diploid cells, each with 46 chromosomes, divide by meiosis to give rise to haploid eggs (ova), each with 23 chromosomes. About once every month, one or other of the ovaries releases an egg, a process called ovulation.

A human egg is approximately 0.1 mm (100 μm) in diameter and can't move of its own accord. Once released from the ovary it is gently wafted into the oviduct – a tube that leads from the ovary to the uterus – by the action of tiny propulsive hairs known as cilia. It is in the oviduct that fertilisation may occur.

In order for fertilisation to take place, sperm need to reach the top of the oviduct within a day or two of ovulation (see Figure 7.32). The structure of sperm is directly related to their function. The head contains a haploid set of 23 chromosomes, the same number as found in the haploid nucleus of the egg. The rest of a sperm is specialised for movement, containing numerous long energy-producing mitochondria and a powerful tail for swimming.

Circulatory system

Humans, in common with other mammals, have their blood entirely contained within tube-like vessels, a system known as a closed circulatory system (see Figure 7.33). Gases and other substances enter and exit from the blood across the walls of the narrowest of blood vessels, called capillaries.

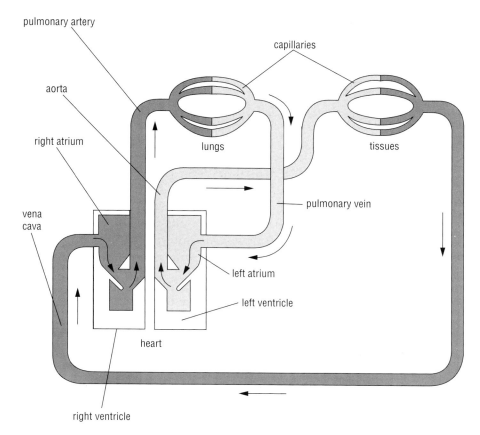

Figure 7.33 *The arrangement of the heart and blood vessels in a mammal, showing a closed, double circulation. Arrows indicate the direction of blood flow. Oxygenated blood is shown in light grey; deoxygenated in dark grey.*

▶ Electrical activity of the heart, page 303

▶ Functions of the cardio-respiratory system, page 316

▶ Case study: Heart attacks, page 325

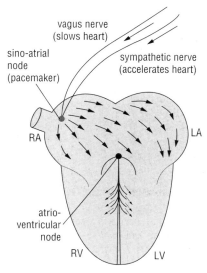

Figure 7.34 *Ventral view of the heart showing how, for each heartbeat, a wave of electrical excitation spreads from the sino-atrial node across the atria to the atrio-ventricular node, and thence to the two ventricles. The heart's natural pacemaker is the sino-atrial node (SAN). It consists of fine cardiac muscle fibre and is situated in the wall of the right atrium, close to where the large veins enter. As a result of the action of the sino-atrial node, two things happen. First, the atria contract, forcing blood into the left and right ventricles. Secondly, the wave of excitation reaches the atrio-ventricular node. From here, electrical excitation begins to spread over the two ventricles. As a result, both ventricles begin to contract. In Figure 7.23, point P corresponds to the wave of excitation that spreads over the atria as a result of the action of the SAN. Points Q, R and S correspond to the wave of excitation that spreads over the two ventricles. The T wave marks the electrical recovery of the ventricles.*

Not only is the circulatory system closed, it is also double, because a complete circuit requires blood to pass through the heart twice. The great advantage of a double circulation is that blood can be pumped to the lungs, to gain oxygen and lose carbon dioxide, and then pumped again before setting off a second time to go round the whole of the rest of the body.

The organ most directly responsible for the operation of the circulatory system is, of course, the *heart* (see Figure 7.34). The electrical activity that occurs during a single heartbeat can be recorded by means of an ECG trace. When the right ventricle contracts, blood is pumped to the lungs via the *pulmonary artery*. When the left ventricle contracts, blood is pumped to the rest of the body via the *aorta*.

We tend to take the functioning of our circulatory system for granted. Only when a baby is born with a hole in the heart, when someone close to us has a heart attack or when something else goes wrong do we realise just how much we depend on it.

Endocrine system

A chemical substance produced in one part of the body and transported, usually in the bloodstream, to another part of the body where it causes a specific response is known as a *hormone*. Hormones are organic compounds and are effective in extremely small quantities. As we shall see, hormones play a vital role in the maintenance of health.

Hormones are secreted into the bloodstream by *endocrine glands*, 'endocrine' meaning 'internal secretion'. So-called *exocrine glands*, such as the salivary glands, have special ducts to carry their secretions. The positions of the main endocrine glands are shown in Figure 7.35. We shall illustrate how hormones work by looking at insulin.

Figure 7.35 *The positions of the main human endocrine glands.*

Endocrine glands have no ducts and they secrete their products – hormones – directly into the bloodstream.

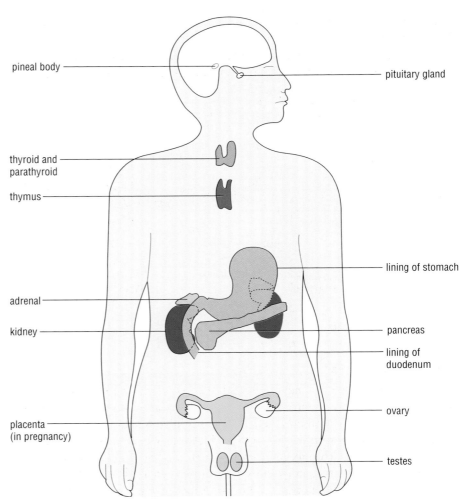

- pineal body
- pituitary gland
- thyroid and parathyroid
- thymus
- lining of stomach
- adrenal
- kidney
- pancreas
- lining of duodenum
- ovary
- placenta (in pregnancy)
- testes

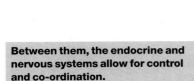

Principles of regulation, page 323

Between them, the endocrine and nervous systems allow for control and co-ordination.

Insulin

The hormone insulin is produced by the pancreas. It lowers blood sugar levels by:
- increasing the uptake of glucose by cells
- increasing the conversion of glucose to glycogen and fat
- inhibiting the formation of glucose from glycogen and other sources.

Insulin operates with another hormone called *glucagon*. Glucagon has the opposite effects to insulin and so raises blood sugar levels. By controlling the relative amounts of insulin and glucagon secreted into the bloodstream, the body is able to keep blood sugar levels close to a constant level, despite the effects of metabolism (which removes glucose from the blood) and eating (which adds glucose to the blood).

Some people cannot synthesise insulin and suffer from insulin-dependent diabetes, also called type 1 diabetes. Without insulin injections their blood sugar levels fluctuate wildly, often being dangerously high.

Nervous system

Hormonal communication within the body is very important, but rather slow. Our **nervous system** allows much more rapid responses to be made. The nervous system is divided into two parts:
- The **central nervous system** (CNS) – made up of the *brain* and *spinal cord*
- The **peripheral nervous system** – made up of *nerves*.

Nerves connect the CNS either to structures known as *receptors* that detect changes in the environment or to *effectors* that cause the body to respond. Examples of receptors are the rods and cones sensitive to light in our eye and chemoreceptors on our tongues for taste. Effectors are either muscles, or glands.

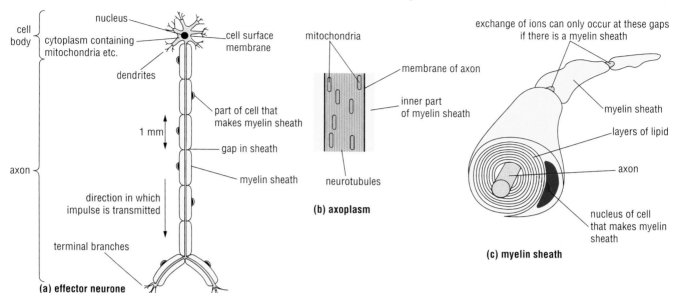

(a) effector neurone

(b) axoplasm

(c) myelin sheath

Nerves are made up of *neurones* (nerve cells). A neurone that connects the spinal cord to an effector such as a muscle is called an effector neurone (see Figure 7.36). An effector neurone is specialised to transmit messages (impulses) from the spinal cord to the effector to which it is attached. Neurones have long, thin axons usually surrounded by a myelin sheath.

The information transmitted by a neurone is carried in the form of electrical pulses, called action potentials, along the axon. The function of the myelin sheath is to provide electrical insulation for the axon, resulting in increased speed of transmission of impulses.

Action potentials can be recorded by means of an *oscilloscope*. Normally the inside of an axon is slightly negatively charged relative to its outside, so that a *resting potential* of about −70 millivolts exists across the membrane of the axon. However, during the passage of an action potential, the resting potential is temporarily reversed, due to changes in the permeability of the axon to sodium and potassium ions (see Figure 7.37).

Figure 7.36 (a) An effector neurone. (b) Detail of the axoplasm as revealed by the electron microscope. (c) Three dimensional representation of the myelin sheath as revealed by the electron microscope.

The nervous system gathers information by means of receptors, processes the information in the central nervous system, and then causes muscles to contract or glands to secrete.

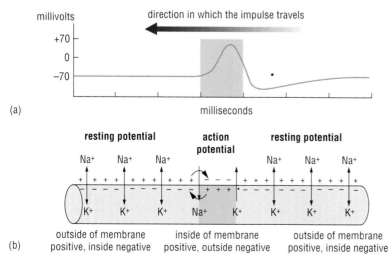

Figure 7.37 Summary of events occurring in an axon which has no myelin sheath. (a) The resting and action potentials as seen on an oscilloscope. (b) Interpretation of the events in (a) in terms of the movement of ions. During a resting potential, potassium ions (K^+) are pumped into the axon and sodium ions (Na^+) out of it. An action potential begins with a sudden rush of sodium ions into the axon, causing the inside of the axon temporarily to become positive relative to the outside. The loss of potassium ions marks the beginning of recovery. The normal distribution is restored by the sodium-potassium pump.

Q 18 How is an oscilloscope able to detect action potentials?

Q 19 Predict the effect on a person of the gradual deterioration over a period of years of the effector neurones which lead from the spinal cord to the muscles of the arms and legs.

Gaseous exchange system

The human gaseous exchange system, sometimes called the *respiratory system*, is shown in Figure 7.38.

Air enters the lungs during *inspiration*. The diaphragm contracts, causing it to lower, and contraction of the *external intercostal muscles* lifts the ribs upwards and outwards. These contractions increase the volume of the thorax and decrease the pressure inside it. It is this fall in pressure that draws air into the lungs via the *trachea, bronchi* and *bronchioles*.

Inspiration is followed by breathing out, *expiration*. This is largely a passive process achieved by the relaxation of the diaphragm and external intercostals. However, the *internal intercostal muscles* may contract, helping to decrease the volume of the thorax and so expel air.

Gaseous exchange itself happens at the tiny air pockets, known as *alveoli*, which are situated at the end of the bronchioles (see Figure 7.39). An alveolus is a sac-like structure covered, on its outside, by a mass of blood capillaries. The blood is brought from the heart by the **pulmonary artery**. On arrival at the **alveoli**, the blood in these capillaries is relatively deoxygenated, its oxygen having being used in respiration by the various organs of the body.

The walls of an alveolus are exceptionally thin. This allows oxygen inside the alveolus to be separated from the red blood cells flowing through the capillaries by the minimum possible distance. As a result, oxygen diffuses the short distance from the air inside the alveolus to the oxygen-carrying haemoglobin molecules that fill the red blood cells. At the same time carbon dioxide diffuses from the blood to the alveolar air.

Q 20 Explain how the structure of the lungs enables blood within them to absorb oxygen and discharge carbon dioxide as rapidly as possible.

Q 21 In the condition known as emphysema, the alveoli break down. Predict the effects of this on a person's health.

Assignment trigger

Asthma

Asthma and related respiratory diseases are said to be on the increase.

Where is the evidence for this?
What are the causes of asthma?
How can the symptoms be identified and how can they be relieved?

If a practical assignment is developed, it is essential that a risk assessment is made and checked by your teacher/lecturer.

Could lead to possible assignments relating to Unit 7.

Deoxygenated blood is supplied to the lungs via the pulmonary artery. In the alveoli, carbon dioxide is exchanged for oxygen.

▶ Health consequences of smoking, page 293

▶ Case study: Atheletes sleep their way to the top, page 326

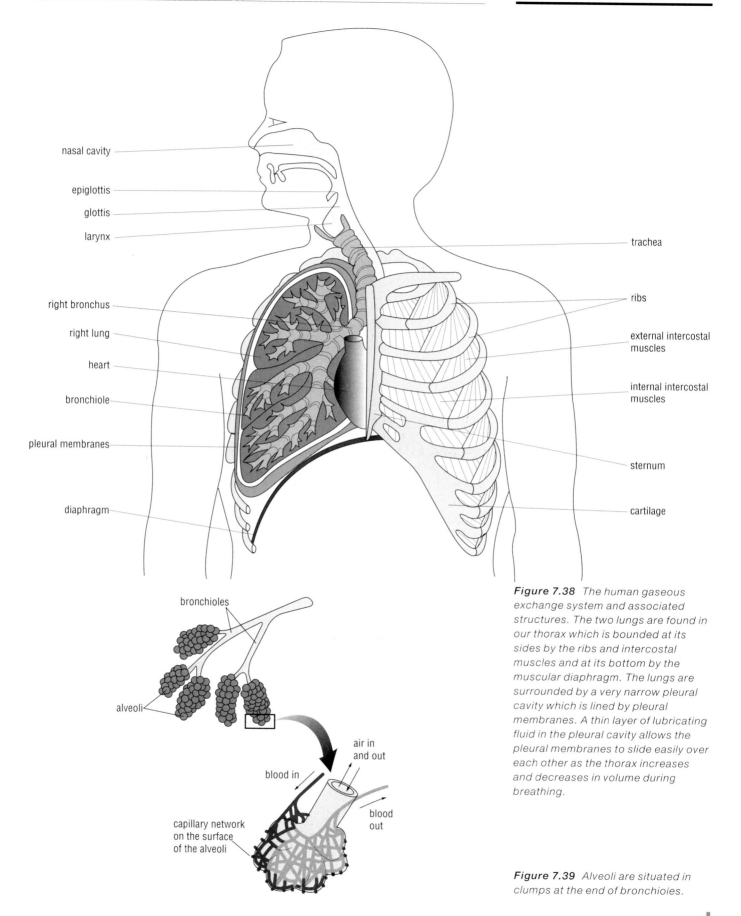

nasal cavity

epiglottis

glottis

larynx

right bronchus

right lung

heart

bronchiole

pleural membranes

diaphragm

trachea

ribs

external intercostal muscles

internal intercostal muscles

sternum

cartilage

bronchioles

alveoli

capillary network on the surface of the alveoli

air in and out

blood in

blood out

Figure 7.38 The human gaseous exchange system and associated structures. The two lungs are found in our thorax which is bounded at its sides by the ribs and intercostal muscles and at its bottom by the muscular diaphragm. The lungs are surrounded by a very narrow pleural cavity which is lined by pleural membranes. A thin layer of lubricating fluid in the pleural cavity allows the pleural membranes to slide easily over each other as the thorax increases and decreases in volume during breathing.

Figure 7.39 Alveoli are situated in clumps at the end of bronchioles.

Functions of the cardio-respiratory system

The circulatory and gaseous exchange (respiratory) system work closely together, and jointly make up the **cardio-respiratory system**. The cardio-respiratory system provides a clear example of how the structure of the body allows good health to be maintained.

In a person completely at rest, the lungs and heart provide the tissues with enough oxygen, glucose and other substances to meet the person's minimum energy needs – their *basal metabolic rate*. During maximum exertion, our rate of metabolism goes up by a factor of over ten.

Q 22 Why is a person's basal metabolic rate not zero?

We have already seen how the heart pumps blood round the body and how our lungs help to keep our blood oxygenated. Here we shall look in more detail at the structure of blood vessels and at the functions of the various blood cell types.

Arteries, veins and capillaries

Blood is carried away from the heart in *arteries*. Veins return blood to the heart, with the exception of the *hepatic portal vein* which transports blood from the small intestine to the liver.

Both arteries and veins have a wall which consists of three layers:
- an outer layer composed mainly of collagen fibres
- a middle layer composed mainly of elastic fibres and smooth muscle
- a very thin inner layer composed of a single layer of epithelial cells and known as the endothelium.

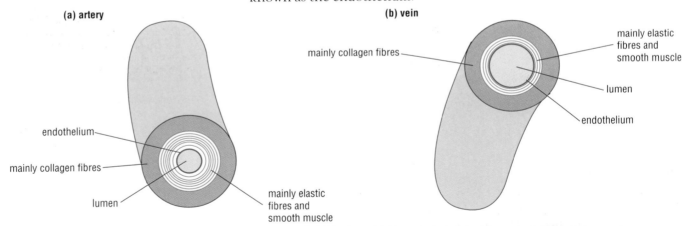

(a) artery

endothelium

mainly collagen fibres

lumen

mainly elastic fibres and smooth muscle

(b) vein

mainly collagen fibres

mainly elastic fibres and smooth muscle

lumen

endothelium

Figure 7.40 Diagrammatic representation of an artery and vein in cross-section showing the similarities and differences.

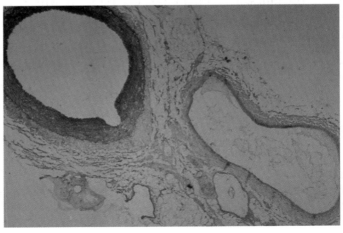

Figure 7.41 Artery and vein seen in transverse section at low power under the light microscope. Which is the artery?

The lumen (hole) of a vein is wider than in its corresponding artery, though the vein has a thinner wall (see Figures 7.40, 7.41). Veins are wider than arteries so blood flows along them more slowly than along arteries. Arteries have more elastic fibres and smooth muscle to help them carry pulses of blood. A final structural difference is that veins possess valves. These help prevent blood from flowing the wrong way, namely away from the heart.

A very important feature of the circulatory system is its capillaries (see Figure 7.42). The heart, arteries and arterioles simply serve to deliver blood to the capillaries; the venules and veins to return blood to the heart. It is the capillaries that enable the passage of materials into and from the surrounding tissues. **Capillaries** are adapted for their functions as follows:

• They are extremely numerous, so presenting a large surface area for diffusion to take place across them.
• They are small, being approximately 10 μm in diameter and having only a single layer of very thin cells – an endothelium – surrounding them (see Figure 7.43). These features minimise the distance over which substances have to diffuse.

In the lungs (see Figure 7.44), capillaries allow carbon dioxide to diffuse from the deoxygenated blood into the alveoli. At the same time, oxygen diffuses into the capillaries, where the concentration of oxygen is lower. Elsewhere in the body, capillaries allow oxygen to diffuse from the blood into surrounding tissues, along with valuable substances such as glucose, amino acids, hormones, minerals and vitamins. At the same time waste products diffuse from metabolically active cells into blood capillaries.

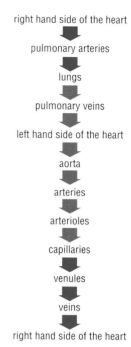

Figure 7.42 The circulation of mammalian blood via arteries, arterioles, capillaries, venules and veins. Arterioles are small arteries; venules are small veins.

Capillaries are numerous and thin-walled. They allow the movement of valuable substances and waste products between blood and surrounding tissues.

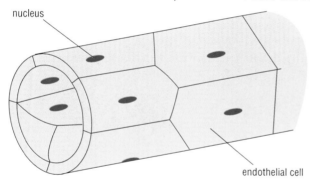

Figure 7.43 A diagrammatic representation of the structure of a capillary showing how capillaries have only a single layer of very thin cells surrounding them.

Blood cell types

The most common type of blood cells are **red blood cells** (see Figure 7.45). These carry oxygen to respiring tissues from the lungs and carbon dioxide back to the lungs. The other blood cell types are **white blood cells** and **platelets.** Platelets are cell fragments and play an essential role in blood clotting.

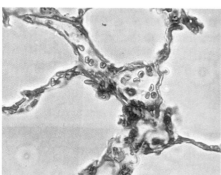

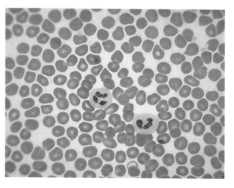

Figure 7.44 (left) Blood capillary in lung

Figure 7.45 (right) Human blood. Red blood cells predominate.

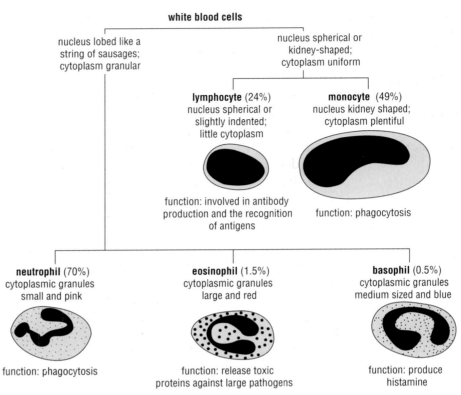

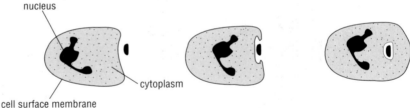

Figure 7.46 *The different types of white blood cell found in human blood. The figures in brackets after the name of each type indicate the percentage of white blood cells belonging to each type.*

Several different types of white blood cells are found (see Figure 7.46). All white blood cells help protect us against disease. The two most common types do so as follows:

- **Neutrophils** try to engulf and digest invading *pathogens*, e.g. bacteria, so destroying them (see Figure 7.47). This is called *phagocytosis*.

Figure 7.47 *A white blood cell destroying a bacterium by phagocytosis.*

> Red blood cells carry oxygen and carbon dioxide. Neutrophils attempt to engulf pathogens. Lymphocytes produce antibodies. Platelets function in clotting.

- **Lymphocytes** produce proteins called **antibodies**. These antibodies recognise particular molecules on the surface of the pathogen known as *antigens*. Antibodies are very specific and will bind only to one particular type of antigen. This allows the body to recognise and destroy pathogens without destroying its own cells. Sometimes, however the process goes wrong. Either the invading pathogen is not recognised in time, and can go on to cause severe damage or even kill us, or we produce antibodies against some of our own antigens. This is the case in *auto-immune diseases* such as *rheumatoid arthritis*.

Q 23 Why do you think there are several types of white blood cell, but only one type of red blood cell?

Mammalian tissues

As we have seen, an organ, such as a heart or lung, is composed of a number of different tissues. In all there are over 200 different types of tissues found in the human body. We have already looked at the different cell types found in blood. Here we shall look briefly at the various sorts of **epithelial, muscle, fibrous connective** and **bone tissue.**

Epithelial tissues

The tissue that lines our organs is known as **epithelial tissue** or **epithelium.** The cells sit on a meshwork of *collagen protein fibres*. Collagen is a protein which consists of three long polypeptide chains, coiled around one another to form a triple helix. It is extremely strong and difficult to stretch. However, when it does return to its original length after having been stretched, it returns almost all the energy it has stored; in other words it is *elastic*. The collagen fibres are embedded in a jelly-like matrix. This structure supports the cells and is known, rather confusingly, as a *basement membrane*.

The simplest sort of epithelial tissue is a single layer of crazy-paving-like cells (see Figures 7.48(a) and 7.49). This is known as *pavement epithelium* or, to give it its technical name, **squamous** epithelium. Squamous epithelium found on the inside of the heart and blood vessels is known as *endothelium*. Squamous epithelium is very thin and permeable.

Cuboidal epithelium is very like squamous epithelium. The only difference is that the cells are more-or-less cube-shaped, and so the tissue is thicker (see Figure 7.48(b)). Glands and ducts are often lined with cuboidal epithelium.

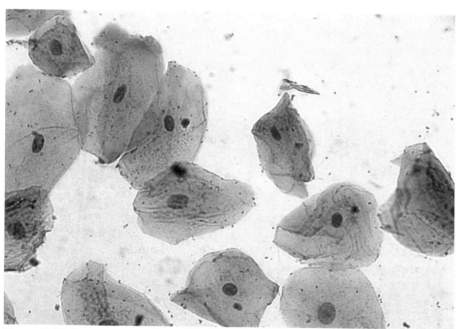

Figure 7.49 Squamous epithelial cells taken from the inside of a human cheek.

In **columnar** epithelium, as the name suggests, the cells are tall (see Figure 7.48(c)). The small intestine is lined with columnar epithelium. Columnar epithelium may also be **ciliated** (see Figure 7.48(d)) or **glandular** (see Figure 7.48(e)). Cilia beat rapidly, so ciliated epithelium transports substances along its surface. For example, ciliated epithelium in our trachea (windpipe) carries dust particles away from our lungs towards our throat. In this way our lungs are protected. Glandular epithelium contains cells which secrete substances.

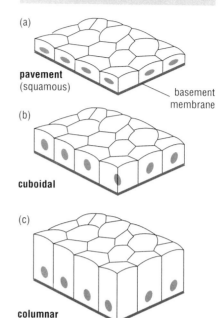
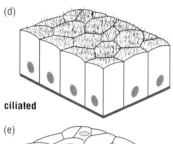
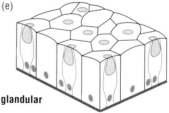

pavement (squamous) — basement membrane

cuboidal

columnar

ciliated

glandular

Figure 7.48 *Five types of simple epithelial tissue.*

319

Muscle tissues

Mammals have three main types of muscle tissues. Some are under voluntary control – we can control them consciously. Others are involuntary, and move without us needing to think about it:

- Muscles under our voluntary control, known as **skeletal muscles**. It is these muscles that we use when moving. The structure of skeletal muscle is summarised in Figure 7.50.

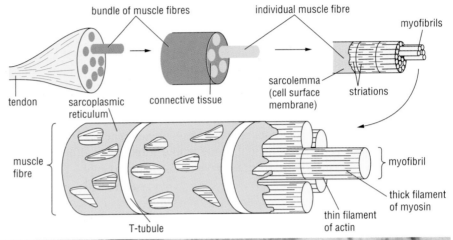

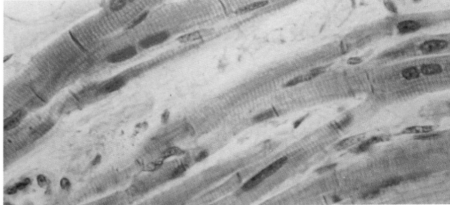

Figure 7.50 Skeletal muscle is attached by tendons to the skeleton. A skeletal muscle consists of a bundle of muscle fibres. Each muscle fibre has a specialised cell surface membrane (the sarcolemma) which surrounds it. An individual muscle fibre itself consists of myofibrils. These contain the proteins actin and myosin. It is the interactions between actin and myosin that cause muscles to contract.

- Involuntary muscle found in the heart and known as **cardiac muscle** (see Figure 7.51). Cardiac muscle can contract rhythmically without fatigue. Indeed it does so about once a second throughout our lives.
- Involuntary muscle found lining our alimentary canal and certain other internal organs and known as **smooth muscle**.

Q 24 What are the advantages of cardiac muscle being involuntary? Can you think of a disadvantage?

Figure 7.51 Mammalian cardiac muscle in longitudinal section under a light microscope at medium power. Notice the bands (striations) within the fibres. These striations are also found in skeletal muscle. One distinctive feature of cardiac muscle is that, as can be seen here in places, fibres join with their neighbours.

Fibrous connective tissue

The tissues and organs in our body are held in the right position by **fibrous connective tissue** (see Figure 7.52). Fibrous connective tissue contains the following structures in a jelly-like matrix:

- Large flat cells called *fibroblasts*. These make the matrix and fibres.
- Long, thin **collagen** fibres. *Tendons*, which attach skeletal muscles to bones, are largely composed of collagen. Try feeling your Achilles tendon and then imagine how it functions when you run.
- Long thin branched fibres called *elastic fibres*. Elastic fibres contain a protein called elastin. **Elastin** is much easier to stretch than collagen –

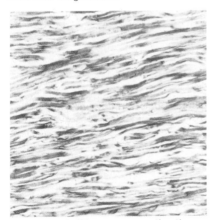

Figure 7.52 Fibrous connective tissue in longitudinal section as seen under a light microscope at medium power. Large numbers of elastic fibres are visible.

Collagen and elastin are proteins found in fibrous connective tissue. Collagen is strong; elastin is stretchy.

hence its name – and is less strong. It is also found in the wall of the bladder – for reasons which should, after a little thought, be obvious to you. As we saw earlier, elastin is also found with smooth muscle in the middle layer of the walls of arteries and veins.

- A number of other cells, including *macrophages* and *mast cells*, both of which help defend the body against disease, and *fat cells*.

How the tissue is arranged in a bone

 Arteries, veins and capillaries, page 316

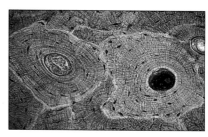

Figure 7.53 *A light micrograph of compact bone showing some 40 or so black spider-like objects. The tiny black dot itself is a lacuna and in living bone contains a single osteoblast.*

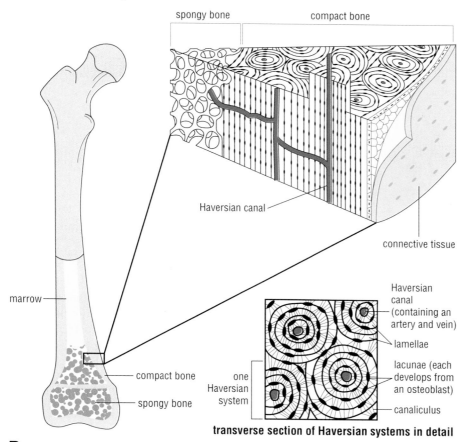

transverse section of Haversian systems in detail

Figure 7.54 *The structure of bone in the mammalian femur.*

Bone

Bone consists of an organic ground substance, or *matrix*, in which various mineral salts are present. The organic matrix contains large numbers of collagen fibres. These help give bone its tensile strength, allowing it to bear heavy loads without breaking. The main mineral salt is *calcium hydroxyapatite* – $Ca_{10}(PO_4)_6(OH)_2$. This exists as tiny crystals and helps make bone very hard.

The organic matrix and various mineral salts found in bone are secreted by specialised cells called *osteoblasts* (see Figure 7.53). Concentric rings of osteoblasts are located around the *Haversian canals*, each of which contains an artery and a vein (see Figure 7.54).

Bone consists of tiny, very hard inorganic crystals in an organic matrix dominated by collagen fibres.

Mammalian cells

Mammalian cells differ widely in their structures, as you can see from the appearance of red blood cells (see Figure 7.45) and neurones (see Figure 7.36), for example. Nevertheless, all mammalian cells develop from cells with essentially the same structure. Indeed, certain types of cells, for example epithelial cells, retain these basic features with little change throughout their lives.

 Epithelial tissues, page 319

Cells have a number of functions including biosynthesis, transport and respiration.

The structure of a generalised mammalian cell is illustrated in Figure 7.55. The roles played by the various cell components can be explained by considering three major functions of the cell: **biosynthesis**, **transport** and **respiration**.

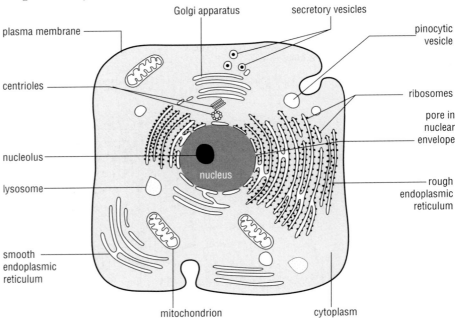

Figure 7.55 *The structure of a typical animal cell as revealed by the electron microscope.*

 DNA and protein synthesis, page 195

Biosynthesis takes place at various places in the cell, including the nucleus, ribosomes and Golgi apparatus.

Biosynthesis

The manufacture of biological compounds is known as biosynthesis. Biosynthesis is carried out almost continuously by most cells, except when they are dividing. It involves a number of cell components. The *nucleus* of a cell contains the *chromosomes*. These contain our genetic material, DNA. Each of our 60 000 or so genes consists of DNA capable of making its own messenger RNA which codes for a particular protein. This messenger RNA then leaves the nucleus via *nuclear pores* and attaches to small structures called *ribosomes* which are usually found on *rough endoplasmic reticulum*. Here the protein coded for by the gene that made the particular messenger RNA is synthesised. The *Golgi apparatus* synthesises glycoproteins, e.g. mucus.

Transport

Substances are continually being moved into and out of the cell across the *plasma membrane* or *cell surface membrane*. A few very small molecules, such as oxygen, carbon dioxide and water, diffuse through the membrane. Most others are carried across by proteins that are found in the membrane (see Figure 7.56). Some substances are taken into the cell by *pinocytotic* and larger *phagocytic vesicles* or are taken out of the cell in *secretory vesicles*.

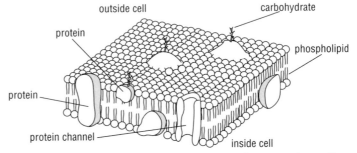

Figure 7.56 *Cell membranes contain proteins and lipids. This model of the cell membrane is known as the fluid mosaic model.*

Some of the vesicles that bring larger particles into the cell join with specialised vesicles called *lysosomes*. Lysosomes contain a range of digestive enzymes and help to break down whatever is in the vesicles they join with.

The Golgi apparatus is involved in modifying, sorting and packaging macromolecules (large molecules). For example, *mucus* is a *glycoprotein*. It consists of a protein to which a carbohydrate component has been added. The **Golgi apparatus** receives the protein component from the rough endo-plasmic reticulum and adds the carbohydrate component. The mucus is then carried in vesicles to the cell surface membrane. Here the vesicles join the cell surface membrane, releasing the mucus to the cell exterior.

> **Cellular transport involves the plasma membrane, vesicles, lysosomes and Golgi apparatus.**

Respiration

The synthesis of ATP in a cell is the main result of respiration. ATP is a valuable compound which can be used for a wide range of processes which require the transfer of energy for them to occur. Such processes include nervous conduction, muscle contraction and the synthesis of many organic compounds. The most efficient form of respiration requires oxygen and is therefore known as **aerobic respiration**. Aerobic respiration takes place in the sausage-shaped structures called **mitochondria** (singular: *mitochondrion*). Mitochondria are the energy-producing powerhouses of cells. As you might expect, very active cells, such as skeletal muscle cells and sperm, have large numbers of mitochondria.

> **Aerobic respiration takes place in mitochondria.**

 25 Identify the cell structures associated with each of the following activities – synthesis of ATP, transport of materials out of the cell, production of DNA, digestion of vesicle contents, synthesis of proteins.

Principles of regulation

In order for us to live, the physical environment that surrounds the cells of our bodies must be kept relatively constant. The most important factors that are regulated in this way are:

- temperature (*thermoregulation*)
- pH
- glucose concentration
- the concentration of ions such as K$^+$ and Na$^+$
- the balance between water and solutes (*osmoregulation*).

At the same time, toxic substances such as carbon dioxide and nitrogenous waste products need to be excreted. The name given to the regulation of all these different factors is **homeostasis**, which literally means 'keeping the same'.

So how does the body achieve homeostasis? A fundamental principle of homeostasis is negative feedback. Negative feedback means that when something changes, the opposite change follows. For instance, a rise in blood sugar levels is followed by a fall in blood sugar levels.

> **Regulation, or homeostasis, is achieved by negative feedback. It involves the body being able to monitor the internal and/or external environment and then respond so that its internal state is kept fairly constant, whatever the conditions outside.**

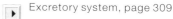 Excretory system, page 309

Figure 7.57 The basic principles of negative feedback

The ideal level of a factor is described as the norm or set point (see Figure 7.57). Suppose that, for whatever reason, there is a rise in the level of a factor – for example, body temperature rises above the optimum as a result of exercise. The essential point about negative feedback is that the higher than normal level of this factor leads to a lowering of it. Similarly, a lower than normal level of a factor results in a raising of that factor.

The regulation of breathing rate

Regulation requires a structure that is able to monitor the levels of whatever it is that is being regulated. Consider the regulation of breathing rate. Breathing, of course, serves to bring oxygen into the body and to expel carbon dioxide from the body. In fact, the body regulates its **breathing rate** *not* so much in response to changes in *oxygen* concentrations in the blood, but mainly in response to changes in *carbon dioxide* concentrations in the blood.

So how precisely does the body regulate its breathing rate? The following steps are involved:

- Specialised cells monitor the level of carbon dioxide in the blood (see Figure 7.58).
- These cells send information to a group of nerve cells called the ventilation centre situated in the brain.
- If the carbon dioxide levels recorded rise above the norm, the brain's ventilation centre sends messages along effector nerves running to the diaphragm and the external intercostal muscles, causing these muscles to contract. As a result, breathing rate and the depth of breathing *increase*. If carbon dioxide levels fall below the norm, the vagus nerve that runs from the ventilation centre to the walls of the bronchi causes a *decrease* in breathing rate.
- Finally, both breathing rate and depth are also under *voluntary* control. So, for example, an athlete may choose to breathe deeply a few times in rapid succession *before* starting a bout of strenuous exercise.

The result of negative feedback is that factors that need to be regulated do not remain exactly at a constant level, but **fluctuate** somewhat about their norm. These fluctuations cause no problems, provided they are minor. It is when something goes wrong and the fluctuations become too great that danger may follow.

We have concentrated on the regulation of breathing rate and depth. Other mechanisms ensure the regulation of many other physiological processes, including heart rate, blood pressure and body temperature.

What happens when body temperature departs from normal?

The average body temperature of a healthy human, whether a baby or adult, is typically 37 °C ± 0.5 °C. A raised body temperature may be the result of strenuous exercise or may indicate an infection. A temperature in excess of 40 °C generally indicates a severe infection. Indeed, such temperatures may be a defence mechanism of the human body, being more dangerous for many disease-causing bacteria than for humans. However, temperatures in excess of 42 °C can lead to irreversible damage or even death.

Body temperatures of less than 36 °C occur after shock. Significantly lower temperatures are indicative of *hypothermia* – a word that simply means 'low temperature'. Death may result with temperatures less than 35 °C. Hypothermia may occur:

- in elderly people on low incomes living on their own in winter
- in people who fall into water less than about 10 °C in temperature
- in people who overdose on certain types of drugs, including barbiturates.

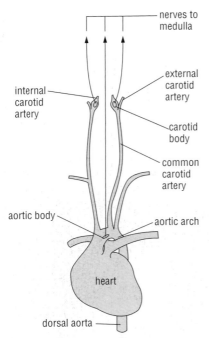

Figure 7.58 *Cells sensitive to carbon dioxide levels in the blood are found in the carotid bodies located between the internal and external carotid arteries on each side of the neck, in the aortic body situated in the wall of the aorta as it leaves the heart, and in the brain itself.*

> Breathing rate and depth are regulated both involuntarily, through specialised cells which monitor the internal concentration of carbon dioxide, and voluntarily.

> Physiological regulation inevitably results in minor fluctuations in the level of whatever is being regulated.

Case study

HEART ATTACKS

In Britain about half a million people have a heart attack each year. Over 100 000 of them die as a direct result. The main symptom of a heart attack is a pain in the centre of the chest, often vice-like in its intensity. This may spread into the neck, jaws and arms. Other symptoms include shortage of breath, dizziness, nausea and feeling cold.

The technical term used by health professionals for a heart attack is a myocardial infarction. The immediate cause of a myocardial infarction is a blockage of a coronary artery by a blood clot – a condition known as coronary thrombosis. As the coronary arteries carry oxygenated blood to the heart, a blockage in one of them means that an area of heart muscle becomes starved of oxygen. This area may die.

So why do people get heart attacks? The most common immediate reason is that one or more of the coronary arteries have narrowed in a process called 'hardening of the arteries' or atherosclerosis. In atherosclerosis fatty plaques, containing a high proportion of cholesterol, are deposited on the insides of some of the larger arteries (see Illustration 1). The presence of these plaques narrows the artery and can stimulate the formation of blood clots. It is when these blood clots beak away and become trapped in a coronary artery that a heart attack may result.

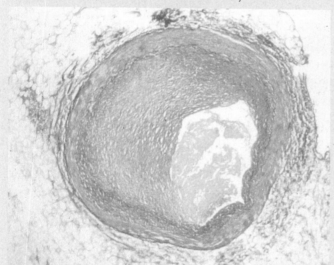

Illustration 1 A human coronary artery affected by atherosclerosis

What causes atherosclerosis?

We have seen that heart attacks often result from atherosclerosis. A number of factors increase the chance of atherosclerosis:

- cigarette smoking
- high blood cholesterol levels
- genetic predisposition (you inherit a tendency towards it)
- hypertension
- being male
- obesity
- lack of exercise
- getting older
- diabetes
- stress/inability to relax.

Treating heart attacks

If a heart attack is suspected, a doctor or ambulance should be called immediately. If a heart attack is confirmed, cardiac massage will be necessary if the person's heart has stopped beating (see Illustration 2). Mouth-to-mouth resuscitation is needed if the person has stopped breathing. Anti-clotting drugs such as aspirin may be given as these have been found to increase survival rates very significantly.

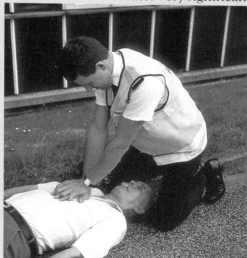

Illustration 2 Ambulance man giving cardiac massage to a patient

Assuming the person is not dead upon arrival at hospital, they will be taken to intensive care or a special coronary unit. Here the patient will be connected to an electrocardiogram (ECG). A cardiac defibrillator may be used to administer an electric shock, so as to 'jump start' the heart. In addition, blood pressure, body temperature, pulse rate and urine output are monitored. Blood samples are taken because the presence of certain enzymes, such as creatine phosphokinase, indicates that a heart attack has happened.

Subsequent treatment may involve the following steps:

- giving the patient oxygen by means of an oxygen mask
- use of drugs to relieve pain
- anticoagulant drugs to reduce the risk of another heart attack
- diuretic drugs to stimulate urine production.

The likelihood of the person suffering another heart attack may be reduced by one or more of three main approaches:

- changes in behaviour
- use of drugs such as beta-blockers, which reduce blood pressure and the oxygen demands of the heart
- surgery (see Illustration 3).

Questions

1 What percentage of people in Britain who have a heart attack die as a direct result of it?

2 Explain why a coronary thrombosis causes a heart attack.

3 Why is a person who has had a heart attack usually connected to an electrocardiogram on arrival at hospital?

4 How do anticoagulant drugs reduce the risk of heart attacks?

5 Suggest five changes in behaviour that would be expected to reduce the chance of another heart attack.

6 Explain the principle behind a coronary artery bypass operation, as shown in Illustration 3.

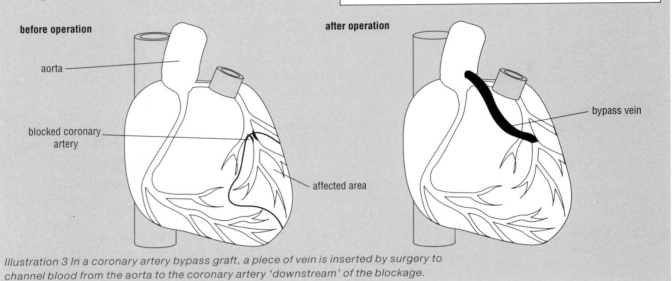

Illustration 3 In a coronary artery bypass graft, a piece of vein is inserted by surgery to channel blood from the aorta to the coronary artery 'downstream' of the blockage.

Case study

ATHLETES SLEEP THEIR WAY TO THE TOP

Athletes and their coaches are forever trying to find new ways to improve performance. Now Igor Gamow, professor of chemical engineering at the University of Colorado, has developed a 'high-altitude' bed (Illustration 1) which he claims improves athletic performance.

Illustration 1 The Gamow bed

ATHLETES SLEEP THEIR WAY TO THE TOP

"Some recent studies have documented that living high and training low is the optimum strategy for the endurance athlete," says Gamow, "As far as I know, this is the only serious training device that will train you while you sleep."

Gamow's sleeping chamber enables an athlete to get the best of both worlds: gaining the advantage of living at high altitude while training at sea level. Athletes who train above 3300 metres cannot get as good a workout as they would at sea level because their bodies cannot absorb enough oxygen from the thinner air.

Being at high altitude for as little as four hours a day stimulates a hormone, erythropoietin, that causes more red blood cells to be produced, Gamow says. This acclimatisation to altitude lasts about two weeks.

The high altitude bed is 80 centimetres in diameter and weighs about 100 kilograms. The bed is designed to simulate altitudes of up to 6000 metres. When a vacuum pump draws air out of the chamber, a latchless door on one end seals automatically as the air pressure begins to drop.

A system of valves maintains pressure levels in the chamber that simulate different altitudes and allows fresh air to circulate inside the bed.

The fibreglass chamber must withstand major stresses, similar to those of a submarine.

The low-pressure chamber complements the Gamow Bag, a portable high-pressure chamber which was also invented by Gamow. The bag, designed to bring climbers with altitude sickness rapidly back to sea level, has saved the lives of scores of mountaineers by simulating lower altitudes.

Jonathan Beard, New York.

A person's aerobic fitness is a measure of how well their body can make use of oxygen when they are exercising. Gamow's sleeping chamber is designed to increase an athlete's aerobic fitness. You can measure your own aerobic fitness using a step-up test as follows:

Required: 16 inch high step if you are female aged 14-17

18 inch high step if you are a male aged 16-17

18 inch high step if you are a female aged 18 or over

20 inch high step if you are a male aged 18 or over

(It is important that the height of the step is accurate to within half an inch and, for safety reasons, that the step is very steady.)

Stopwatch or watch with a second hand

Some way of taking your pulse rate (see page 300).

Method:

1 Step onto and off the step at a steady rate equivalent to 30 complete steps per minute, where a step includes stepping up and stepping down. Make sure you stand fully upright each time at the top of the step.

2 If you can, carry on stepping for 5 minutes. If you find this too much, measure for how long you can carry on.

3 At the end of the stepping, rest in a sitting position for 60 seconds.

4 Then take your pulse rate for 30 seconds.

5 Use the following formula to calculate your fitness index (FI):

$$FI = \frac{(\text{duration of test in seconds}) \times 100}{(\text{pulse count for 30 seconds}) \times 5.5}$$

6 Use the following table to work out your approximate aerobic fitness:

Fitness Index	Aerobic Fitness
180 or over	Superb
160–179	Excellent
140–159	Very good
120–139	Good
100–119	Creditable
80–99	Reasonable
Less than 80	Room for improvement!

Questions

1 Why do people who live at high altitude have more red blood cells than people who don't?

2 Explain the thinking behind Gamow's sleeping chamber.

3 Why does Gamow's sleeping chamber have to withstand stresses similar to those of a submarine?

4 Propose an experiment to test whether Gamow's sleeping chamber works. You will need to think about such things as the number of subjects, the nature of your control, and what statistical test to use.

5 Gamow's sleeping chamber costs around $10 000. Do you think its use by athletes should be allowed or prohibited?

6 Explain why the step-up test provides a measure of a person's aerobic fitness.

7 In what other ways could you measure how fit someone is?

8 | Communicate information

In all your scientific work you will be acquiring, using and generating information. If the work of scientists is to be of any value this information must be *reliable* and *valid*. Scientists rely on each other as well as having others relying on them. However good your information is, it must be communicated effectively to be of any use. Whatever job you have, you will have to gather, process and communicate data electronically.

The sharing or *dissemination* of information is vitally important to the progress of science. Scientists need to be able to *receive* up-to-date information in their field and to be able to *transmit* their own new data to the widest possible audience. This is because science works through *critical appraisal*. Any new idea is tested and reflected on by other scientists. In this way it can be refined and may eventually be replaced by a better idea, or it can be rejected if it is shown to be wrong.

Figure 8.1 *Free interchange of scientific ideas is vital. Mendel was the first geneticist. He made the most important breakthrough in the understanding of how characteristics are passed on from parents to offspring. Unfortunately, he published his findings in the* Proceedings of the Natural History Society of Brünn! *They remained in obscurity for forty years.*

Advances in the technology of communications systems have made the acquisition and transfer of data increasingly efficient. Computers have become central to most methods of communication. This is thanks to the convergence of three technologies: *computing*, *micro-electronics* and *telecommunications*. You are living in an *information technology revolution* that may prove to be even more important to human history than the industrial revolution.

The Elements

Element 8.1 Gather data for scientific purposes
You will need to:
- explain why you need a particular set of data
- choose a suitable method and use it to collect your data safely
- assess the reliability of your source of data.

Gathering information for scientific purposes, page 330

Element 8.2 Transfer scientific data electronically
You will need to:
- explain why data are being transmitted from one place to another
- describe what each stage does and explain the features of a communications system
- transfer data using a communications system.

Transferring data electronically, page 331

Element 8.3 Process, display and evaluate data
You will need to:
- estimate the size of errors in your data
- use formulae, graphs and statistics to process data
- explain why you have chosen a particular method to display your data
- display your data in a suitable form
- draw valid conclusions from your data.

Making the best of your data, page 345

Gathering data for scientific purposes

Whenever you gather data you will have some purpose in mind. You should be able to explain why the data are required if you are to be sure that they are appropriate to that purpose.

Figure 8.2 *Sometimes scientists obtain their data from laboratory investigations or fieldwork. They might make direct observations or use electronic devices such as dataloggers connected to sensors. This is called primary data.*

Figure 8.3 *Scientists also check the scientific literature. For example, they use databases, textbooks, journals and databooks to find the data they need. This information from published sources is called secondary data.*

As a scientist, you may have many different types of task to perform. For example a pharmacist may need to *analyse* a drug sample to check its purity. An agrochemicals company would want a team to conduct a *survey* to determine the potential market for a new product. *Problem solving* is a common scientific purpose. When a problem arises, specific data are needed in the search for a solution. The continuing struggle to test for and find wheat strains resistant to new varieties of rust fungus is an example.

Reliable and valid data

Scientific work must be reliable and valid. If data are **reliable**, they are *consistent*. It should be possible to obtain the same information again. Factors you should bear in mind are:

- have sources of error been recognised?
- has the precision of any measuring instruments been taken into account?
- has the currency (how up to date) of any information used been determined?
- has information used been checked against a number of sources?

The reliability of your data depends on:
- the extent of your survey leading to the data;
- your sources of error;
- the precision of the measuring instruments that you used;
- the currency of the data.

If data and conclusions are *valid*, they are *good for their purpose*. They actually give you the information that you need. Factors you should bear in mind are:

- Were the data collected in an appropriate way so that they are accurate?
- Are conclusions based solely on the data obtained?
- Are they relevant to the purpose of the investigation?

You must be certain that the data that you obtain are good for their purpose. They must not only be of the correct kind but must also be *precise* and *accurate*. A pharmacist might be checking a sample for purity to prevent their company from poisoning rather than curing their clients!

As a scientist you have to be aware of any potential sources of *errors* in your work, and take them into account. Sampling is important here. How representative are your data of the range of values occurring in all cases, not just that in the sample that you are testing?

1 On-line electronic sensors such as ion-sensitive electrodes have come into common use for testing such things as drinking water supplies obtained from treated water. How often would you like your water supply to be tested?

In **primary data** you need to know the precision of your instruments and you should check for *random* or *systematic* errors and *anomalous results*. In **secondary data** you need to check the currency of your sources (how up to date are they?), the *status* of the original work (is the author an acknowledged expert, is the publisher/publication reputable?) and the extent of your survey (have you compared different sources?).

Good scientists will have indicated the precision and reliability of the data they publish, to make it as useful as possible to others.

Gathering your own data

You should have plenty of opportunities to gather primary and secondary data. You will want to use electronic measurement devices whenever you can. Can you think of any examples? You should have no trouble meeting this requirement of this Unit!

Transferring scientific data electronically

Modern communications systems rely on the electronic transfer of data. This can take place almost instantaneously. Computer networks can operate to transfer information over short distances, such as within a school or college, but they can also cross international boundaries, particularly if signals are transmitted via radio waves and satellites.

Facsimile machines (faxes) are now in common use to transmit documents cheaply and rapidly.

2 How much does it cost to send an A4 document through the post and by fax in the UK? How long does it take? What are the relative costs and times for sending it to Australia?

Computer networks

For data to be transmitted from one computer to another requires a number of main stages. Computer systems consist of a central processing unit (CPU) connected to a number of peripheral devices. These allow data to be moved in

Measuremer precision

Primary data is new information that you have determined for yourself. It is based on your own observations and measurements.
Secondary data is obtained from other sources such as books or word of mouth. Someone else has done the original work to find out that information.

Remember that as a scientist you should be able to explain the purpose of your data gathering, then select suitable methods and assess their reliability.

and out of the computer. They include input devices (for example, keyboard, light pen, mouse, scanner, touch screen, voice, joystick, disk drive) and **output devices** (for example, printer, plotter, disk drive, visual display unit (VDU), loudspeaker).

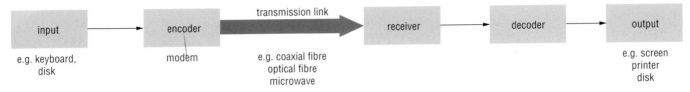

Figure 8.4 *The main stages necessary for data transmission in a computer network*

Digital data
The micro-processor of the CPU uses data in digital (numerical) form. It is composed of many thousands of transistor units linked by microscopic circuitry, all on the surface of a tiny silicon chip. This is packaged in a holder that has all the necessary electrical connectors to link it to other devices.

The transistors units can act as switches, so that the data can be coded using two digits, 0 and 1. Usually a current of up to 10 mA at a voltage of $\simeq 0V$ represents the digit 0. A current of up to 0.1 mA at a voltage of $\simeq 5V$ represents the digit 1. The 0s and 1s in a binary number are called **bits** (BInary digiTS).

Figure 8.5 *A microchip, thousands of transistor units in a tiny space.*

Binary numbers are used to code digital data in computers. They consist of a byte formed from bits.

Table 8.1 Binary and decimal digits

Decimal	Binary	8 bit binary
0	0	00000000
1	1	00000001
2	10	00000010
3	11	00000011
4	100	00000100
5	101	00000101

Typically, computers use 8 bit binary numbers. For example, using the keyboard to type the letter C will use the code 01000011. Each group of 8 bits is called a **byte**. There are 256 different binary codes possible when using 8 bits. More powerful computers use 16 or 32 bit bytes, giving 65 536 and 4 294 967 296 combinations respectively.

 3 Another measure of the power of a computer is the number of bytes that it can store in its memory. 1 kilobyte (kb or kbyte) of memory means about 1 000 bytes can be stored (in fact it is 1 024). 1 megabyte (Mb or Mbyte) is about 1 million bytes. How many bytes are 1 gigabyte?

Connecting computer communication equipment

Equipment sited a few hundred metres or more apart is usually connected by a telephone line by using a *modem* (MOdulator/DEModulator) at each end. *Modulation* is the change in a carrier wave caused by a signal. This is discussed later in this unit.

Ordinary telephone lines are designed to communicate the human voice. This causes problems which make them unsuitable for the transmission of digital signals. A modem acts as an *encoder* to convert the digital data into a suitable form for transmission (by modulation) and then as a *decoder* (for demodulation) after the signal has reached the *receiver*. The receiver is tuned to pick up a carrier wave of a particular frequency. In this way large numbers of signals can be carried down the same wire together, using different frequencies for each. This is discussed further later in this unit.

For shorter distances other cables can be used. However, both ends of the transmission line must still be able to behave *as though* they are connected to a modem. This is because other control signals are transmitted by modems. Devices called null modems, modem eliminators or drivers are used.

▶ Capacity, page 336

Data can be coded in digital or analogue form.

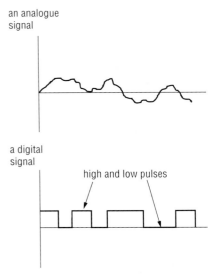

Figure 8.6 *Digital and analogue signals compared*

Analogue data and facsimile machines

The digital data used by computers consists of discrete high/low pulses. Much data is originally in **analogue** form. Rather than being discrete, it varies continuously with time(see Figure 8.6).

A transducer converts one form of energy to another. *Input transducers* are needed to convert data such as temperature changes to electrical signals, so that these can be transmitted to a datalogger or a computer. A temperature probe containing a thermistor could be used for this purpose. There are an infinite number of signal levels between the maximum and minimum values obtainable. These can be represented by gradual changes in voltage or current. This contrasts with the discrete, separate changes found in digital data.

Facsimile machines (fax)

Fax machines use *optical readers* (input transducers) which scan a document. They use either analogue *or* digital data. In one type a photoelectric cell converts black through shades of grey to white (analogue data) into electric signals. These are encoded (by modulating a telephone carrier wave) and transmitted using telephone lines.

The machines also act as *receivers*, *decoders* and *output transducers*. They pick up the incoming signals, demodulate them and print an image. A printer acts as an output transducer by converting electrical signals into marks on paper.

The hands of the analogue watch make continuous movements. The digital watch changes by discrete whole number units.

Figure 8.7 *Analogue and digital watches. The difference between analogue and digital data is most easily seen in comparing analogue and digital watches.*

Fax machines are classified in four groups. Group 1 machines are high quality but slow. Group 2 machines are faster but give lower quality results. Both of these are the analogue type, reproducing shades of grey. If you have used a fax machine, it was probably from Group 3 or 4. These are used for text, as they give black and white tones only. They are the cheap popular machines in common use today. They are digital machines, converting black or grey to a binary 1 and white to a binary 0. Transmission time is much reduced and cost is low.

 4 Fax machines are even more popular in Japan than in countries like the UK and USA. Can you explain why?

5 Figure 8.4 shows the main stages in communication in a computer network. Sketch a similar diagram to summarise the main stages in transmission of data using a fax machine.

Analogue data and computers

If you want to monitor changes such as temperature or pH using sensors, you must be able to convert this analogue data to digital signals before the computer can use them. Many computers have ports connected to *analogue to digital converters* (ADC's). These act as **encoders** which convert analogue fluctuations in voltages into binary numbers.

6 The ADC of a BBC computer gives 12-bit resolution to make accuracy of 1 in 4096 possible. Try to explain this statement as fully as you can to someone else. If you find it difficult, ask another student to explain it to you.

> Input transducers such as temperature probes, movement sensors and optical readers in fax machines transmit changes in voltage. These vary directly with changes in the quantity being measured. These analogue signals must be transmitted to encoders which convert them to digital form for use in the computer.

Assignment trigger

Process control

Modern industrial processes are complex and their management sophisticated. Yet they can be controlled by a handful of people. This is owing to modern electronic systems.

What operations in a process are controlled in this way?
What are the advantages and disadvantages?

If a practical assignment is developed, it is essential that a risk assessment is made and checked by your teacher/lecturer.

Could lead to possible assignments relating to Unit 8.

Reliability of analogue and digital systems

The everyday use of any system requires it to be reliable, and the information on it to be clearly accessible.

Fidelity

A variety of problems arise which affect the **fidelity** of a signal when data are eventually decoded and obtained through an output device. In music systems you expect 'hi-fi', that is , HIgh FIdelity. The playback should correspond as closely as possible to the original performance. This is not always necessary: sometimes all we need is to retain the essential meaning of the data. This can be done at low fidelity. As long as the 'message' remains intact, the data do not need to be in exactly the same form as the original. This is why ordinary telephone signals are 'voice quality' only. You may

> Music requires high fidelity signal reproduction, but telephone systems do not.

have experienced difficulty in recognising a familiar voice when you heard it on the telephone, but you will have been able to understand what they wanted to say.

Noise and distortion

Any transmission of electrical signals is subjected to **noise**. A large number of factors contribute to this. Resistors and transistors both generate noise. Resistor noise, for example, is caused by thermal fluctuations in free electron density in a conducting material. From one moment to the next, a particular piece of conductor may have more or fewer electrons than the average, lowering or raising its voltage. The size of these fluctuations increases as more thermal energy becomes available. So noise increases with rises in temperature.

Fluctuations in noise are caused by changes in neighbouring electrical apparatus and by thunderstorms. Neighbouring cables suffer from 'cross talk' caused by capacitance and inductance effects.

Factors that affect noise levels may also interfere with the signal itself, causing *distortion* so that fidelity is reduced.

White noise and the signal to noise ratio

For any signal, there is usually a reasonably steady mean level of noise over the frequency waveband being used. This is known as white noise. What matters is that the signal is strong enough to be detected against this background noise. The **signal to noise ratio** (SNR) can be found by comparing the level of the signal to the level of the noise alone:

$$\text{SNR} = \frac{\text{signal} + \text{noise}}{\text{noise}} \quad \text{(usually measured in decibels)}$$

 7 FM radio (VHF) is less noisy than AM radio (for example, Medium Wave). Will higher quality transmission give you a high or a low SNR?

Attenuation and amplification

Resistance, current leakage, capacitance effects and so on mean that some of the energy of a signal in a wire is dissipated as heat. As the frequency of the alternating current of a signal increases, these losses also increase. *Coaxial cables* are designed to reduce the losses and are therefore used for high frequency signals.

Such cables still offer resistance, so electrical signals in all cables gradually lose energy and become **attenuated** (weakened). Because of this, telephone companies such as BT use *repeaters* every few kilometres on older trunk lines. These amplify and retransmit the signals.

To avoid the need for cables, signals can be transmitted using radio waves. This also allows the signals to be dispersed over a wide area. However, dispersal causes attenuation, so radio signals must amplified to produce powerful transmissions. Radio signals travel in straight lines, so radio blind spots can occur owing to the irregular nature of the Earth. Furthermore, radio signals will not travel around the curve of the Earth's surface. This can be overcome by bouncing them off the ionosphere. This ionised layer in the upper atmosphere reflects radio waves, which can then bounce back off the ground. Repeated bouncing will carry them around the Earth's curvature (see Figure 8.9). This only works for shorter frequencies, as higher ones pass through the ionosphere.

These signals will eventually become attenuated, so relay stations such as those used by the BBC in Cyprus boost the signals. Satellites can also be

> *Noise* is the sum total of all the unwanted electrical energy in a system that is added to a signal.

> Noise may mask a signal. The *signal to noise ratio* determines whether meaningful data can still be obtained from a transmission. It must not be allowed to fall below a minimum level.

> All transmitted signals become progressively attenuated the further they travel.

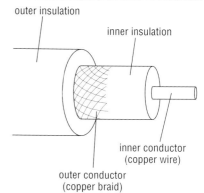

Figure 8.8 Structure of a coaxial cable

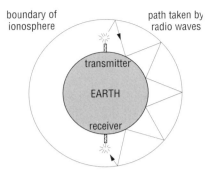

boundary of ionosphere

path taken by radio waves

transmitter

EARTH

receiver

In practice, relay stations are used to boost the signal which becomes very attenuated over such long distances.

Figure 8.9 *Sending short wave radio round the curvature of the earth*

used to amplify signals and overcome curvature. By these means, short wave radio can be sent around the earth.

8 It may seem a simple solution to amplify attenuated signals at regular intervals, but what will happen to the signal to noise ratio? See if you can work out why this is important before you read on.

Problems with amplification

The white noise in a system will remain at roughly the same level as the signal attenuates. So the signal to noise ratio becomes less (worse). Amplification will boost noise and signal together, so that this lower SNR will be unchanged. Gradually, weak signals will become lost in the background of noise.

Reliability of analogue and digital systems compared

The reasons for the greater reliability of **digital** transmissions when compared to analogue transmissions are summarised in Table 8.2, though distortion of an analogue signal may not prevent it from being recognisable. You can still understand a voice on a noisy telephone line or radio broadcast, up to the point where the signal-to-noise ratio becomes very small. On the other hand, certain noise, such as static, can completely obliterate bits (binary digits) so that digital codes are altered. Even a tiny change in the code for part of a computer program can have disastrous effects. You may well have first-hand experience of this!

Table 8.2 Analogue and digital transmissions compared

	Analogue		Digital	
Factor	Feature	Consequences	Feature	Consequences
Signal	signal varies with each small change in data transmission	sophisticated, finely-tuned apparatus required; more prone to failure	signal discrete pulses of voltage or current	simpler, cheaper, more reliable equipment
Noise	permanently alters signal	signal cannot faithfully be regenerated	noise unlikely to have significant effect on pulses	signal can usually be regenerated perfectly
	noise will not usually alter the essential features of a signal	distorted signals can still be recognised	noise can sometimes obliterate bits	signal code can be altered

Communications systems transmitting digital signals are more reliable than those transmitting analogue signals.

Error detection devices can be used to prevent problems arising from inaccurate transmission of digital data. For example, ASCII (American Standard Code for Information Interchange) is an internationally accepted system for coding for microcomputers. All computers exchange 8-bit codes down modem links, even though ASCII only uses 7 of the available 8 for character coding. The eighth bit often codes for non-ASCII characters. In addition, it is standard practice to have a ninth parity bit which codes characters as odd or even. A change in the code for any character can give rise to an error warning.

Capacity

The **capacity** of a transmission link to carry data depends on the nature of the connection and of the signal being sent.

Carrier waves, modulation and multiplexing

A large number of simultaneous signals can be transmitted down cables or through the air or space. This can be done by using different high

Multiplexing refers to techniques which allow two or more signals to occupy the same transmission link, thereby increasing capacity.

noise

The signal **attenuates** and becomes **distorted** by the noise

analogue signal

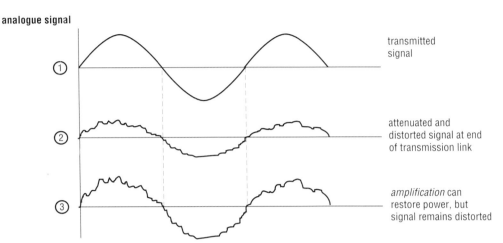

transmitted signal

attenuated and distorted signal at end of transmission link

amplification can restore power, but signal remains distorted

Noise will permanently alter an analogue signal, so that it can never be faithfully reproduced. It is impossible to regenerate the original signal.

digital signal

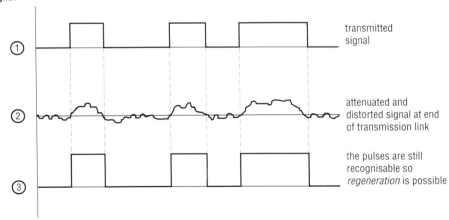

transmitted signal

attenuated and distorted signal at end of transmission link

the pulses are still recognisable so *regeneration* is possible

When digital pulses are used, low level noise will be totally ignored. Only the difference between the pulses needs to be recognised. High fidelity reproduction of the original signal is possible even for a highly attenuated signal. So even after repeated amplification accurate regeneration with 100% accuracy is possible.

*Amplifiers in analogue transmission links are usually called repeaters. In a digital system a regenerator can be used. It is possible not only to amplify the signal, but to restore it to its original form.

Figure 8.10 *Amplification of analogue and digital signals*

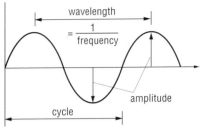

A simple sinusoidal wave is shown.
The *amplitude* of a wave is related to the power of the signal. The vertical movement (positive or negative) is greater the more energy that is being transferred.

A *cycle* is one complete movement or oscillation.

Wavelength (symbol λ) is the distance moved for one complete cycle. It is measured in *metres*.

Frequency (symbol *f*) is the number of cycles completed every second. It is measured in hertz (Hz).

$$\lambda = \frac{1}{f}$$

Figure 8.11 *Characteristics of a wave*

frequency waves to *carry* each signal separately from the rest. Signals generated by computers, fax machines, phones and so on are used to modulate *carrier waves* of different fixed frequencies. Various modulation methods are used, including *amplitude*, *frequency* and *pulse code modulation*. Characteristics of a wave are shown in Figure 8.11.

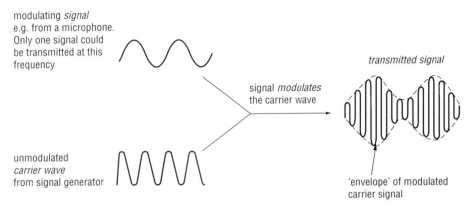

The modulated carrier wave still has its original frequency, but the *amplitude* varies according to the changes in the original signal. These can be decoded at the end of the transmission link.

Figure 8.12 *Amplitude modulation (AM)*

Amplitude modulation is shown in Figure 8.12. This is used for radio broadcasts in the UK on the short, medium and long wavebands. A form of it is also used in the telephone system. Unfortunately it can be badly affected by noise generated by electrical equipment and atmospheric static.

Use of AM in telephones and radio

Amplifiers have distinct input and output connections and operate one-way only. This meant that early telephone lines required pairs of copper wires and amplifiers for each conversation! Later *coaxial cable* was used for long distance trunk lines, to allow many conversations to be transmitted simultaneously. This is because coaxial cable can transmit electrical signals at radio frequencies whilst insulating them from radio station broadcasts.

The ability of radio waves to transmit signals simultaneously is used in the domestic radio services. The 'medium' waveband has a *system bandwidth* between 525 kHz and 1606 kHz. It is divided into 121 *channels* each with a *bandwidth* of 9 kHz. Each of these can carry a separate signal for a different radio station. This is called *frequency division multiplexing* (FDM) (see Figure 8.13). Each *signal bandwidth* must lie within the *channel bandwidth* to remain separate from other signals.

Many signals can be transmitted at the same time by using different carrier frequencies.

FDM restricts the bandwidth available for each channel.

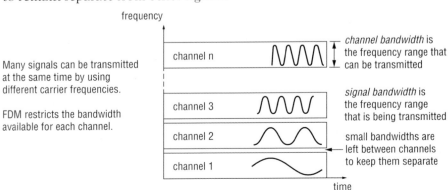

Figure 8.13 *Frequency division multiplexing (FDM)*

A bandwidth of 9 kHz for radio allows transmission of reasonable quality sound and speech, but this is much wider than that required for the telephone system. Telephone microphones act as input transducers to transmit electrical signals at much the same frequencies as the human voice. Human speech ranges from about 0.1 kHz to 10 kHz. Using frequencies between 0.3 kHz and 3.8 kHz, a bandwidth of 3.5 kHz, gives adequate quality, though not high fidelity. Ordinary telephone lines are therefore designed to carry analogue signals between these frequencies and the carrier waves to be modulated must lie between these frequencies.

To make *long distance* lines efficient, the use of coaxial cable was combined with the use of high frequency electrical signals at radio wave frequencies. This dramatically increased the number of channels available. In this way single amplifiers could be used in each direction to transmit thousands of calls simultaneously!

Frequency modulation (FM)

Figure 8.14 shows how FM works.

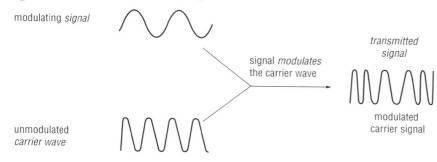

The modulation of the carrier wave leaves the original constant amplitude, but the frequency varies according to the changes in the original signal.

Figure 8.14 *Frequency modulation (FM)*

9 Wider bandwidths are needed for frequency modulation than are necessary for amplitude modulation. Why is this?

FM uses *very high frequency* (VHF) transmissions to provide the wider bandwidths that are needed. Increasing bandwidth also increases the amount of information that can be transmitted. Listening to your favourite music on AM is very different to hearing it on FM! AM radio broadcasts are of significantly poorer quality than FM.

Television requires transmission of even more information, so even broader bandwidths are used, at *ultra high frequencies* (UHF). Microwave transmission gives yet higher frequencies. This provides even larger bandwidths and makes even more channels possible, so that still more information can be carried. This need for transmission of high volumes of information is the reason for using towers with microwave dishes in cities. Television, data and voice signals are transmitted from these towers.

Time division multiplexing

Time division multiplexing is shown in Figure 8.15. This can be used to maintain broad bandwidths and therefore a high volume of information transmission. Signals are split into short, interleaved packets and occupy separate channels at different time intervals. This is suitable for digital transmissions, where bandwidth is equivalent to the number of bits transmitted per second (the *bit rate*).

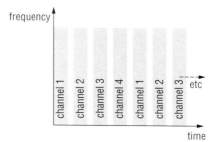

TDM allows wider band widths to be used but transmission of a signal can take a long time if there are many channels competing.

Figure 8.15 *Time division multiplexing*

Pulse code modulation (PCM)

A British engineer called Alex Harvey Reeves proposed the PCM system to code voice signals as long ago as 1938. He saw it as a method which would overcome the problems of noise in telephone systems. At the time the necessary equipment was not available.

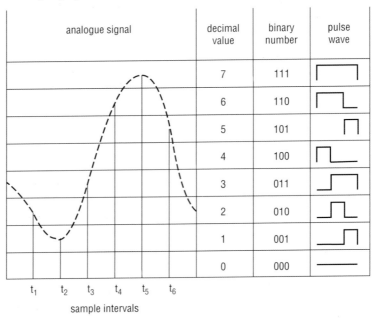

analogue signal	decimal value	binary number	pulse wave
	7	111	
	6	110	
	5	101	
	4	100	
	3	011	
	2	010	
	1	001	
	0	000	

sample intervals

The amplitude of the analogue signal is measured at short time time intervals (t_1, t_2, t_3 ...) and given a decimal value (it is 'digitised').
Here, at time t_1 amplitude is 2

t_2	1
t_3	3
t_4	6
t_5	7
t_6	5

These values are converted to binary numbers which are used to generate a *pulse code* of 'off' for 0 and 'on' for 1. 010 is ⊓. This process is called *pulse code modulation*. The PCM signal for the analogue signal shown is:

PCM signal
binary code 0 1 0 0 0 1 0 1 1 1 1 0 1 1 1 1 0 1

Figure 8.16 *Pulse code modulation*

Figure 8.16 explains *pulse code modulation*. This is a system for converting analogue signals to digital signals. You can see that this involves measuring the amplitude of a signal at regular intervals. A decimal value is given to the amplitude found at each time interval, then this is converted to a binary number. Each sampled amplitude is then represented by a pulse code. This is a digital signal representing the code for the bits of a binary number.

The amplitude of the analogue signal has to be measured and stored. The faster this can be done the greater the sampling rate can be. The fidelity of conversion depends on the *sampling rate*.

Telephone transmissions use bandwidths of about 4 kHz. To enable the signal to be successfully decoded at the end of the transmission link, sampling is done at **twice** the bandwidth of the signal being used. As this is about 4 kHz for a telephone voice, PCM sampling is at 8 000 times per second, or once every 125μs. A pulse can be generated every 1μs. Using 8 bits for each sample means that this takes only 8μs. This leaves 117μs for time division multiplexing with other signals before the next sample is taken.

For PCM, the bit rate is the number of bits per sample multiplied by the sampling frequency. For a single PCM telephone signal this would be $8 \times 8\,000 = 64\,000$ bits s^{-1}, that is 64 kbits s^{-1}.

Q 10 Table 8.3 below compares bit rates for different communications channels. If a high quality music transmission requires 16 bits to encode each sample with a bandwidth of 15 kHz, what *bit rate* should be shown in the table?

Table 8.3 Bit rates compared

System	Bit rate per PCM channel
Telephone voice	64 kbits s^{-1}
Music	? kbits s^{-1}
TV	70 Mbits s^{-1}

Q 11 Why will a low sampling rate give poor fidelity? The BBC computer was mentioned earlier. It has a 12-bit ADC. When you use a CD system you are using 16-bit converters. Why not use 8 bits for these two applications?

Digital to analogue conversion

Transmission of binary data between computers can be accomplished by using modems linked by telephone lines. This requires conversion of the digital signals used by the first computer to analogue signals and then back to digital again. Amplitude and frequency modulation are possible ways to carry the analogue signals, though computers are usually linked by phase modulation. These techniques are shown in Figure 8.17.

Improving transmission speeds and capacity

The basic capacity of a digital system for information transfer depends on the bit rate. Data transmission speeds also depend on the number of bits per byte and the number of bits required (such as 'starts' and 'stops') in addition to the data.

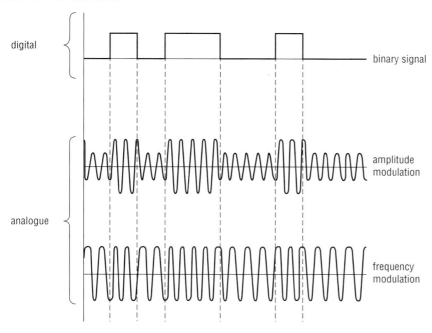

Figure 8.17 *Digital to analogue conversion*

The optical fibre revolution

Coaxial cables transmitting high-frequency signals revolutionised telephone trunk lines. Use of microwaves at extremely high frequencies has been even more efficient, thanks to the increased bandwidths made available. *Optical fibres* using *laser* light make even larger numbers of broad bandwidths available.

Table 8.4 Comparison of carrier waves

Carrier wave	Frequency	Wavelength possible	Bandwidth	Number of voice channels
HF Radio	3 MHz	30 m	16 kHz	4
Microwave radio	6 GHz	5 cm	4 MHz	960
Digital microwave	140 Mbits sec^{-1}	5 cm	40 MHz	2100
Optical fibre	100 000 GHz	1 μm	$> 10^3$ MHz	$>10^5$

Laser light can be pulsed on and off very rapidly indeed. Most systems use wavelengths of 1.3 μm, which is actually in the infrared part of the spectrum. These extremely high frequencies make enormous bandwidths available. Table 8.4 compares the bandwidths of different carrier waves. No wonder BT has laid optical fibre cables across the country to link telephone exchanges. These cables are fibre bundles around a central steel wire and protected by a tough outer sheath.

Early fibres suffered from two main problems. *Impurities* in the glass attenuated the signal. Removing nearly all of these impurities has enormously increased the distances that can be covered. The early fibres were also wider, which allowed the light to reflect from side to side. These reflections caused the light to take different paths (modes) with different total lengths. A sharp pulse entering such a fibre can spread out. This problem is called *multimode dispersion* and it also causes attenuation. This is shown in Figure 8.19. To overcome this problem, modern fibres are made very narrow, about 10 μm in diameter, so that they have a single modal guide path . Fibres in commercial use can typically transmit over 50 kilometres without amplification.

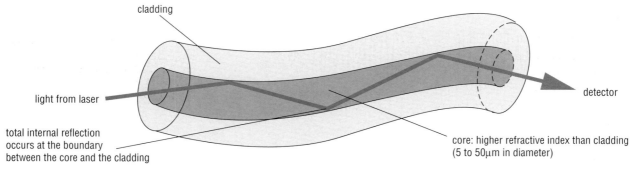

Figure 8.18 Structure of an optical fibre. The individual fibres consist of a single very narrow glass thread inside a plastic cover. The centre of the glass is a core that is slightly denser than the outside. The difference between the refractive index of the inner and outer glass prevents the light from leaving the fibre, so that light from the signal cannot escape. It can therefore travel around bends.

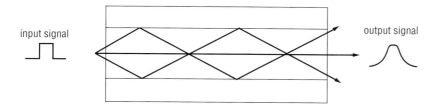

With wider cores light can follow several routes (modes) of different length giving
multimode dispersion and broadening the signal.

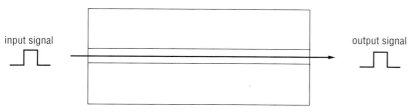

A narrow core prevents modal dispersion

Figure 8.19 *Multimode dispersion*

Optical fibres carrying digital signals overcome the three main problems
of telecommunications:
- *attenuation* of the signal is reduced
- laser pulses are not subject to interference by electromagnetic *noise*
- very large bandwidths are available for enormously expanded *capacity*.

Assignment trigger

Telephones

On the telephone the quality of the sound appears to be independent of
the distance it travels.

Why is this?
Has it always been like this?
How many changes does the voice signal actually make?
What is the difference when computers or fax machines are linked?

*If a practical assignment is developed, it is essential that a risk assessment is
made and checked by your teacher/lecturer.*

Could lead to possible assignments relating to Unit 8.

Security

As more and more information is transmitted through public channels of
communication, the need to preserve privacy and protect sensitive
information increases.

There are five main areas of risk:
- human error (for example using the incorrect procedure, accidental
  deletion)
- natural disasters (for example fire, flood)
- hardware failure (for example power cut, computer breakdown)
- software failure (for example program bugs)
- crime (for example sabotage, fraud, espionage, hacking).

There are three main ways in which data can be protected:

**Security is a major problem not only
because of the possible loss of
confidential data, but also because
of the risk of sabotage or the
introduction of viruses.**

343

Figure 8.20 *Even members of the royal family can have their telephone conversations intercepted.*

- *Physical controls* are necessary to protect systems and storage methods. Floppy disks are easily corrupted if handled inappropriately, for example by placing them on hi-fi speakers or near other magnetic fields.
- *Logical controls* can be built into the system. These include the use of security codes or passwords which can help to prevent unauthorised access. You must choose them carefully. A hacker was able to gain access to Prince Philip's private files on Prestel because the password was 2222222222! A dial-back system is an effective security measure. It can be used to protect data even when a password has been discovered. This disconnects the caller and then dials the number that is allocated to the password that has been used.
- *Administrative controls* include the use of regular backup procedures. Everyone who works on computers needs to make regular backups - that includes you! Cash card and other sensitive systems can be protected from fraud by division of responsibility. Several programs are combined to form the total final program. This way, no single person has complete knowledge of the whole. Regular checking of systems is called computer system auditing.

Leakage of signals

Signals transmitted through the air can be intercepted by unauthorised users. Scanning devices can be used to pick up telephone calls or police messages. This is a major problem for the military, who have to use codes, scrambling and waveband switching to achieve security. Copper cables are easy to tap into, but optical fibres offer extra security.

The Data Protection Act

> The Data Protection Act was passed by parliament in 1985 to deal with some of the problems arising from the storage of personal data on computer.

Under the terms of the **1985 Data Protection Act**, data users, that is, people or organisations who keep information about others on computer files, are obliged to:

- register with the Data Protection Registrar
- obtain data fairly and lawfully
- take security measures to prevent unauthorised access to or alteration of the data
- hold data for specified purposes only
- use the data for the specified purposes only
- keep the data accurate and up to date
- allow individuals access to any data held on them and correct it or delete it if necessary
- keep the data no longer than is necessary for the specified purpose.

Further stages in the IT revolution

Mobility

> Mobility, cost, accessibility and ease of use are important features of a computer system.

Improvements in **mobility** have led to increased use of information technology (IT). Miniaturisation has resulted in the development of high-powered portable 'lap top' and 'palm top' micro-computers, which have helped to increase access to data and therefore user convenience. You can carry them from place to place easily and use them in such places as trains. You can store very large amounts of information on floppy disks, which can be readily transported from place to place.

Q 12 Disks are much more portable than books or files. How many pages of A4 can you store on one floppy disk?

Ease of use

Software has become increasingly sophisticated and *user-friendly*, improving ease of use. As software and hardware technology improves and prices fall, the number of computers in use is increasing, and the rate of increase is accelerating. Increased accessibility leads to an increase in the number of applications for which computers are used, and demand for the machines rises accordingly. The increase in market size has also led to further reductions in cost.

All this has meant that within a few years the number of computers and computer literate people has increased enormously. The IT revolution is here now, and *you* are part of it!

Making the best of your data

Handling data efficiently and effectively is essential to the scientist. The key considerations that you should check when handling data are as follows:

- You should estimate the extent of any **error** in measurements and note how these may be compounded by any calculations .
- You should process data manually and electronically. You will need to substitute in formulae and rearrange them. You will construct tables and plot graphs. You will need to interpret these, for example by finding intercepts and gradients, interpolating and extrapolating and so on. You will **display** your data in many different forms, depending on your needs at the time. You will use not only paper, but VDU's, print-outs and calculator displays.
- Through your skilful processing of your data you will be able to form **valid conclusions**. You will be able to show that these are based on the data, serve their purpose and fall within stated confidence limits.

In all of this the computer will become your friend. It will take much of the tedious number handling away. The use of spreadsheets will help you to compile tables, plot graphs and carry out calculations in a painless way to a high professional standard.

 Measurement: accuracy, precision and errors, page 31

In processing, displaying and evaluating your data you will take into account:
- **errors**
- **the best methods to display the data**
- **how to draw valid conclusions.**

 Using graphs, page 37

Case study

SECURE NETWORKS

Internet Wide Open To Hacker Attack

Lax security is threatening the credibility of the Internet, the global computer network. Computer managers have failed to install safeguards to improve the network's defences, and US government controls on cryptography have blocked development of new security measures, security experts told a Congressional committee in Washington DC last week.

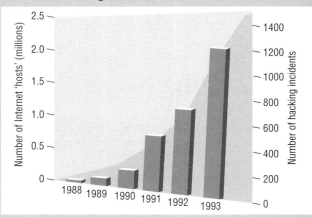

The Internet links computer systems in 70 countries and carries data from a wide variety of sources, including research organisations, government bodies and businesses. But because the system is loosely organised and not controlled by any single government or company, there is no way to force organisations linked to the network to improve the security of their systems.

The network's failings have recently been exposed in glaring fashion by hackers, just as the Clinton administration is seeking to use the Internet as a "laboratory" for new technologies for the National Information Infrastructure, better known as the information superhighway.

"As the Internet is increasingly relied upon to transmit sensitive information, the security stakes will grow," says Democratic Congressman Rick Boucher, who chaired the hearing. "If scientists cannot be certain that their research data will not be altered, if patients do not trust the privacy of their medical records, and if the safety of financial information is in doubt, then the value of the Internet will be sharply curtailed."

The Internet has 20 million users – 45 per cent of them outside the US – and is adding new users at the rate of 15 to 20 per cent a month. Illicit use of the Internet is also rising (see Graph). During 1993, the US government's Computer Emergency Response Team Coordination Center at Carnegie Mellon University in Pittsburgh received reports of 1334 security breaches. Presumably, some incidents were harmless break-ins by students. But the FBI estimates that in 80 to 90 per cent of the computer crimes it is investigating, the criminals used the Internet to gain access to computers. In many cases, gaps in security could be closed easily, says Dain Gary of the response team. But computer managers are often too busy, or too complacent, to make the improvements. They also worry that tighter security will be costly or will make computers more difficult to use.

Vinton Cerf, one of the architects of the network that has developed into the Internet, says the US government's stranglehold on exports of cryptographic technology must also bear some of the blame. Washington prohibits exports of even basic cryptographic technology, preventing its use on the Internet. Without these techniques, says Cerf, "the entire system will suffer from the weakest-link syndrome".

The shortcomings of the Internet were emphasised in early February, when the response team announced that unknown hackers had installed "sniffer" programs around the Internet that secretly recorded the passwords for tens of thousands of computers. Gary says that at least 27 computers have been infected with the sniffer. The hackers planted the sniffer program in computers that form junctions on the network and carry high volumes of data – including the passwords.

It is not yet known how many computers the hackers broke into using the stolen passwords, Gary says. And there is no guarantee that the sniffer assaults have ended. "The crisis is not over," he says.

Open secrets

Activists trying to embarrass the US government over its plans for eavesdropping on electronic communications have used the Internet global communications network to distribute a confidential manual produced by the National Security Agency, the government's chief eaves-dropper.

Hackers say the stunt was intended to highlight the inability to keep secrets even at the NSA, which has played a key role in developing the controversial Clipper Chip, which would give police access to confidential electronic transmissions such as telephone calls and e-mail.

Judi Emmel, a spokeswoman for the security agency, shrugs off the break-in. She says that though the NSA document was sent to dozens of newspapers and media outlets, no secrets were leaked. "It's not a classified document," she says.

Thieves run amok on Internet

Computer hackers have stolen the passwords to tens of thousands of computers connected to the global Internet computer network, warn security officials.

Last week's warning sent computer operators around the world scurrying to check whether their computers were infected with the rogue program used by the thieves – and to change any passwords that might have been compromised.

The program eavesdrops on transmissions between computers. When one computer tries to gain access to another by transmitting an account number and password, the program records the information.

One consolation is that the program monitors only those computers that are permanently connected to Internet. People who use a home computer and modem to dial into Internet are safe.

Revision of passwords offers limited protection, because a new infection could wreak havoc all over again, say officials at the Computer Emergency Response Team at Carnegie Mellon University. The problem cannot be finally solved until new systems are adopted, in which a user's password is changed each time the computer is used.

Questions

1a) What does the Internet do?

 b) What kind of people use the Internet and why?

2a) What different kinds of security problems do the articles illustrate? Give some examples of the reasons why security of data is important and how security can be breached by unauthorised persons.

 b) What methods can be used to increase security?

3a) Optical fibres are considered to offer greater security than copper cables. Why?

 b) Why isn't this relevant to making the Internet more secure?

4 How does the Data Protection Act protect private individuals in the UK?

Case study

TELEPHONES

Today's telephone network includes a combination of old and new technologies. The telephone system was originally entirely analogue, with electrical signals varying continuously in intensity. In recent years telephone companies have begun including digital systems, which encode conversations as a series of ones and zeroes. Users of computers have turned to the telephone network to transmit digital data, encoded into audio signals by modulator/demodulators (or 'modems').

The spread of digital electronics has stimulated interest in an all-digital network that could carry voice and data signals more efficiently. The International Telecommunications Union developed the Integrated Services Digital Network (ISDN) standard. It includes two channels carrying data at 64 kbits s^{-1} and one 16 kbits s^{-1} channel. Fibre optics will provide this service in Southern Bell's Heathrow system.

The International Consultative Commission on Telephone and Telegraph is considering a proposed broadband ISDN that would add three digitised video channels, carried over single mode optical fibres. Each video channel would require about 45 Mbits s^{-1}, and the entire B-ISDN would be at about 150 Mbits s^{-1}.

Illustration 1 Fibre optics being tested

An optical fibre consists of a single glass thread inside a plastic cover. In the centre of the glass is a core of slightly denser glass that carries the light. The difference in refractive index between the core and the surrounding glass guides the light along the fibres core. The purity of the glass ensures that the core absorbs virtually no light.

STL installed the first working fibre-optic system in Britain in 1975 to connect video display units to the Dorset police department's central computer. American companies put the first fibre-optic links into the world's telephone system in 1977.

In these links lasers or light-emitting diodes produced light with wavelengths of 800–900 nm which was passed through fibres with cores 50–150 μm

in diameter. These cores were large enough to allow the light to take on different shapes or 'modes'. Each mode travelled at different velocities along the fibre. This modal dispersion caused the signals to spread out. Light could only be sent for a few kilometres before it needed to be amplified.

Second generation systems also had large-core multimode fibres, but operated at 1300 nm, at which attenuation of light is much reduced. Signals could therefore travel much further without amplification. These systems went through a brief boom in the early 1980's.

Today, virtually all new telecommunications systems use third-generation technology. This uses light at a wavelength of 1300 nm and fibre cores of about 10 μm. These are so small that they carry only a single waveguide mode. Some commercial systems can carry over 100 million pieces of information per second for 50 kilometres. Single mode technology appears widely in telephone networks. At present, BT transmits information at up to 565 MHz, but it may be installing 2.5 GHz equipment later in 1994. The light signals are generated simply by switching lasers on and off.

Questions

1a) What is the difference between an analogue and a digital signal?

b) Why are digital transmissions preferred to analogue ones? (Use these terms in your answer: reliability, noise, attenuation, distortion, amplification, signal to noise ratio, regeneration, fidelity.)

2 How can distant computer users exchange their digital data? What stages must computer data pass through before it can be transmitted in this way.

3 What do modems do?

4 How can large numbers of signals be transmitted through the same transmission link at the same time? Write brief notes to answer this question. (Use these terms in your answer: signal bandwidth, channel bandwidth, amplitude modulation, frequency modulation, pulse code modulation, multiplexing.)

5 What are the bit rates used in the ISDN channels? A broadband ISDN was under discussion. Why was it needed?

6a) What caused attenuation in early optical fibres?

b) How is it reduced in modern ones?

7a) What is meant by the capacity of a communications system?

b) How have optical fibres increased capacity?

Bibliography/ useful addresses

1 Useful journals and magazines

New Scientist
Guardian (on Tuesday)
Chemistry Review, Phillip Allen
Education in Chemistry, Royal Society of Chemistry
Biological Sciences Review, Phillip Allen
School Science Review, Association for Science Education
Focus

2 Further Reading

Author	Title	Publisher	Year of publication
AFRC and National Centre for Biotechnology Education	*Practical Biotechnology, A Guide for schools and colleges*	AFRC	1993
Alexander, W. and Street, A.	*Metals in the Service of Man*	Penguin	
Allen, J.	*University of Bath Science 16-19 Telecommunications*	Nelson	1990
Andrews, C. and Smith, J	*Medical Nursing: A Concise Nursing Text, 11th edn*	Bailliere Tindall	1992
Association of the British Pharmaceutical Industry	*Medicines, Health and You* poster series	ABPI	1991 and 1993
Association of the British Pharmaceutical Industry	*Medicines and Drugs*	ABPI	1994
Barrett, D and Spencer, P.	*Genetics and Evolution*	Nelson Blackie	1992
Barrett, D. and Spencer, P.	*Plant Science*		1992
Black Report	*Inequalities in Health*	Penguin	1980
Brimicombe, M.	*Introducing Electronic Systems*	Nelson	1987
Brimicombe, M.	*Physics in Focus*	Nelson	1990
British Medical Association	*Complete Family Health Encyclopedia*	Dorling Kindersley	1992
British Telecom	*The Physics of Telecommunications*	BT Education Service	1994
British Telecom Education Service	*Booklets: Communicating by Light; Satellite Microwave Link; Submarine Optical Fibre Link; Terrestrial Microwave Link; Telecom Link Technical Background*	BT Education Service	
Budavari, S. et al	*The Merck Index: An Encyclopedia of Chemicals, Drugs and Biologicals 11th edn*	Merck and Co Inc	1989
Clegg, F.	*Simple Statistics: A Course Book for the Social Sciences*	Cambridge University Press	1982
Collins, M. and Wood-Robinson, V.	*Human and Social Biology*	Nelson Blackie	1993
Comfort, A.	*The Biology of Senescence 3rd edn*	Churchill Livingstone	1979
Freeland, P.	*Investigations in Applied Biology and Biotechnology.*	Hodder and Stoughton	1990
	Micro-organisms in Action: Investigations.		
Freemantle, M.	*Chemistry in Action, 2nd edn*	Macmillan	1995
Fox, E.L.	*Sports Physiology, 2nd edn*	Wm. C. Brown	1988
Gadd, K. and Gurr, S.	*University of Bath Science 16–19, Chemistry*	Nelson	1994
Gordon, J.E.	*The New Science of Strong Materials or Why You Don't Fall Through the Floor*	Pelican	1968
Griffin, M. and Redmore, A.	*Human Systems*	Nelson Blackie	1993
Hayward, G.	*Applied Genetics*	Nelson	1990
Hill, D.W. and Summers, R.	*Medical Technology: A Nursing Perspective*	Chapman and Hall	1994

Hill, G. and Holman, J.	*Chemistry in Context, 4th edn*	Nelson	1995
Hill, G. and Holman, J.	*Chemistry in Context Laboratory Manual, 3rd edn*	Nelson	1995
Holman, J. (ed.)	*Salter's Advanced Chemistry, Chemical Storylines Activities and assessment pack, Teacher's Guide*	Heinemann	1994
Hill-Cottingham, D. and Hill-Cottingham, P.	*Plant Science*	Nelson Blackie	1993
Hunt, A. (ed.)	*SATIS 16–19 files 1–4*	Association for Science Education	1990–2
Hutchings, R.	*University of Bath Science 16–19, Physics*	Nelson	1992
Katz, J.	*Fitness Works!* ™	Leisure Press Publications	1988
Langley, G.	*Telecommunications Primer*	Pitman	1990
Lewington, A	*Plants for People*	Natural History Museum	1990
Liptrot, G.F.	*Modern Inorganic Chemistry 4th edn*	Harper Collins Publishers	1983
Liptrot, G.F., Thompson, J.J. and Walker, G.R.	*Modern Physical Chemistry*	Harper Collins Publishers	1982
Mansfield, P.	*The Good Health Handbook,*	Grafton Books	1988
McAvoy and Donalson	*Health Care for Asians*	Oxford Medical Publications	1990
Roberts, M.B.V., Reiss, M.J. and King, T.J.	*Advanced Practical Biology*	Nelson	1994
Roberts, M.B.V., Reiss, M.J. and Monger, G.	*Biology: Principles and Processes*	Nelson	1993
Rogers, E.	*Physics for the Inquiring Mind*	Oxford University Press	1960
Rowland, M.	*University of Bath Science 16-19 Biology*	Nelson	1992
Rowntree, D.	*Statistics without Tears*	Penguin	1983
Science Museum	*Health Matters*	Science Museum	1994
Secretary of State for Health	*The Health of the Nation: A Strategy for Health in England*	HMSO	1992
Smith, A. and Jackson, B. (eds)	*The Nation's Health: A Strategy for the 1990s. (A report from an Independent Multidisciplinary Committee)*	King Edward's Hospital Fund for London	1988
Sony (UK)	*The Science of Audio Systems*	Sony (available from the ASE)	1993

Standard Telephones and Cables plc in association with the Microelectronics Education Programme	*Patterns of Communication*		1983
Swain, J., Finkelstein, V., French, S. and Oliver, M.	*Disabling Barriers: Enabling Environments.*	Sage	1993
Taylor, D.	*Human Physical Health*	Cambridge University Press	1989
The Department of Transport	*The Highway Code*	HMSO	
Thorburn, K.	*The Most Useful Science. Chemical and Biological Science in the future's food industry*	Northern Foods	1988
Tomkins, S., Reiss, M. and Morris C.	*Biology at Work*	Cambridge University Press	1993
Unilever	*Fats and Oils*	Unilever Educational Liaison	1994
Wallwork, J. and Stepney, R.	*Heart Disease: What it is and How it's Treated,*	Basil Blackwell	1987

3 Health and Safety Executive publications

HS(R)25 Memo of Guidance on the Electricity at Work Regulations (1990)

L21 Management of Health and Safety at Work Regulations 1992: Approved Code of Practice (1992)

L25 Personal Protective Equipment at Work Regulations 1992: Guidance on Regulations (1992)

Control of Substances Hazardous to Health and Control of Carcinogenic Substances; Control of Substances Hazardous to Health Regulations (1988): Approved Code of Practice 4th edition (1993)

PM32 The Safe Use of Portable Electrical Equipment

GS23 Electrical Safety in Schools (1990)

IND9G 160 Maintaining Portable Electrical Equipment in Offices and Other Low Risk Environments (1994)

4 Useful organisations and their addresses

Action for ME
PO Box 1302
WELLS
Somerset BA5 2WE

Action on Smoking and Health
(ASH)
109 Gloucester Place
LONDON W1H 3PH

Age Concern
Astral House
1268 London Road
LONDON SW16 4ER

Alcohol Concern
Waterbridge House
32–36 Loman Street
LONDON SE1 OEE

Alzheimer's Disease Society
158–160 Balham High Road
LONDON SW12 9BN

Arthritis and Rheumatism
Council
Copeman House
St Mary's Court
St Mary's Gate
CHESTERFIELD S41 7TD

Asthma Research Council
St Thomas's Hospital
Lambeth Palace Road
LONDON SE1

Association of the British
Pharmaceutical Industry
12 Whitehall
LONDON SW1A 2DY

Association for Science
Education (ASE),
College Lane,
HATFIELD AL10 9AA

British Agrochemicals
Association
4 Lincoln Court
Lincoln Road
PETERBOROUGH PE1 2RP

BBC
Engineering Information
Broadcasting House
LONDON W1A 1AA

The Biochemical Society
59 Portland Place
LONDON W1N 3AJ

BNFL Education Unit
Risley
WARRINGTON
WA3 6AS

BP Educational Service
Britannic House
1 Finsbury Circus
LONDON EC2M 7BA

British Diabetic Association
10 Queen Anne Street
LONDON W1M OBD

British Gas plc
326 Holborn
LONDON WC1V 7PT

British Gas,
Education Liaison Officer
Room 707A, 326 High
Holborn
LONDON WC1V 7PT

British Heart Foundation
14 Fitzhardinge Street
LONDON W1H 4DH

British Steel Education
Service
PO Box 10
WETHERBY LS23 7EA

BT Education Service
British Telecommunications
plc
81 Newgate St
LONDON EC1A 7AJ

The Butter Council
Tubs Hill House
London Road
SEVENOAKS
Kent TN13 1BL

Centre for Research
Education and Training in
Energy (CREATE)
Kenley House
25 Bridgeman Terrace
WIGAN WN1 1SY

Centre for Science
Education
School of Science
Sheffield Hallam University
36 Collegiate Crescent
SHEFFIELD S10 2BP

The Chartered Society of
Physiotherapy
Room 422 Fulton House
Jessop Avenue
CHELTENHAM GL50 3SH

Chemical Industry
Education Centre
Dept of Chemistry
University of York
Heslington
YORK YO1 5DD

The Chemical Industries
Association
King's Buildings
Smith Square
LONDON SW1P 3JJ

Child Poverty Action Group
4th Floor, 1–5 Bath St
LONDON EC1V 9PY

Commission for Racial
Equality
Elliot House
10–12 Allington Street
LONDON SW1E 5EH

Coronary Prevention Group
Plantation House
31–35 Fenchurch Street
LONDON EC3M 3NN

Council for Educational
Technology (CET)
3 Devonshire Street
LONDON W1N 2BA

Customer Services
Department
Hobsons Publishing plc
Bateman Street
CAMBRIDGE CB2 1LZ

Cystic Fibrosis Trust
Alexandra House
5 Blyth Road
BROMLEY BR1 3RS

Daniels Publishing
38 Cambridge Place
CAMBRIDGE CB2 1NS

The Engineering Training
Authority
Engineering Careers
Information Service
Vector House
41 Clarendon Road
WATFORD WD1 1HS

Eurotunnel Exhibition
Centre
St Martin's Plain
Cheriton High Street
FOLKESTONE CT19 4QD

Health Education Authority
Hamilton House
Mabledon Place
LONDON WC1H 9JP

Health and Safety Executive
PO Box 1999
SUDBURY CO10 6FS

HMSO Publications Centre
PO Box 276
LONDON SW8 5DT

Peter Honey
Ardingley House
10 Linden Avenue
MAIDENHEAD SL6 6HB

ICL
West Avenue
Kidsgrove
STOKE-ON-TRENT ST7 1TL

Institute of Biology
20–22 Queensbury Place
LONDON SW7 2DZ

Institute of Biomedical
Science
12 Coldbath Square
LONDON EC1R 5HL

Institute of Chiropodists
27 Wright Street
SOUTHPORT PR9 0TL

Institute for Complementary
Medicine
PO Box 194
LONDON SE16 1QZ

Institution of Electrical
Engineers (Schools,
Education and Liaison)
Michael Faraday House
Six Hills Way
STEVENAGE SG1 2AY

The Institute of Food
Science and Technology
5 Cambridge Court
210 Shepherd's Bush Road
LONDON W6 7NL

The Institute of Materials
1 Carlton House Terrace
LONDON SW1Y 5DB

Institute of Physics Publishing
Techno House
Redcliffe Way
BRISTOL BS1 6NX

The Institute of Physics
47 Belgrave Square
LONDON SW1X 8QX

Leukaemia Research Fund
43 Great Ormond Street
LONDON WC1N 3JJ

MERV Plastics
201 Station Road
Beeston
NOTTINGHAM NG9 2AB

The Meteorological Office
Education Service
Sutton House
London Road
BRACKNELL RG12 2SY

National Centre For
Biotechnology Education
Department of Microbiology
University of Reading
Whiteknights
READING RG6 2AJ

National Council for
Educational Technology
(NCET)
Sir William Lyons Road
University Of Warwick
Science Park
COVENTRY CV4 7EZ

National Dairy Council
5–7 John Princes St
LONDON W1M OAP

National Extension College
18 Brooklands Avenue
CAMBRIDGE CB2 2HN

Network Educational Press
Network House
PO Box 635
STAFFORD ST17 0JR

The Newspaper Society
Bloomsbury House
Bloomsbury Square
74–77 Great Russell Street
LONDON WC1B 3DA

Nirex
Information Office
Curie Avenue
Harwell
DIDCOT OX11 ORH

Release (drugs and legal
helpline)
169 Commercial Street
LONDON E1 6BW

Royal Society for the
Promotion of Health
RSH House
38A St George's Drive
LONDON SW1V 4BH

ROSPA (Royal Society for
the Prevention of Accidents)
Cannon House
Priory Queensway
BIRMINGHAM B4 6BS

RSPCA (Royal Society for
the Prevention of Cruelty to
Animals) Education
Department
Causeway
HORSHAM RH12 1HG

RTZ Educational Resources
for Schools
Intermail Ltd
10 Fleming Road
NEWBURY RG13 2DE

Royal Society of Chemistry
Burlington House
Piccadilly
LONDON W1V OBN

Royal Society for the
Promotion of Health
RSH House
38A St George's Drive
LONDON SW1V 4BH

Science and Plants for Schools
(SAPS)
Homerton College
Hills Road
CAMBRIDGE CB2 2PH

Education Officer
The Science Museum
LONDON SW7 2DD

Scottish Power
Public Affairs Dept
Cathcart House
Spean Street
GLASGOW G44 4BE

Shell Education Service
Shell UK Ltd
Shell-Mex House
Strand
LONDON WC2R ODX

Sickle Cell Society
54 Station Road
LONDON NW10 4UA

Society of Chiropodists and
Podiatrists
53 Welbeck Street
LONDON W1M 7HE

Speak out and Listen
PO Box 7
Winchcombe
CHELTENHAM GL54 5HY

Standard Telephones and
Cables plc
STC House
190 Strand
LONDON WC2R 1DU

The Standing Conference on
Schools' Science and
Technology
76 Portland Place
LONDON W1N 4AA

Terrence Higgins Trust
(AIDS and HIV)
52–54 Gray's Inn Road
LONDON WC1X 8JU

The Tidy Britain Group
The Pier
WIGAN WN3 4EX

Understanding Electricity
Education Service
30 Millbank
LONDON SW1P 4RD

Unilever Educational
Liaison
PO Box 68
Unilever House
LONDON EC4P 4BQ

The Community Affairs
Department
The Wellcome Foundation Ltd
PO Box 129
160 Euston Road
LONDON NW1 2BP

Wessex Publications
Elwell House
Stocklinch
ILMINSTER TA19 9JF

WWF UK (World Wide
Fund for Nature)
Panda House
Weyside Park
GODALMING GU7 1XR

Zoological Society
University of Bristol
BRISTOL BS8 1 MG

Index